OPTICAL MASERS

Advances in Electronics and Electron Physics

Edited by

L. MARTON

National Bureau of Standards, Washington, D.C.

Assistant Editor

CLAIRE MARTON

SUPPLEMENT 1

Electroluminescence and Related Effects. 1963

HENRY F. IVEY

SUPPLEMENT 2

Optical Masers. 1964

GEORGE BIRNBAUM

OPTICAL MASERS

George Birnbaum

NORTH AMERICAN AVIATION SCIENCE CENTER
THOUSAND OAKS, CALIFORNIA

1964

ACADEMIC PRESS   New York and London

ACADEMIC PRESS INC.
111 Fifth Avenue, New York, New York 10003

United Kingdom Edition published by
ACADEMIC PRESS INC. (LONDON) LTD.
Berkeley Square House, London W.1

LIBRARY OF CONGRESS CATALOG CARD NUMBER: 64-14569

First Printing, 1964

Second Printing, 1965

PRINTED IN THE UNITED STATES OF AMERICA

FOREWORD

About two years ago I first announced, in the foreword to our latest volume of *Advances*, a contribution on lasers. All those who have a nodding acquaintance with the subject are well aware of the phenomenal growth and of the accompanying difficulties entailed in preparing a good critical review. The author of the present review had my full sympathy, and when he announced that the subject could not be treated within the space limitations of a "standard" contribution, we immediately agreed to issue it as a monograph-supplement to our regular series.

The emphasis in this volume is more on the physical principles and less on the applications, although some of the important applications to date are discussed in detail. As the years go by we will attempt to cover further advances and the principal applications whenever this appears desirable.

L. MARTON

Washington, D. C.

July, 1964

v

PREFACE

This book is concerned with the new and rapidly developing field of optical masers. Although its origins may be said to spring from the development of microwave masers, it was only after the demonstration of optical maser action in ruby in 1960 that many investigators turned their attention to this new field. In the few years since 1960, maser action has been observed in an enormous number of materials resulting in the production of coherent radiation at substantial power levels from the ultraviolet to the far infrared regions of the spectrum.

Concomitant with these advances, much had to be done in the realms basic to maser processes—spectroscopy and the electronics and physics of optical circuit elements. From the outset, there was interest in controlling and modulating optical maser radiation, in optical heterodyning, and in exploring the many ways in which this new type of optical radiation could be used. In particular, the enormous intensity of the optical maser made possible the observation, for the first time, of harmonic generation, stimulated Raman emission, and other nonlinear effects, and thereby produced a new field of investigation and applications. The purpose of this book is to present a systematic account of the experimental and theoretical results which have been developed thus far, and to make this information readily available to students, research workers, and those interested in the many areas to which optical masers may be applied.

The furious activity in optical masers has made it particularly desirable to digest and coordinate the extensive literature. This task has been made very difficult not only by the rapid development of ideas and techniques themselves, but also by the fact that this has often resulted in the publication of incomplete or fragmentary treatments of problems. However, the field appears to have matured to the point where the major trends are now clearly discernible.

Since the emphasis in this book is on fundamentals rather than devices, an effort has been made to treat the diverse aspects of maser theory in an integrated way. Accordingly, following the introduction in Chapter I, the theory is developed in Chapters II to VIII somewhat separately from the experimental results, which are discussed systematically and critically in the subsequent chapters. Nevertheless, theory and experiment are closely correlated throughout the book. Two subjects, although important, required treatments too detailed for inclusion in the main body of the book. These subjects, which are discussed, respectively, in Appendices III and IV, are: the theory of induced and spontaneous transitions in resonators and in free space, and the theory of the interaction of electromagnetic waves in nonlinear dielectrics. A theory of oscillation in imperfect crystals is published here for the first time. Since almost all of the material is developed from "first principles," it is felt that most of the discussion can be profitably read with only an elementary knowledge of physics.

Considerable effort has been directed towards making this volume a reference work that is of value to a variety of users. Attention has been directed to making each chapter and section as independent of other sections as is practicable, although the treatment is a continuously developed one. Thus, some definitions of symbols and expressions are repeated. Tables of optical masers, summarizing their operating characteristics and the spectroscopic information pertinent for maser action, are given in Appendix I.

I thank the following colleagues for their comments on a preliminary draft of this book: Dr. E. R. Cohen, Prof. B. A. Lengyel, Dr. G. F. Smith, and Dr. J. S. Margolis. I am grateful to Dr. W. G. Wagner for valuable discussions and criticism on several aspects of the theory, Dr. J. O. McCaldin for an informative discussion of p-n junction diodes, and Mr. D. R. Johnson for assistance in the preparation of the tables.

Valuable criticism and important suggestions concerning the entire manuscript were made by Dr. Milton Birnbaum, to whom I express my deep gratitude.

I thank Dr. H. Reiss for his encouragement and helpful interest in the writing of this book. For providing the environment that made this work possible, I am grateful to North American Aviation, Inc. Not least of all, my wife and two daughters contributed time, patience, and encouragement, and I gratefully acknowledge my indebtedness to them.

GEORGE BIRNBAUM

July, 1964

CONTENTS

ERRATA

p. 2, line 24 should read:

The first to observe spectral narrowing, a reduction in lifetime, and oscillation . . .

p. 2, the sentence beginning on line 27 should read:

These observations were very quickly extended by Maiman, Hoskins, D'Haenens, Asawa, Evtuhov (*150*), and by Collins, Nelson, Schawlow, Bond, Garrett, and Kaiser (*55*), who demonstrated the . . .

I. Introduction

A. Definitions

The terms *maser* or *optical maser* and *laser* have been used interchangeably to describe the quantum electronic devices which generate coherent electromagnetic radiation in the infrared, visible, and ultraviolet regions. The words have evolved as acronyms of the phrases "microwave (or molecular) amplification by the stimulated emission of radiation," or "light amplification" by such processes. In this book the term *optical maser* or *maser* is generally used, although popular usage now seems to favor *laser* to describe devices in the infrared and optical regions and *maser* for those in the microwave and millimeter regions.

Laser oscillation is marked by a dramatic narrowing of the spectral and angular distribution of the spontaneous emission radiation at a particular level of excitation called the *threshold*. The specific process of laser oscillation designating the behavior of a laser above a well defined threshold is distinguished from the general process of stimulated emission.

A final matter of terminology is the use of the word *atom* to denote in a generic sense the active species of the maser, which may in fact be an atom, ion, exciton, or molecule.

B. Some Highlights in the Development of Optical Masers

It has been speculated that the development of masers was not possible before the 1940's, although lasers could have been developed many years earlier. It was in the 1940's that good microwave sources became generally available and that the exacting microwave art came to maturity. The spectroscopic exploration of substances in the microwave region followed very quickly on the heels of these developments. On the other hand, classical optical spectroscopy was a well-established field at the advent of the Bohr theory in 1913, and the optical resonator, the Fabry-Perot interferometer, had been invented in the latter part of the 19th century. Of course, what was lacking was the idea of amplification by the stimulated emission of radiation, although the notion of stimulated emission was advanced as early as 1917 by Einstein. It appears that definite proposals of applying the phenomenon of stimulated emission to produce amplification were made independently by Basov, Fabrikant, Prokhorov, Townes, and Weber, several decades later.

The first successful application of stimulated emission was made in 1954 by Gordon, Zeiger, and Townes (36) who used the inversion transition of ammonia to obtain continuous maser oscillation at 24 Gc/s. It is understandable that it was in the microwave rather than in the optical region that stimulated emission devices were first developed (2–6). The idea of amplification is associated with circuits, and a great deal of work had been done in treating guided wave structures as circuit elements. Optical structures, on the other hand, had been regarded in terms of geometrical or physical optics until Schawlow and Townes in 1958 (1) analyzed the Fabry-Perot interferometer as a highly overmoded rectangular resonator and concluded that optical maser action should be possible using the Fabry-Perot interferometer. The design principles of such a device were illustrated by reference to a system using potassium vapor excited by optical pumping. Such a maser using cesium has since been developed (261).

The first to observe spectral narrowing and a reduction in lifetime due to an inverted population in the optical region was Maiman (54) in 1960, who excited a ruby rod with plane parallel ends coated with silver with intense pulses of light from a flash lamp. His observations were very quickly extended by Collins, Nelson, Schawlow, Bond, Garrett, and Kaiser (55) in 1960, who demonstrated the coherence and directionality of the stimulated radiation and also observed the characteristic relaxation oscillation in the amplitude of the output radiation. Thus optical oscillations had been observed for the first time and the era of quantum electronics in the optical region had begun. Similar behavior has since been observed in many new solid state lasers using rare earth metal ions in a variety of hosts.

Working along different lines, Javan, Bennett, and Herriott (237) in 1961 developed the first gas laser, and also the first continuously operating laser, by exciting a mixture of helium and neon in a discharge located between the mirrors of a Fabry-Perot interferometer. The spectral purity (of the order of 1 part in 10^{14}), beam directionality, and spatial coherence are enormously superior to that of the solid state lasers and are found to approach theoretical expectations in a number of respects. These results are due almost entirely to the fact that the gas represents a practically perfect optical medium in contrast with solids which suffer from strains and inhomogeneities. Maser oscillation has been observed in a wide variety of gas systems all excited by discharge but one (an optically pumped cesium maser).

Another important advance was the development of the p–n junction laser in 1962 by Hall, Fenner, Kingsley, Soltys, and Carlson (287), Nathan, Dumke, Burns, Dill, and Lasher (288), and Quist, Rediker, Keyes, Krag, Lax, McWhorter, and Zeiger (289). By injecting high current densities in GaAs p–n diodes they demonstrated a striking line narrowing accompanied by a strong directionality of the recombination radiation. Laser oscillation was quickly obtained in other p–n diodes. The laser diode is an especially simple and compact device which converts electrical current to light with a quantum efficiency approaching unity.

With such a variety of excitation methods and types of atomic transitions suitable for maser action, a very large number of optical masers have been rapidly developed (7–16). They now span the wavelength range from 0.3 to 85μ, i.e., from the ultraviolet to the far infrared, but one may confidently anticipate extentions at both ends of the spectrum.

C. The Optical Resonator

The mode theory of the Fabry-Perot interferometer as an optical resonator was developed in 1961 by Fox and Li (83) and Boyd and Gordon (84), and others. From the microwave point of view it seems plausible that the optical interferometer may be described in terms of modes. From the classical optical point of view, the description in terms of modes never arises because excitation with broadband and unpolarized radiation washes out the essential features of the mode structure. To indicate some of the characteristics of the optical interferometer as a resonator, imagine that a microwave resonator is forced to oscillate in its lowest order mode at an optical frequency. There will now be an enormous number of nodal planes in the axial direction but no nodes in the transverse direction, with the result that the energy in the transverse components of the field will be very much greater than that in the axial components. This suggests that the side walls of the resonator can be removed without seriously degrading the Q. As a matter of fact, the Q of the optical resonator is orders of magnitude larger than that of the microwave resonator, since the Q may be shown to be proportional to the number of axial half-wavelengths. The fact that there are no side walls in the optical resonator provides for great flexibility in the maser device configuration. It becomes simple to excite the maser substance by optical pumping, rf discharges, or current injection, and to insert various components inside the cavity for modulating the radiation or controlling the mode excitation.

Because the optical resonator or interferometer is such a highly overmoded structure, there is a great tendency for the maser to oscillate in more than one mode if particular care to avoid this is not taken. The closely spaced modes may be coupled by a number of linear and nonlinear mechanisms which gives rise to a variety of phenomena generally observed in optical masers.

D. RADIATION CHARACTERISTICS OF THE OPTICAL MASER

The maser oscillator, like an electronic oscillator, may be regarded as an extremely high gain amplifier driven by internal noise. This noise is circuit or Johnson noise in the microwave region, and spontaneous radiation from excited maser atoms in the optical region. The gain of the maser increases with increasing population inversion until the amplified noise power becomes equal to the total resonator losses. At this point the system breaks into oscillation, and because of the positive feedback or regeneration the gain may be very large. Since the product of the gain and bandwidth is a constant in an amplifier or oscillator, the spectral narrowing of the maser oscillator may be extreme and continues to increase with increasing power output or gain. (See, however, Section XI, D, 4.)

Without enlarging upon the idea of coherence at this point, it suffices to say that the very narrow bandwidth of the maser oscillating in a single mode implies a very high degree of time coherence by the time-bandwidth uncertainty relation, i.e., the radiation field at a given point in space is very well correlated with that at earlier and later times. That there must also be spatial coherence, i.e., correlation at a given instant of the field in a direction perpendicular to the direction of propagation, follows from the specification that the maser is oscillating in a single mode. In other words the spatial coherence is simply the property of the field in the resonator.

In the infrared and optical regions, the wavelength of the radiation is so much less than the dimensions of the structure, that the radiation leaving the partially transmitting mirror of the optical resonator is diffracted through a very small angle to form a well collimated beam. On the other hand, if the field were to radiate through the end wall of a microwave resonator, it would be diffracted through a large angle since the wavelength is of the same order as the dimensions of the resonator. Thus from the viewpoint of the microwave engineer the only new feature of laser radiation is its extreme collimation. From the viewpoint of the opticist, laser radiation is profoundly different from anything that had been obtained heretofore. Whereas the usual optical radiation has an intensity characterized by effective temperature of the order of thousands of degrees, the laser output can be described as having an effective temperature of 10^{18} °K or more, signifying that the laser generates highly coherent radiation at substantial power levels.

E. NONLINEAR OPTICAL EFFECTS

The enormous effective temperature of laser radiation affords many orders of magnitude more radiant power per unit frequency per unit solid angle per unit area than was previously available. It makes common a variety of nonlinear effects previously never detected. The first of these was the observation of Franken, Hill, Peters, and Weinrich (*396*) in 1961 that the second harmonic of the 6943Å radiation from a ruby laser could be generated by focusing the beam in crystalline quartz. Observations of third harmonic generation and other nonlinear optical effects followed quickly. It has been found that the laser beam can induce higher order Raman effects which produce coherent radiation at the Stokes and anti-Stokes lines of several orders. Thus starting with a high intensity laser and using frequency mixing techniques in combination with Raman laser action, one could in principle obtain coherent radiation at any frequency from the far infrared to the ultraviolet regions.

II. Threshold Conditions for Oscillation

A. General Relations

The threshold conditions for oscillation of masers have been given in a variety of somewhat different but equivalent forms all expressing the fact that oscillation can occur when the power produced by the stimulated emission of radiation is equal to or greater than the power loss in the resonant structure. We will discuss these oscillation conditions from several points of view not only because of the heuristic value, but also as a way of summarizing a number of spectroscopic and electromagnetic relations useful in the theory of masers.

Consider a parallel beam of monochromatic light of frequency v traveling in the positive x-direction through a layer of atoms of thickness dx. Suppose there are n_1 atoms per cc in the lower state and n_2 atoms per cc in the upper state capable of respectively absorbing and emitting this radiation. If the effect of spontaneous emission is neglected since it takes place in all directions, the decrease in the power per unit area of the beam, $-dS$, according to the Einstein theory of radiation, is given by*

$$-dS = hv\, dx(n_1 \Gamma_{12}^i - n_2 \Gamma_{21}^i). \qquad (2.1)$$

Γ_{12}^i is the probability per second that the incident radiation induces a transition in the atom from state 1 to 2, and Γ_{21}^i is the probability per second that the incident radiation induces a transition in the atom from state 2 to 1, thereby emitting a quantum in the same direction as the stimulating quantum. The transition rate is given by

$$\Gamma_{12}^i = B_{12}wS(v), \qquad (2.2)$$

where w is the energy density and $S(v)$ is the normalized shape factor

---

* A more general expression including the effect of spontaneous emission, and suitable for anisotropic media is given in Section IV,B,3. The theory of induced and spontaneous transitions in free space and resonators is treated in Appendix III.

of the atomic resonance. For radiation which is not monochromatic, w is replaced by $w(\nu)\,d\nu$, the energy density in the frequency range ν to $\nu + d\nu$. The quantity B_{12} is the Einstein B coefficient for induced absorption and will be defined subsequently.

In a plane wave the energy density stored in the electric field at any point of the wave is equal to the energy density stored in the magnetic field at that point. The time average of the total energy density for fields which vary sinusoidally in time is given in unrationalized Gaussian units by*

$$w = \frac{\epsilon'}{8\pi} E^2 = \frac{\mu'}{8\pi} H^2, \tag{2.3}$$

where E and H are, respectively, the peak electric and magnetic field strengths, and ϵ', the dielectric constant, and μ' the magnetic permeability, are dimensionless quantities. The energy flow per unit area transported by the light wave, which is represented by the Poynting vector $\mathbf{S}$, is related to the energy density by

$$\mathbf{S} = \mathbf{s}vw, \tag{2.4}$$

where $\mathbf{s}$ is a unit vector in the direction of propagation, and v is the velocity of light in the medium. In a resonator the average values of the energy stored in the electric and magnetic fields are equal, and the total energy is given by

$$W = \frac{1}{8\pi} \int \epsilon' E^2 dV = \frac{1}{8\pi} \int \mu' H^2 \, dV. \tag{2.4a}$$

From (2.1) and (2.2) we have, provided dS/dx does not vary appreciably,

$$P = h\nu VwS(\nu)\,(n_1 B_{12} - n_2 B_{21}), \tag{2.5}$$

where V is the volume of the substance illuminated by the beam. P is the power absorbed or emitted depending on whether $n_1 B_{12}$ is greater than or less than $n_2 B_{21}$, respectively. This expression also

---

* In mks units (2.3) becomes

$$w = \epsilon'\epsilon_0 E^2/2 = \mu'\mu_0 H^2/2,$$

where $c = (\epsilon_0\mu_0)^{-1/2} = 3 \times 10^8$ meters/sec, $(\mu_0/\epsilon_0)^{1/2} = 120\,\pi$, E is in volts/meter, and w is in joules/meter³.

applies for a resonator of volume V completely filled with the substance provided $wV = W$ is replaced by $\int w dV$, the energy stored in the resonator.

Now the fundamental quantity describing the power loss P_c of a resonant structure is its Q or damping time τ_c, which are defined by the relations

$$P_c = \frac{dW}{dt} = -\frac{\omega W}{Q} = -\frac{W}{\tau_c}, \tag{2.6}$$

where we have used the relation $Q = \omega \tau_c$. If the cavity, whose resonance frequency is set equal to that of the atoms, is filled with atoms which can emit power, the condition $P = P_c$ gives the minimum population density required to produce oscillation, viz.,

$$n_2 - n_1 \frac{B_{12}}{B_{21}} = [\hbar Q B_{21} S(\nu)]^{-1}. \tag{2.7}$$

The Einstein B coefficient is a fundamental measure of the interaction of the atom with the radiation field. For electric dipole transitions,* the B coefficients for induced emission and absorption are, respectively,

$$B_{21} = \frac{2\pi |\mu_{21}|^2}{3\hbar^2 g_2}, \qquad B_{12} = \frac{2\pi |\mu_{12}|^2}{3\hbar^2 g_1}. \tag{2.8}$$

Here g is the degeneracy of the initial state, and $|\mu_{21}|^2 = e^2 |\mathbf{r}_{21}|^2$ is the total dipole moment matrix element squared, which is summed over all degenerate final and initial substates. Equations (2.8) hold for an isotropic medium and consequently apply for a polarized unidirectional beam as well as isotropic and unpolarized radiation. Since $|\mu_{21}|^2 = |\mu_{12}|^2$ and

$$B_{21}g_2 = B_{12}g_1, \tag{2.9}$$

power is emitted, or the absorption is negative when

$$n_2 > n_1 g_2/g_1. \tag{2.10}$$

At thermodynamic equilibrium, the population N_m in the energy level E_m is given by the Boltzmann distribution

$$N_m = \frac{N g_m e^{-E_m/kT}}{\sum_m g_m e^{-E_m/kT}}. \tag{2.11}$$

---

* The B and A coefficients for electric and magnetic dipole and electric quadrupole transitions are discussed by Kemble (17), and Condon and Shortley (18).

When a pair of levels is not in thermodynamic equilibrium, an effective temperature T_e may be defined in terms of the populations N_1 and N_2 by the relation

$$N_2 g_1/N_1 g_2 = \exp\left[-(E_2 - E_1)/kT_e\right],$$

where $E_2 > E_1$. T_e is then positive or negative depending on whether N_2/g_2 is, respectively, smaller or greater than N_1/g_1. The concept of negative temperature has been frequently used in the discussion of microwave masers.

The Einstein A coefficient, defined as the probability per second that an atom in an upper state will spontaneously emit in a random direction a photon and change to a lower state, is

$$A_{21} = \frac{1}{\tau_{21}} = \frac{64\pi^4 \nu^3 \mid \mu_{21} \mid^2}{3hv^3 g_2}. \tag{2.12}$$

TABLE I. RADIATIVE LIFETIMES OF EXCITED STATES

($\mu = 10^{-18}$ esu corresponds to an electric dipole transition appropriate for vibrational or rotational transitions of polar molecules and for electronic transitions of free atoms. $\mu = 10^{-20}$ esu corresponds to a magnetic dipole transition or a forbidden electronic transition of an ion in a crystal.)

λ cm	$\mu = 1 \times 10^{-18}$ esu	$\mu = 0.01 \times 10^{-18}$ esu
1	3×10^6	3×10^{10}
10^{-2}	3	3×10^4
10^{-4}	3×10^{-6}	3×10^{-2}
10^{-5}	3×10^{-9}	3×10^{-5}

τ_{21} is the mean lifetime of an atom in state 2 if only the spontaneous transition $2\rightarrow1$ occurs. Typical values of τ_{21} are given in Table I. The A coefficient is related to the B coefficient by

$$A_{21} = \left(\frac{8\pi\nu^2}{v^3}\right) h\nu\, B_{21}, \tag{2.13}$$

where the factor in parenthesis is the density of radiation modes per unit frequency range.

Although (2.8) and (2.12) allow one to estimate transition rates, the relevant matrix elements in particular cases are often unknown.

However, as will be shown later, B may be evaluated from the integrated absorption.

Suppose that the atomic resonance has the Lorentz shape,

$$S(\nu) = \frac{1}{\pi} \frac{\Delta\nu}{(\nu_0 - \nu)^2 + \Delta\nu^2}, \qquad (2.14)$$

where $\Delta\nu$ is the half-width at half maximum, and $\int S(\nu)\,d\nu = 1$. This shape is appropriate, for example, for an ensemble of atoms with the same resonance frequency but whose radiation lifetimes are interrupted at random. Then from (2.7) and (2.8) the excess population density required to sustain oscillation is

$$n_2 - \frac{n_1 g_2}{g_1} = \frac{3\hbar g_2}{4\pi\tau_c \,|\,\mu_{12}\,|^2} \frac{\Delta\nu}{\nu_0}. \qquad (2.15)$$

In a gas at low enough pressure, infrared or optical transitions will have a line shape determined by the Doppler effect arising from the thermal motion of the atoms. The atomic frequency response is Gaussian in this case,

$$S(\nu) = \frac{1}{\pi^{1/2}} \frac{(\ln 2)^{1/2}}{\Delta\nu_D} \exp\left\{ - \left[\frac{\nu - \nu_0}{\Delta\nu_D} (\ln 2)^{1/2} \right]^2 \right\}, \qquad (2.16)$$

and has a half-width at half-maximum, $\Delta\nu_D$, given by

$$\Delta\nu_D = \frac{\nu_0}{c} \left(\frac{2kT}{m} \ln 2 \right)^{1/2} = 3.581 \times 10^{-7} \nu_0 (T/M)^{1/2}, \qquad (2.17)$$

where m is the atomic mass, M is the atomic weight, and $(2kT/m)^{1/2}$ is the most probable speed. Because of the Gaussian line shape, the oscillation condition becomes

$$n_2 - n_1 \left(\frac{g_2}{g_1} \right) = \frac{3\hbar g_2}{4\pi^2\tau_c \,|\,\mu_{12}\,|^2} \left(\frac{\pi}{\ln 2} \right)^{1/2} \frac{\Delta\nu_D}{\nu_0}. \qquad (2.18)$$

If the expression for $\Delta\nu_D$ is inserted in (2.18), it may be noted that the number of excited systems required for oscillation is independent of the frequency.

To obtain an estimate for τ_c, consider that the optical resonator is a Fabry-Perot interferometer with plane parallel plates, whose power reflection coefficient is R. Assume that a plane parallel wave exists between the plates and is reflected back and forth many times. Then the rate of loss of energy W is given by

$$\frac{dW}{dt} = - \frac{v(1 - R)W}{D},$$ (2.19)

where D is the distance between the plates. The decay time is then

$$\tau_c = \frac{D}{v(1 - R)}.$$ (2.20)

If, for example, $D = 3$ cm, $R = 0.98$, and $v = c = 3 \times 10^{10}$ cm/sec, then $\tau_c = 5 \times 10^{-9}$ sec, and $Q = 1.5 \times 10^7$ for $\lambda = 6.3 \times 10^{-5}$ cm^{-1}. This value is orders of magnitude greater than the values realized in the microwave region for the single mode, enclosed resonator. There is an additional loss in an open type resonator arising from diffraction by the end plates, and it may be estimated as follows. The rate of energy loss from a plane wave due to its spilling off the edges of a square reflecting surface of dimension L may be represented in the approximation of geometrical optics by

$$\frac{dW'}{dt} = - \frac{4c\theta W'}{L},$$ (2.21)

where $\theta = \lambda/L$ is the angle corresponding to the first Fraunhofer diffraction minimum. The Q due to diffraction, Q', is then

$$Q' = 2\pi \left(\frac{L}{2\lambda}\right)^2.$$ (2.22)

For $L = 1$ cm and $\lambda = 6.3 \times 10^{-5}$ cm, $Q' = 4.0 \times 10^8$, a value an order of magnitude greater than that due to power loss in the end plates. Thus the losses due to diffraction in this case may be neglected in comparison with the power loss in the end plates. In general, however, there are a number of loss mechanisms which are operative in attenuating the field in the resonator. These mechanisms, which include in addition to transmission, absorption, and diffraction by the mirrors, mode conversion effects, and dielectric absorption in the maser material, will be discussed in various parts of this report and summarized in Section VII, B. It is sufficient here and elsewhere to characterize all the loss mechanisms by the single parameter Q or τ_c, which is the value for a single mode assuming that the maser medium is neutral, i.e., $n_1 g_2 = n_2 g_1$.

The threshold condition may also be obtained in the following way according to Schawlow and Townes (*1*). The rate of stimulated emission due to a single quantum in a single mode is exactly equal to the rate of spontaneous emission into the same mode. This rate is just A, the spontaneous emission rate, divided by p, the number of modes which are effective in producing spontaneous emission. The condition for instability can then be written

$$\frac{[n_2 - n_1(g_2/g_1)] \, Vh\nu}{\tau_{21}p} = \frac{h\nu}{\tau_c} . \tag{2.23}$$

For an atomic line with a Lorentzian shape

$$p = \int p(\nu) \frac{\Delta\nu^2 \, d\nu}{(\nu - \nu_0)^2 + \Delta\nu^2} , \tag{2.24}$$

where the number of cavity modes between ν and $\nu + d\nu$ is

$$p(\nu) \, d\nu = \frac{8\pi\nu^2 V}{v^3} \, d\nu. \tag{2.25}$$

Evaluating (2.24), we have for the number of modes within the line

$$p = 8\pi^2\nu^2 V\Delta\nu/v^3. \tag{2.26}$$

Substituting this result in (2.23), we obtain

$$\frac{n_2 - n_1(g_2/g_1)}{\tau_{21}} = \left(\frac{8\pi^2\nu^2\Delta\nu}{v^3} \right) \frac{1}{\tau_c} , \tag{2.27}$$

which reduces to (2.15) by substituting (2.12) for τ_{21} .

According to Kastler (*19*), the number of modes, and consequently, the threshold relation, should be corrected for the dispersion of the phase velocity v.

Consider next the modifications in the relations that must be made in dealing with the interaction of radiation with atomic systems embedded in a dielectric medium. These modifications (*20, 21*) take a particularly simple form when the atomic centers are not in resonance with the host medium and when the interactions among the centers may be neglected. First, the dipole matrix element squared should be divided by $\epsilon' = n^2$, the dielectric constant of the host. Also the matrix element squared should be multiplied by $(E_{eff}/E_0)^2$, where E_{eff} is the magnitude of the field effective in inducing transitions, and E_0 is the average field in the medium. If the crystal has cubic symmetry,

$$\frac{E_{\text{eff}}}{E_0} = 1 + \frac{n^2 - 1}{3} + \dots , \qquad (2.28)$$

where the first two terms on the right constitute the Lorentz local field correction, and additional terms which are difficult to evaluate are not shown. It is thought, however, that (2.28) does not represent an adequate approximation for most systems. For simplicity, the refractive index will not be explicitly shown in most of the equations in this book. However, it is easy to show the dependence on n by making the substitutions $v = c/n, \lambda = \lambda_0/n$ and $\mu^2 = \mu_0^2/n^2$.

It is instructive to derive the oscillation condition from the requirement that the amplification during one passage of the wave through the medium be sufficient to replenish the reflection loss, namely,

$$e^{\alpha D} = R^{-1}, \qquad (2.29)$$

where α is the negative absorption per cm^{-1}. For R close to 1, (2.29) is approximately

$$\alpha D \simeq 1 - R. \qquad (2.30)$$

The absorption coefficient may be obtained from (2.1) and (2.2) in the form,

$$k(v) = -\frac{1}{S}\frac{dS}{dx} = \frac{hv}{v}\,S(v)\,(n_1 B_{12} - n_2 B_{21}). \qquad (2.31)$$

The absorption coefficient $k(v)$ and the negative absorption coefficient $\alpha(v)$ are related by $k(v) = -\alpha(v)$. At resonance the negative absorption coefficient may be put in the form, from (2.31), (2.13), and (2.26),

$$\alpha(v_a) = \frac{A_{21}}{pv}\left(N_2 - N_1\frac{g_2}{g_1}\right). \qquad (2.32)$$

The following forms of the threshold condition for oscillation may be useful. Letting k_0 be the absorption coefficient when the populations in the absence of pumping are n_1^0 and n_2^0, we have from (2.30) and (2.31),

$$\frac{n_2 - \dfrac{g_2}{g_1}\,n_1}{n_1^0\,\dfrac{g_2}{g_1} - n_2^0} = \frac{1 - R}{k_0 D}. \qquad (2.33)$$

From the following relation between the absorption coefficient and the cross section, σ, viz.,

$$k = \left(n_1 \frac{g_2}{g_1} - n_2\right) \sigma, \tag{2.34}$$

(2.33) becomes

$$n_2 - \frac{g_2}{g_1} n_1 = \frac{1 - R}{\sigma D}. \tag{2.35}$$

Also since

$$\alpha = 2\pi\epsilon''/\epsilon'\lambda \tag{2.36}$$

when $\epsilon''/\epsilon' \ll 1$, where ϵ' and ϵ'' are respectively the real and imaginary parts of the complex dielectric constant, the threshold relation may be written as

$$(\epsilon''/\epsilon')Q = 1, \tag{2.37}$$

by using (2.20) and (2.30). The ratio ϵ'/ϵ'' is the material Q.

An important relation exists between the integrated absorption, and the lifetime of the excited state and the population densities (22). From (2.31) the integrated absorption is seen to be

$$\int_0^\infty k(\nu)\,d\nu = \frac{h\nu_{21}}{v}\, n_1 B_{12} \left(1 - \frac{g_1 n_2}{g_2 n_1}\right), \tag{2.38}$$

which may be put in the form

$$\int_0^\infty k(\nu)\,d\nu = \frac{\lambda_{21}^2}{8\pi} \frac{g_2}{g_1} \frac{n_1}{\tau_{21}} \left(1 - \frac{g_1 n_2}{g_2 n_1}\right). \tag{2.39}$$

by using (2.13). Since in the optical region the population in the excited state is exceedingly small, the second term in the parenthesis may be neglected in comparison with the first. In any case, once the integrated absorption has been determined, the B value or the lifetime may be obtained from (2.38) or (2.39), respectively, provided the populations are known.

The strength of an atomic line is often given in terms of the f-value, a quantity which arises in the classical electron theory of dispersion. The f-value is related to the integrated absorption by (22, 23)

$$\int_0^\infty k(\nu)\,d\nu = \frac{\pi e^2}{mv}\, n_1 f \tag{2.40}$$

when the excited state is empty. From (2.39) and (2.40), the connection between the f-value and the lifetime is seen to be

$$f\tau_{21} = \frac{mv}{8\pi^2 e^2} \frac{g_2}{g_1} \lambda_{21}^2 , \qquad (2.41)$$

where λ_{21} is the wavelength of light in the medium. From the relation for the classical lifetime of an electron, τ_{cl}, and taking $g_2 = g_1 = 1$, we may write (2.41) in the form $f = \tau_{cl}/3\tau_{21}$.

B. DIELECTRIC LOSS IN IONIC CRYSTALS

Whereas it is possible to select an ionic host lattice which has negligible absorption in the infrared and visible portions of the spectrum, it is impossible to avoid the very strong absorption in the far infrared region, say 50 to 500 cm^{-1}, arising from the optically active lattice modes. Let us examine the effect of this loss on the threshold condition for oscillation.

Suppose that the host crystal is doped with one of the rare earth ions, which in general have energy level separations in the far infrared region. Also suppose that the populations between a pair of these levels are inverted. The resulting negative absorption may be calculated from the expression,

$$\alpha(\nu_a) = \frac{4\pi |\mu_{21}|^2}{3h\nu} \frac{\nu_a}{\Delta\nu} \left(\frac{n_2}{g_2} - \frac{n_1}{g_1} \right) , \qquad (2.42)$$

which is obtained from (2.31) and (2.8). To obtain some idea of the possible magnitude of α, we take $g_1 = g_2$, $n_2 - n_1 \sim 1.5 \times 10^{19}$ cm^{-3}, $\mu \sim 10^{-20}$, $\nu_a/\Delta\nu \sim 10^3$, in which case $\alpha \sim 1$ cm^{-1}. This result is to be compared with the far infrared absorption of NaCl, for example, for which experimental results over an especially wide wavelength region have been obtained (24). It may be concluded in this particular instance that since lattice absorption in the region roughly 10μ to 300μ is larger than 1 cm^{-1}, maser action in this region is not possible.

Data on the lattice absorption of CaF_2, SrF_2, and BaF_2, which are frequently used as host lattices for ions of the rare earth and actinide groups, has been obtained by Kaiser et al. (25) in the region 9.5 to 80μ. Although at 9.5μ, the absorption in CaF_2, for example, has decreased to 1 cm^{-1}, it is much higher than this value at 80μ.

From a theoretical equation for the lattice absorption, whose validity at wavelengths too far removed from the resonance region may be questionable, we find that the absorption should decrease to 1 cm^{-1} at roughly 250μ. Thus with CaF_2 as the host lattice, and within the accuracy of this estimate, also SrF_2 and BaF_2, maser action would be precluded in the region 10 to 250μ. Despite the roughness of this estimate, it seems clear that maser action may not be possible in a considerable portion of the infrared spectrum with ionic crystals.

However, these estimates of lattice absorption are undoubtedly too pessimistic inasmuch as they are based on data obtained at room temperature. Measurements at submillimeter wavelengths in the low frequency wing of the main absorption band show a pronounced decrease in absorption in cooling to low temperatures (25a, 25b).

Thus far we have been concerned with the absorption of the ionic host crystal in the infrared region due to lattice vibrations. However, charge transfer bands and interband transitions in the ultraviolet region (21) make the crystal opaque as the band edge is approached.

III.   Spectral Line Shape

We have seen in the previous section that the radiation-induced transition rate and, consequently, the population excess required to sustain maser oscillation depend on the width and shape of the atomic spectral line. In particular, we employed the Lorentz and Doppler shapes, which represent limiting cases of more complex line shapes that are often encountered in gases and solids. In this chapter we will consider a line shape which represents a folding of the Lorentz and Gaussian distributions, allowing us to discuss gases and solids (and for that matter liquids) from a unified point of view. In addition, a number of aspects of line shape of significance in the behavior of masers will be discussed.

A. THE FOLDED LORENTZ-GAUSSIAN DISTRIBUTION

It has been well established that the Lorentz line shape results from processes which limit the lifetime of an excited state, and which randomly modulate the energy states (26). Processes limiting the lifetime include spontaneous emission of radiation and/or various types of collisions, such as collision of the radiating atom in a gas with neutral atoms, ions, and electrons, and with the walls of the container; or collisions of the radiating atom with the lattice in a solid. In addition, there are collisions whose effect is to change the phase of the emitted radiation and thereby modulate its frequency. On the other hand, the Gaussian shape may arise from mechanisms which create a distribution of atomic frequencies. Examples of such mechanisms are the Doppler effect resulting from the Maxwellian distribution of atomic velocities in a gas, and a random variation in the environment of atoms in a solid. It should be emphasized that other line shapes are often encountered despite the apparent ubiquitous nature of the Lorentz and Gaussian shapes. However, it is often possible to approximate the actual line profile by the Lorentz or Gaussian shapes, or a combination of both.

In real situations, mechanisms resulting in the Lorentz shape and mechanisms resulting in the Gaussian or Doppler shape are both present. Insofar as they are entirely independent, the resulting shape may be calculated by considering either every infinitesimal frequency band of the pure Doppler line broadened by random interruptions, or every infinitesimal band of the Lorentz curve broadened by the Doppler effect. In this circumstance, it can be shown that the normalized shape factor is given by (22)

$$S(\nu) = \frac{1}{\pi^{3/2}} \frac{\sqrt{\ln 2}}{\Delta\nu_D} \int_{-\infty}^{+\infty} \frac{\Delta\nu \left\{ \exp\left[-\left(\nu_D \frac{\sqrt{\ln 2}}{\Delta\nu_D} \right)^2 \right] \right\} d\nu_D}{\Delta\nu^2 + (\nu - \nu_0 - \nu_D)^2}, \qquad (3.1)$$

where some frequency band is selected at a distance $\nu - \nu_0$ from the center of the line showing only Lorentz broadening, and the Doppler broadening of this frequency band is represented by a variable distance ν_D from the point $\nu - \nu_0$. Transforming to the new variables, $\xi = \nu_D/\Delta\nu$ and $x = \Delta\nu \sqrt{\ln 2}/\Delta\nu_D$, and specializing for the resonance condition $\nu = \nu_0$, we obtain

$$S(\nu_0) = \frac{1}{\pi^{3/2}} \frac{\sqrt{\ln 2}}{\Delta\nu_D} \int_{-\infty}^{+\infty} \frac{e^{-x^2\xi^2}}{1 + \xi^2} d\xi. \qquad (3.2)$$

This expression may be transformed to a form easier to evaluate (27), namely

$$S(\nu_0) = \frac{1}{\pi\Delta\nu} xe^{x^2} \left(\sqrt{\pi} - 2 \int_0^x e^{-\xi^2} d\xi \right)$$

$$= \frac{2}{\pi\Delta\nu} xe^{x^2} \int_x^\infty e^{-\xi^2} d\xi. \qquad (3.3)$$

If both frequency distributions in (3.1) are Lorentzian, the line shape resulting from the folding of two Lorentz distributions is again a Lorentz distribution with a width that is the sum of the widths of the two components.

B. Line Shape in Gases

In the microwave and far infrared regions, the width of the resonance is controlled by collisions at all but the lowest pressures. In this case, $\Delta\nu_D \sim 0$, and $\Delta\nu = \Delta\nu_c$, where $\Delta\nu_c$, at pressures that are not too high, is proportional to the pressure. Thus $x \gg 1$, in which case an asymptotic expansion of (3.3) gives

$$S(\nu_0) = \frac{1}{\pi \Delta \nu} \left[1 - \frac{1}{2} \left(\frac{\Delta \nu_D}{\Delta \nu \sqrt{\ln 2}} \right)^2 + \frac{3}{4} \left(\frac{\Delta \nu_D}{\Delta \nu \sqrt{\ln 2}} \right)^4 \cdots \right], \qquad (3.4)$$

where the first term is the Lorentz contribution. At the shorter wavelengths of the infrared and optical regions, the spontaneous emission rate $\tau_{21}^{-1} = \Delta \omega_{21}$ becomes significant (see Table I), and the total Lorentz width must be written as $\Delta \nu = \Delta \nu_c + \Delta \nu_{21}$. However, in gases at low pressures, the Doppler line width is likely to be considerably larger than the total Lorentz width. In this case $x \ll 1$, and

$$S(\nu_0) = \frac{\sqrt{\ln 2}}{\pi \Delta \nu_D} \left[\sqrt{\pi} - 2 \left(\frac{\Delta \nu \sqrt{\ln 2}}{\Delta \nu_D} \right) + \sqrt{\pi} \left(\frac{\Delta \nu \sqrt{\ln 2}}{\Delta \nu_D} \right)^2 \cdots \right], \qquad (3.5)$$

where the first term is just the Doppler contribution.

C. NATURE OF LINE BROADENING IN SOLIDS

Whereas the question of the shapes and widths of spectral lines in gases and plasmas has been the subject of numerous theoretical and experimental investigations for many years, the case of solids has been attacked relatively recently and rather little is understood quantitatively. Mechanisms which can broaden the optical lines of rare earth ions in ionic crystals have been discussed qualitatively (28). The present theoretical position of line broadening in solids has been reviewed in detail by Dexter (29). Presented here is a qualitative discussion of the following mechanisms affecting line width and shape: (a) transitions in which a change in vibrational quantum number is superimposed on the pure electronic transition, (b) phonon transitions between neighboring Stark levels in rare earth ions which reduce the lifetime of such levels, (c) variation of local electric fields in different sites which render the Stark splitting nonuniform, and (d) adiabatic modulation of electronic transitions by lattice vibrations.

(a) For ions subject to the electrostatic crystal field but isolated from the phonon spectrum, the line width would be very small, essentially the inverse lifetime for spontaneous emission, and the line shape would be Lorentzian. However, the ions are in fact coupled to a vibrating lattice, and in the general case of optical transitions both electronic and vibrational wave functions change. Thus, for a given electronic transition one might expect a series of lines involving pairs of vibrational states. Although discrete lines of this type may be observed at low temperature, the common situation is the occurrence of thermally broadened bands composed of many unresolved lines. Broadband vibrational structure due to phonon excitation is often observed on the low frequency side of sharp fluorescent lines. As the temperature is increased, this background of emission increases in intensity relative to the sharp line and decreases the efficiency of fluorescence from it.

Sharp fluorescent lines are produced by electronic transitions, accompanied by Raman scattering, in which the total number of phonons do not change. However, since the energies of the emitted and absorbed phonons are in general not equal, these lines are thermally broadened by a transfer of energy to the lattice, and by the fact that there is an uncertainty in the amount of this energy transfer (*29a, 29b*).

(b) In the rare earth ions there are groups of levels which result from stark splitting by the crystal field and which have typical spacings from 10 to 100 cm^{-1}. It may be expected that relaxation transitions to neighboring states within a Stark manifold involving absorption or emission of phonons will sufficiently reduce the lifetime of such levels to the point where the optical transitions are broadened. In particular, a lifetime of the order of 10^{-10} sec is short enough to have an observable effect on a line 1 cm^{-1} in width. This broadening mechanism has been recently considered by Yatsiv (*30*).

(c) A mechanism responsible for the width of a fluorescent line without affecting its lifetime is that due to strains in the crystal. The width arises from the situation that different ions are subject to different local crystal fields and hence different resonant frequencies. If these frequencies have a Gaussian distribution, the fluorescent line shape may be described by (3.1), where $2\pi\Delta\nu$ is now the inverse lifetime of the excited state. A way of illustrating these two types of broadening is shown in Fig. 3, where the narrow natural line (dashed) represents the line shape of a packet of atoms whose resonance frequencies lie in a very small range, and the broad envelope represents the distribution of atomic frequencies.

(d) It is possible for an interaction to cause adiabatically slow variations in energy without affecting the lifetime of a state as, for example, the random modulation of optical energy levels by collisions in a gas. In a crystal the local electric field at the position of an ion depends on the instantaneous position of its neighbors. Due to the lattice vibrations, the effective crystal field is a function of time and varies throughout the crystal at a given instant. The vibrational period is so short compared with the time of measurement that one observes a broadened line about some average frequency. The magnitude of the line broadening is approximately equal to the energy variation in the excited state. This type of broadening clearly increases with temperature. The question of adiabatic and strain broadening of excited states in crystals have been discussed quantitatively by Kiel (*31*).

It is expected that the line shapes resulting from the various line broadening mechanisms discussed here may, in general, be approximated by the folded Lorentz-Gaussian distribution (3.1). Using this equation plus the appropriate matrix elements, one can estimate transition rates from (2.2) or discuss the threshold conditions for oscillation from (2.7) in a unified way for gases and solids (*32*).

D. SATURATION

The details of the behavior of a system of atoms illuminated with intense monochromatic radiation, i.e., its saturation behavior, depend markedly on the nature of the broadening mechanism. If the broadening arises from transitions limiting the lifetime of the excited state, or from some mechanism which is fluctuating rapidly compared with the time associated with an atomic transition, then the energy absorbed from the radiation field will be distributed to all atoms. This case, an example of which is the adiabatic modulation of the electronic transition by lattice vibrations, is called homogeneous broadening. When there is a static distribution of atomic frequencies, the inhomogeneous case, energy will be transferred only to those atoms whose local fields satisfy the resonance condition.

Consider an assembly of atoms with only two energy states, and with a homogeneously broadened line. In the presence of an applied signal the density of atoms in the ground state 1 and excited state 2 will be governed by

$$\frac{dn_2}{dt} = - (\Gamma_{21}^i + \Gamma_{21}^l)\, n_2 + (\Gamma_{12}^i + \Gamma_{12}^l)\, n_1\,, \qquad n_1 + n_2 = n_0 \qquad (3.6)$$

where n_0 is the total population, Γ_{12}^i and Γ_{21}^i are the induced transition rates due to the applied signal, and Γ_{12}^l and Γ_{21}^l are the transition rates which tend to maintain the system in thermal equilibrium. In the language of magnetic resonance the Γ^l's are related to T_1, the longitudinal relaxation time, by $(T_1)^{-1} = \Gamma_{12}^l + \Gamma_{21}^l$; another relaxation time T_2, the transverse relaxation time or the dephasing time is related to the line width by $T_2 = \Delta\omega^{-1}$. Solving (3.6) for the steady state, and using n_1^0 and n_2^0 for the populations in thermal equilibrium, we have for the population difference,

$$n_1 - n_2 = \frac{n_1^0 - n_2^0}{2\Gamma_{12}^i T_1 + 1}, \tag{3.7}$$

which is now a function of frequency because $\Gamma_{12}^i = B_{12} w S(\nu)$. Now according to (2.1), the rate at which energy is absorbed per unit volume from the radiation field is proportional to $n_1 - n_2$, neglecting the degeneracy factors. Thus from (2.1) and (3.7), we find that

$$-\frac{dw}{dt} = h\nu \frac{(n_1^0 - n_2^0) B_{12} w S(\nu)}{1 + 2T_1 B_{12} w S(\nu)}. \tag{3.8}$$

If there is a distribution of atomic frequencies described by the normalized function

$$\int_0^\infty H(\nu - \nu_0)\, d\nu = 1, \tag{3.9}$$

then the power absorbed by the inhomogeneously broadened line is

$$-\frac{dw}{dt} = (n_1^0 - n_2^0)\, h\nu B_{12} w \int_{-\infty}^\infty \frac{S(\nu - \nu_0 - \nu_D)\, H(\nu_D)\, d\nu_D}{1 + 2T_1 w B_{12} S(\nu - \nu_0 - \nu_D)}. \tag{3.10}$$

We see from (3.8) and (3.10) that the way in which an atomic system saturates will be quite different depending on whether the atomic system is homogeneously or inhomogeneously broadened.

If $H(\nu_D)$ and $S(\nu)$ are Lorentzian, (3.10) becomes

$$-\frac{dw}{dt} = \frac{(n_1^0 - n_2^0) h\nu B_{12} w}{(1 + w/w_0)^{1/2}} H_{\Delta\nu'}(\nu - \nu_0), \tag{3.11}$$

where $H_{\Delta\nu'}(\nu - \nu_0)$ is a Lorentzian whose half width is $\Delta\nu' = \Delta\nu_D + \Delta\nu(1 + w/w_0)^{1/2}$, and $w_0^{-1} = 2T_1 B/\pi\Delta\nu$. If $S(\nu)$ is regarded as a delta function, (3.11) is again obtained from (3.10), where $H(\nu)$ is now an arbitrary line shape function. Assuming that $\Delta\nu_D \gg \Delta\nu(1 + w/w_0)^{1/2}$, we see that the shape of the absorption curve does not change with saturation, and its absolute value varies as $(1 + w/w_0)^{-1/2}$. On the other hand (3.8) shows that the shape of the homogeneously broadened line changes with saturation, and its absolute value at resonance saturates as $(1 + w/w_0)^{-1}$. The saturation behavior in emission when there is a population inversion and an externally applied signal is similar to that in absorption. It may be noted that when there are standing waves or traveling waves with a transverse field variation, the degree of saturation will be a function of position.

In obtaining the equations for the saturated power output it was assumed that levels 1 and 2 are either nondegenerate or have equal degeneracies. When these conditions do not apply, n_2 and n_2^0, must be multiplied by g_1/g_2 in (3.7), (3.8), (3.10), and (3.11), and $2\Gamma_{12}^i$ and $2B_{12}$ in the denominators must be replaced by $\Gamma_{12}^i + \Gamma_{21}^i$ and $B_{12} + B_{21}$, respectively.

The behavior of an atomic system when subject to intense radiation has been described in terms of populations. However, such a description is correct provided the radiation field does not appreciably mix the atomic states and introduce coherent phase factors in the wave functions. The new effects which arise when this occurs are discussed in Chapter XIII.

IV.   Steady State Theory of the Optical Maser

A. Introduction

In the microwave region, the maser oscillator* which has received the greatest attention is the NH_3 beam type where the molecules traverse a single mode cavity with an electric field of essentially constant phase. In such an arrangement, Doppler broadening is practically eliminated and the width of the atomic resonance is determined largely by the time interval that the atom interacts with the electric field in its passage through the cavity. The resulting resonance, which is of the homogeneous type, is considerably sharper than the cavity resonance. Townes and co-workers (36, 37) have analyzed the spectral and frequency pulling characteristics of such an oscillator, in particular the ammonia beam maser. In the microwave solid state maser, which has been employed mostly as a low noise amplifier, the atomic width is usually greater than the cavity width. However no more than one or a few cavity modes are contained within the atomic line width.

The situation in the optical region differs in several important respects from that which obtains in the microwave region. The optical atomic resonance with a Q of perhaps 10^3 to 10^5 has a width some orders of magnitude greater than the width of a single resonator mode, and as may be estimated from (2.26) there may be more than 10^{11} cavity modes within the atomic resonance in typical situations. Gases in the optical region have a width which is due predominantly to Doppler rather than collision broadening. Clearly the detailed behavior of an inhomogeneously broadened resonance coupled to a resonator with a large number of modes may be expected to have

---

* The theory of microwave masers has been reviewed by Troup (5), Vuylsteke (6), and Lamb (33). The theory of induced and spontaneous emission in a coherent field has been extensively developed by Senitzky (34) in a number of papers. An interesting comparison of the quantum and semiclassical theories of radiation with application to the beam maser has been made by Jaynes and Cummings (35).

features considerably different from the case of a single mode resonator and an homogeneously broadened line.

In addition to the nature of the broadening, a variety of linear and nonlinear effects which couple the modes play an important role in determining the detailed properties of optical masers. Notwithstanding such complications, much can be learned by considering the simplest case of an homogeneously broadened atomic system in a resonator where the modes are taken to be orthogonal. However, the inherent nonlinear behavior of the system, i.e., the saturation of the gain, is retained thus allowing a detailed examination of the distribution of the power in the various resonator modes. Later we will discuss in a qualitative way, the effects of inhomogeneous broadening, and various effects which couple the cavity modes.

The theory of the optical maser may be approached from the mode or wave points of view, both of which should give, of course, equivalent results. However, situations arise where one viewpoint may be more suitable or appropriate than the other. Because it is valuable to understand the many facets of the optical maser problem, both approaches will be employed in the following developments.

B. WAVE ANALYSIS

1. Power Spectrum

In the case of the ammonia beam maser, Gordon, Zeiger, and Townes (36) analyzed the output spectrum by considering the device as a linear amplifier driven by circuit or thermal noise. In the optical region, where the thermal noise is inconsequential compared with the spontaneous emission from the maser material, it is natural to consider the maser as an amplifier driven by spontaneous emission. In particular, consider the open sided resonator of the Fabry-Perot type shown schematically in Fig. 1, consisting of plane parallel, partially transmitting mirrors whose complex transmission and reflection coefficients are, respectively, t' and r'.* Let the resonator be uniformly filled with a material whose complex propagation constant is $\kappa = (k - \alpha)/2 + i\beta$, where α is the negative absorption due to the maser atoms, k is the dielectric loss of the host material, and β is the

---

* The properties of a Fabry-Perot interferometer containing an amplifying medium have been discussed by a number of authors (38-41).

phase shift due to the maser atoms and the host material. We wish to calculate the amplitude of the waves, i.e., a self-reproducing field pattern, in a single cavity mode, generated by the spontaneous emission noise from a slab of active material, dz in length. Then by the method of adding the complex amplitude of repeatedly reflected waves, we find that the wave transmitted through mirror 2, emanating from the right and left sides of the slab are, respectively,

$$\frac{t_2 A e^{-\kappa(D-z)}}{1 - r_1 r_2 e^{-2\kappa D}}, \tag{4.1}$$

$$\frac{r_1 t_2 A e^{-\kappa(D+z)}}{1 - r_1 r_2 e^{-2\kappa D}}. \tag{4.2}$$

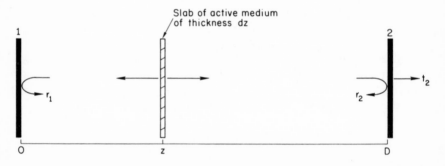

Fig. 1.   Diagram of the Fabry-Perot Resonator.

Multiplying (4.1) and (4.2) by their complex conjugates and adding we find that the power per unit length of material per unit frequency range transmitted through mirror 2 is given by

$$P_{\nu, z} = \frac{A^2 t_2^2 e^{(\alpha-k)D} \big(e^{-(\alpha-k)z} + r_1^2 e^{(\alpha-k)z}\big)}{(1 - r_1 r_2 e^{(\alpha-k)D})^2 + 4 r_1 r_2 e^{(\alpha-k)D} \sin^2 \beta D}, \tag{4.3}$$

where $t_2 = |t_2'|$, $r_1 = |r_1'|$, and $r_2 = |r_2'|$. The quantity A^2 is defined by

$$A^2 \, dz \, d\nu = \frac{n_2 a \, dz \, h\nu}{p'\tau} \frac{1}{\pi} \frac{\Delta\nu_a \, d\nu}{(\nu - \nu_a)^2 + \Delta\nu_a^2}, \tag{4.4}$$

where p' is the number of modes in cross sectional area a, and is given by

$$p' = \frac{a 4\pi\nu^2}{v^2}. \tag{4.5}$$

The quantity βD is the single pass phase shift, and for a standing wave to build up in the cavity, i.e., to obtain resonance, βD must be an integral multiple of π. The phase shifts due to reflection, like that due to the host medium, are independent of frequency over the frequency range of interest. The reflection phase shifts have only a very slight influence on the resonance frequency of the resonator and for simplicity are omitted, although their effect may be represented by using an adjusted value for the refractive index of the host medium. The power reflection coefficient, $r_2{}^2 = R_2$, and the power transmission coefficient, $t_2{}^2 = T_2$, are related by

$$R_2 + T_2 + A_2 + F_2 = 1, \tag{4.6}$$

where A_2 and F_2 are, respectively, the fraction of light absorbed and diffracted by the mirror.

With the assumption that $k = 0,{}^*$ $\alpha D \ll 1$, $r_1 r_2 \simeq 1$, and that the system is operating near resonance, we obtain from (4.3) by performing the integration over z,

$$P_\nu \, d\nu = \frac{2A^2 t_2^2 D \, d\nu}{[(1 - r_1 r_2) - \alpha D]^2 + [2\Delta\beta D]^2}. \tag{4.7}$$

We have used the relation that the phase shift, $\phi = \beta D$, near resonance is

$$\beta D = \beta_c D - \Delta\beta D, \tag{4.8}$$

where $\beta_c D = q\pi$ and $\Delta\beta D \ll 1$. Now the phase shift for a wave traveling once through a resonator of length D and waveguide wavelength, λ_g, is

$$\phi = \frac{2\pi D}{\lambda_g} \simeq \frac{2\pi\nu Dn}{c}, \tag{4.9}$$

where in the type of highly overmoded resonator of interest here we have taken λ_g to be $c/\nu n$, the plane wave value in a medium of refractive index n. Hence the cavity has resonance frequencies separated by $c/2Dn$. Small changes in phase measured from the phase at the cavity frequency are given by

$$\frac{\partial\phi}{\partial\nu}(\nu - \nu_c) + \Delta\phi = 0. \tag{4.10}$$

* If $kD \ll 1$, then $1 - r_1 r_2$ should be replaced by $1 - r_1 r_2 + kD$ in the expressions which follow.

Pulling of the oscillation frequency, which is treated in the following section, is neglected here by assuming that the cavity frequency and atomic frequency, and consequently the oscillation frequency, are all equal.

From (4.9) and (4.10) we have for the change in phase shift due to the dispersion of the resonator

$$\Delta\phi_c = (\nu_c - \nu)\,\frac{2\pi n_0 D}{c} \tag{4.11}$$

where n_0 is independent of frequency. To calculate the phase change due to the dispersion of the amplifying medium, we write for a Lorentzian line,

$$\alpha(\nu) = \alpha(\nu_a)\,[1 + (\nu_a - \nu)^2/\Delta\nu_a^2]^{-1}, \tag{4.12}$$

and

$$\Delta\phi(\nu) = (n_\nu - 1)\,\frac{2\pi\nu D}{c} = -\frac{\alpha(\nu)\,D}{2}\,\frac{\nu_a - \nu}{\Delta\nu_a}, \tag{4.13}$$

provided that $\alpha(\nu) \ll 1$, $\nu + \nu_a \simeq 2\nu$, and where $\alpha(\nu_a)$ is the absorption coefficient at the atomic resonance. The total change in phase which is substituted in (4.7) is the sum of (4.11) and (4.13). Thus we obtain from (4.7) and (4.4)

$$P_\nu\,d\nu = \frac{t_2^2}{1 - r_1 r_2}\,\frac{GN_2 h\nu_a}{Y}\,\frac{8\pi^2\mu^2\nu_a}{3hV\Delta\nu_a}\,\frac{1}{\pi}\,\frac{(\Delta\nu_c/GY)\,d\nu}{(\Delta\nu_c/GY)^2 + (\nu - \nu_c)^2} \tag{4.14}$$

where

$$Y = [1 + (\Delta\nu_c/\Delta\nu_a)],$$

and G is the gain given by

$$G = \left[1 - \frac{\alpha(\nu_a)\,D}{(1 - r_1 r_2)}\right]^{-1}. \tag{4.15}$$

In obtaining (4.14), we have neglected $(\nu_a - \nu)^2/\Delta\nu_a^2$ in comparison with 1 on the basis that $G \gg 1$. The limiting case $G \to \infty$ will be recognized as the oscillation condition. In accordance with (2.20), the half cavity width at half amplitude, $\Delta\nu_c$, is given by

$$\Delta\nu_c = \frac{c(1 - r_1 r_2)}{4\pi n_0 D}$$

Equation (4.14) describes the frequency distribution of the power output for a homogeneously broadened atomic system driving a single cavity mode by spontaneous emission noise. The power spectrum has a Lorentzian shape with a half width $\Delta\nu_{os}$ given by

$$\Delta\nu_{os} = \frac{\Delta\nu_c}{G\left(1 + \dfrac{\Delta\nu_c}{\Delta\nu_a}\right)},\qquad(4.16)$$

which is just the usual gain-bandwidth product of linear amplifier theory. These results have been obtained by another method described in ref. (42). When $\Delta\nu_c \ll \Delta\nu_a$, the case appropriate for the optical region, (4.16) is simply

$$\Delta\nu_{os} = \Delta\nu_c/G.\qquad(4.17)$$

Upon performing the integration in (4.14), and for simplicity omitting the factor $t_2^2/(1 - r_1 r_2)$, the power resulting from amplified spontaneous emission is seen to be

$$P = N_2 h\nu G[(8\pi^2\mu^2\nu_a)/(3hV\Delta\nu_a)] \, [1 + (\Delta\nu_c/\Delta\nu_a)]^{-1}.\qquad(4.18)$$

The term $8\pi^2\mu^2\nu_a/3hV\Delta\nu_a$ is the induced transition rate resulting from one photon per unit volume, and when multiplied by $N_2 h\nu$ represents the emitted power for N_2 atoms in the excited state. This power multiplied by the gain of the system is the total power in the cavity mode. Solving (4.18) for G, we may put the expression for oscillator spectral width, (4.16), in the form

$$\Delta\nu_{0s} = \frac{8\pi^2\mu^2 n_2 \nu_a^2}{3P\Delta\nu_a} \frac{\Delta\nu_c}{[1 + (\Delta\nu_c/\Delta\nu_a)]^2}.\qquad(4.19)$$

When expressed in terms of the degree of inversion, $(n_2 - n_1)_{th}$, required for the gain to become infinite, (4.19) becomes

$$\Delta\nu_{0s} = \frac{n_2}{(n_2 - n_1)_{th}} \frac{h\nu_a}{\tau_c P} \frac{\Delta\nu_c}{[1 + (\Delta\nu_c/\Delta\nu_a)]^2}\qquad(4.20)$$

2. Shifts in the Oscillation Frequency

The method used by Bennett (43) for analyzing frequency pulling effects nicely fits in with the previous developments. Now the total change in single-pass phase shift at the actual frequency of oscillation ν_{os} which is caused by the insertion of the medium, may be expressed in the form

$$\Delta\phi_T(\nu_{os}) \equiv (2\pi D/c) \left[(n_0 - 1) + (n_\nu - 1) \right] \nu_{os}$$
$$\equiv (2\pi D/c) (n_0 - 1) \nu_{os} + \Delta\phi(\nu_{os}). \tag{4.21}$$

The first term arises from the host material and from atoms in the ground and excited states of the active material which can participate in transitions other than the maser transition. The second term is due to the dispersion of the maser transition. Including the effects of n_0 by defining $\nu_c = \nu_{0c}/n_0$ and $\Delta\nu_c = \Delta\nu_{0c}/n_0$, we have for the oscillation frequency from $(\partial\phi/\partial\nu)(\nu_{os} - \nu_{0c}) = -\Delta\phi_T(\nu_{os})$ and (4.21),

$$\nu_{os} = \nu_c - (2\Delta\nu_c/\zeta) \, \Delta\phi(\nu_{os}), \tag{4.22}$$

where ζ, the fractional energy loss per pass, is from the definition of Q

$$\zeta = 4\pi\Delta\nu_{0c}D/c. \tag{4.23}$$

On making a Taylor expansion of $\Delta\phi(\nu_{os})$ about ν_c and substituting in (4.22), we have to the second order

$$\nu_{os} = \nu_c - (2\Delta\nu_c/\zeta) \, \Delta\phi(\nu_c) \left[1 - (2\Delta\nu_c/\zeta) \, (\partial\Delta\phi/\partial\nu)_{\nu_c} + \cdots \right]. \tag{4.24}$$

Threshold for oscillation occurs at that frequency ν_{th} satisfying both (4.22) and the requirement

$$g(\nu_{os}) = \zeta, \tag{4.25}$$

where $g(\nu_{os})$ is the single pass fractional gain. (4.25) is another way of writing $\alpha(\nu_{os}) \, D = (1 - r_1 r_2)$. The characteristics of the amplifying medium may be specified by the complex propagation coefficient or by the single pass fractional energy gain and phase constant, namely,

$$g = \alpha D, \qquad \phi = \beta D. \tag{4.26}$$

Equations (4.13), (4.22), and (4.25) give for a Lorentz line

$$\nu_{os} = \frac{\nu_c\Delta\nu_a + \nu_a\Delta\nu_c}{\Delta\nu_a + \Delta\nu_c}, \tag{4.27}$$

a result which has been obtained previously by another method (42).

A good approximation for $\Delta\phi$ for a Gaussian line when the frequency deviation is within the line width is (43)

$$\Delta\phi(\nu) \cong -0.28_2 g_a \sin\left(\frac{\nu_a - \nu}{0.6\Delta\nu_a}\right). \tag{4.28}$$

The fractional energy gain per pass for the Gaussian is

$$g(\nu) \cong g_a \exp\left[-\left(\frac{\nu_a - \nu}{1.2\Delta\nu_a}\right)^2\right], \tag{4.29}$$

where $1.2 \simeq (\ln 2)^{-1/2}$. Then (4.22), (4.25), and (4.28) yield

$$\nu_{os} = \nu_c + 0.56\Delta\nu_c \exp\left[\left(\frac{\nu_a - \nu_{os}}{1.2\Delta\nu_a}\right)^2\right] \sin\left(\frac{\nu_a - \nu_{os}}{0.6\Delta\nu_a}\right). \tag{4.30}$$

Thus for a Gaussian line shape, the pulling is nonlinear even for a homogeneously broadened line. However, for frequencies very near the line center and $\Delta\nu_c \ll \Delta\nu_a$, (4.30) becomes linear, viz.,

$$\nu_{os} = \nu_c + (\nu_a - \nu_c)\left(0.94\,\frac{\Delta\nu_c}{\Delta\nu_a}\right)\left[1 - 0.94\,\frac{\Delta\nu_c}{\Delta\nu_a} + \ldots\right]. \tag{4.31}$$

This result is similar to that obtained for the Lorentz shape under the same conditions, except for a 6% reduction in the pulling factor.

Maser behavior when the atomic resonance is inhomogeneously broadened differs from the case of homogeneous broadening. When the latter condition obtains the increase of gain at ν_{os} necessary to satisfy (4.25) produces a proportionate increase of gain at all other frequencies. Thus, for homogeneous broadening the oscillation frequency is always given by its value at threshold and there is no power-dependent pulling effect. In addition, a second cavity mode would generally not go into oscillation with increasing power because condition (4.25) would prevent another cavity resonance from reaching threshold. For inhomogeneous broadening, the oscillation condition is satisfied by burning a hole in the line, i.e., $g(\nu_{os})$ saturates at ν_{os} whereas the gain over the rest of the line continues to increase with pumping power.

We have seen that the extent to which the frequency of the stimulated emission oscillation from a maser approaches that of the center of the normal emission line depends on the nature of the broadening and on the widths of the atomic line and cavity resonance. However, even if the cavity and atomic frequencies were equal and the frequency pulling were consequently zero, the precise oscillation frequency would still not be that of the normal emission line. One reason for this arises from the circumstance that the Lorentz field in a dielectric medium makes the atomic frequency depend very slightly on the population of the levels between which the transition occurs (44). Another frequency pulling effect arises from a time-dependent Stark effect due to the coherent field, the electric analog of the Bloch-Siegert effect, which causes the atomic frequency to increase very slightly with the energy in the electric field (45).

3. The Traveling Wave Amplifier

We suppose that a medium interacts with a beam of radiation incident in a direction θ and ϕ, having an energy density per unit frequency range per unit solid angle $w(\nu, \theta, \phi, \mathbf{e})$ where ν is the frequency and $\mathbf{e}$ is a unit vector which defines the polarization of the radiation. Then the equation for the rate of anisotropic emission becomes

$$\frac{dw(\nu, \theta, \phi, \mathbf{e})}{dt} = w(\nu, \theta, \phi, \mathbf{e})\, h\nu\, S(\nu)\, [n_2 B_{21}(\theta, \phi, \mathbf{e}) - n_1 B_{12}(\theta, \phi, \mathbf{e})]$$
$$+ n_2 h\nu A_{21}(\theta, \varphi, \mathbf{e})\, S(\nu). \tag{4.32}$$

$A(\theta, \phi, \mathbf{e})$ is the spontaneous emission rate per unit solid angle for radiation with polarization $\mathbf{e}$ emitted in a direction specified by θ and ϕ, and $B_{21}(\theta, \phi, \mathbf{e})$ is the B coefficient for induced emission in a direction specified by θ and ϕ and for radiation with polarization $\mathbf{e}$. The anisotropic A and B coefficients are related by

$$A_{21}(\theta, \phi, \mathbf{e}) = \left(\frac{\nu^2}{v^3}\right) h\nu B_{21}(\theta, \phi, \mathbf{e}). \tag{4.33}$$

If the transition is isotropic, then $A_{21}(\theta, \phi, \mathbf{e}) = A_{21}/8\pi$. To find the gain, the portion of (4.32) due to stimulated emission is integrated to give (46)

$$\int_{w_0}^{w} \frac{dw(\nu, \theta, \phi, \mathbf{e})}{w(\nu, \theta, \phi, \mathbf{e})} = \int_0^{D(\theta,\phi)/v} [n_2 B_{21}(\theta, \phi, \mathbf{e}) - n_1 B_{12}(\theta, \phi, \mathbf{e})]\, h\nu\, S(\nu)\, dt,$$

where $w_0(\nu, \theta, \phi, \mathbf{e})$ is the incident energy density, and $D(\theta, \phi)$ is the length of the medium in the direction considered. The gain in db is consequently

$$G_{db}(\nu, \theta, \phi, \mathbf{e}) = (10 \log e) \frac{D(\theta, \phi)}{v} S(\nu) \, h\nu[n_2 B_{21}(\theta, \phi, \mathbf{e}) - n_1 B_{12}(\theta, \phi, \mathbf{e})],$$

(4.34)

and by comparing (4.34) with (2.31), the gain is also seen to be

$$G_{db}(\nu, \theta, \phi, \mathbf{e}) = (10 \log e) \, \alpha(\nu, \theta, \phi, \mathbf{e}) \, D(\theta, \phi). \qquad (4.34a)$$

For a Lorentzian line shape the bandwidth B_L over which the gain is within 3 db of the peak gain is given by

$$B_L = 2\Delta\nu_L \left(\frac{3}{G_{db,max} - 3}\right)^{1/2},$$

whereas for a Gaussian line shape the bandwidth B_G is given by

$$B_G = 2\Delta\nu_G \left(\frac{\log \dfrac{G_{db,max}}{G_{db,max} - 3}}{\log 2}\right)^{1/2}.$$

$G_{db,max}$ is given by (4.34) by letting ν be the frequency at the center of the line. It may be seen from these expressions that the bandwidth of the traveling wave amplifier is not very much less than the bandwidth of the atomic resonance. This result is to be contrasted with the very narrow bandwidths which obtain when there is regeneration. For large gain the expression for B_G assumes the same form as that for B_L, apart from the factor $(\log 2)^{-1/2}$. For large gain, the frequency dependence near ν_a of the radiation leaving the amplifying medium takes the Gaussian shape independently of whether the atomic line shape is Gaussian or Lorentzian.

At high levels of radiation intensity, saturation becomes important and the gain characteristics of the maser amplifier become nonlinear, as discussed by Prokhorov (46a) and Rigrod (46b). To treat the problem of gain saturation, we follow the method of Rigrod (46b) by writing the negative absorption coefficient in the form,

$$\alpha(\nu) = \frac{\alpha_0(\nu)}{(1 + w/w_0)^n}, \qquad (4.34b)$$

where w is the energy or power density, $n = 1$ for a homogeneously broadened line, and $n = \frac{1}{2}$ for an inhomogeneously broadened line.

The unsaturated absorption coefficient $\alpha_0(\nu)$ and the saturation parameter w_0 are different for homogeneously and inhomogeneously broadened lines. Equation (4.34b) follows from the discussion of Section III, D, and will be considered further in Chapter VIII. Letting k represent the various losses due to scattering and dielectric absorption, the net gain is given by

$$\frac{1}{w}\frac{dw}{dx} = \frac{\alpha_0(\nu)}{(1 + w/w_0)^n} - k . \qquad (4.34c)$$

When $k = 0$, (4.34c) integrated over a path D gives for a homogeneously broadened line

$$\alpha_0(\nu)D = \ln(w_2/w_1) + (w_2 - w_1)/w_0 .$$

This expression shows that at high amplification levels where $w_2/w_1 \gg 1$, the power increases approximately linearly with distance rather than exponentially as in the small signal limit. When medium losses are present and $k \neq 0$, the maximum possible intensity in the amplifier corresponding to zero gain is $(w_2)_{max} = (\alpha_0/k - 1)w_0$. For an inhomogeneously broadened line, (4.34c) integrated over a path D gives at high levels of intensity

$$\alpha_0(\nu)D \simeq 2[(1 + w_2/w_0)^{1/2} - (1 + w_1/w_0)^{1/2}] ,$$

which gives a relatively faster increase of gain with $\alpha_0(\nu)D$ than for homogeneous broadening.

4. Amplification of Spontaneous Radiation by Traveling Waves

If one or both of the mirrors of the interferometer are removed, and if reflections due to the discontinuity of the medium are negligible, there is clearly no possibility of oscillation, although the spontaneous radiation will be amplified by traveling waves if $e^{(\alpha-k)D} > 1$. This amplified noise power per unit frequency interval is from (4.3) with $r_1 = r_2 = 0$ and $k = 0$ given by *

$$P_\nu = \frac{e^{\alpha(\nu)D} - 1}{\alpha(\nu)\,D}\,\frac{N_2 h\nu}{\tau p'}\,\frac{1}{\pi}\,\frac{\Delta\nu}{(\nu - \nu_a)^2 + \Delta\nu^2} . \qquad (4.35)$$

* Equation (4.35) may be written in the form $P_\nu = 2P_\nu'(e^{\alpha(\nu)D} - 1)$, where $P_\nu' = h\nu N_2[N_2 - N_1(g_2/g_1)]^{-1}$ is the noise power per mode per unit bandwidth given by the theory of black body radiation.

Now spontaneous emission noise excites all waveguide modes, or equivalently excites the plane waves contained in the whole solid angle. The solids commonly used for masers have relatively large indices of refraction, and consequently internal reflections may occur for large angles of incidence; for ruby, for example, the critical angle is approximately 60°. Multiply reflected rays should experience larger gain therefore than the rays which travel through the crystal without reflection from the side walls. However, the variation of gain with direction will not be too great and the power will be more or less uniformly distributed among the many strongly propagating modes. To treat this situation in a rough approximation, it is assumed that the plane waves that are excited are contained in the solid angle $2\pi(L/D)^2$, where L is the diameter and D is the length of the crystal. Thus from (4.35) and the fact that the solid angle associated with one radiation mode is $4\lambda^2/\pi L^2$, we obtain

$$P_\nu \, d\nu = \frac{e^{\alpha(\nu_a)D} e^{-\alpha(\nu_a)D[(\nu_a-\nu)/\Delta\nu]^2}}{\alpha(\nu_a)\, D} \frac{N_2 h\nu_a}{2\tau} \left(\frac{L}{D}\right)^2 \frac{d\nu}{\pi\Delta\nu}, \qquad (4.36)$$

where we have assumed that $e^{\alpha(\nu_a)D} \gg 1$, and have expanded $\alpha(\nu)$ for small departures from the resonance value. The resulting frequency distribution is Gaussian whose half width is $\Delta\nu_a(\ln 2/\alpha(\nu_a)D)^{1/2}$. Thus, the rather modest line narrowing in the traveling wave case occurs via the dispersion in the single pass gain factor. Because there is no cavity in this case there is no frequency pulling, and the peak frequency is equal to the atomic frequency.

The total power in the amplified spontaneous radiation is obtained from (4.36) by a simple integration, with the result

$$P = \frac{h\nu_a N_2}{\tau} \left[\frac{e^{\alpha D}}{2\pi^{1/2}(\alpha D)^{3/2}} \left(\frac{L}{D}\right)^2 \right] = \frac{h\nu_a N_2}{\tau'}, \qquad (4.37)$$

where the quantity $(\tau')^{-1}$ may be regarded as an enhanced spontaneous emission rate. Equation (4.37) gives the power that must be supplied to maintain N_2 atoms in the excited state, and it can be very large if the gain is high.

The mode of operation described in this section, i.e., the amplification of spontaneous emission by traveling waves, may be important in the far ultraviolet and shorter wavelength regions of the spectrum where resonant structures may not be available.

C. Mode Analysis

1. *Oscillation in a Multimode Cavity*

In the previous section, we analyzed the situation where a wave is reflected many times from mirrors with plane faces oriented parallel to the wave surface of constant phase, and arrived at an expression for the coherent power output of an optical maser. To discuss in more detail the problem of spontaneous radiation and induced emission in an optical structure which contains an enormous number of modes, we will follow the treatment of Wagner and Birnbaum (W-B) (*42*). The essential results of their analysis show how the regeneration process selects the highest Q mode for oscillation, and how the threshold pumping power and power output spectrum depend on the loss rates of the various modes.[*]

The starting point in the W-B analysis is the expansion of the field distribution in the optical resonator in terms of a set of damped modes. The discussion of the nature of these modes will be deferred to the section on optical resonators; it is sufficient here to note only that the existence of such modes in the open-sided resonator has been established. In essence, we consider that the fluctuating dipoles associated with spontaneous emission drive every mode of the optical resonator, and investigate how the regeneration due to a negative absorption coefficient gives rise to oscillation in the mode or modes of highest Q. We treat the case in which the second level is homogeneously broadened, and the atomic resonance has a Lorentz shape. The equations of motion from Appendix III are seen to be[†]

$$\ddot{q}_m + \gamma_m \dot{q}_m + \omega_m^2 q_m = \sum_i 2\pi^{1/2} \mu \, {}^i\!f_m^i \omega_m \, . \tag{4.38}$$

---

[*] The problem of maser oscillation in a multimode resonator has been treated by a number of authors. Fain and Khanin (*46c*) have derived the condition for oscillation, McCumber (*46d*) has emphasized the energy spectrum of the oscillator and the frequency dependence of the linear response of the amplifier, Lamb (*46e*) has developed a general theory of gaseous masers including a variety of nonlinear mode coupling effects, Haken and Sauermann (*46f*) have investigated the nonlinear interaction between two modes brought about by the space dependent distribution of excited atoms in a solid, and Lugovoy (*48*) has treated the case of two modes coupled to a homogeneously broadened atomic system with a uniform population distribution.

[†] The difference between the formulas here and in reference *42* is due to the use here of unrationalized rather than rationalized units.

Here q_m is the amplitude of the electric field of the mth mode and $\gamma_m = 2\,\Delta\omega_m$ is the damping rate. The dipole moment of the ith atom is μ^i, which is the sum of an induced part, μ_i^i, and a spontaneous part μ_s^i. On making the substitutions for the induced dipole term (III.21) and for a field oscillating as $\exp(-i\omega t)$, the following coupled equations are obtained:

$$-\omega^2 q_m - i\omega\gamma_m q_m + \omega_m^2 q_m = \sum_n i\omega_m\omega_n \frac{4\pi\mu^2\langle f_m^i f_n^i\rangle (N_1 - N_2)\, T}{\hbar[1 - iT(\omega - \omega_a)]}\, q_n$$

$$+ \sum_i 2\pi^{1/2}\mu_s^i(\omega)\, f_m^i\omega_m \,, \tag{4.39}$$

where the sum is taken over all cavity modes including $n = m$. The quantity T is the inverse atomic line width $\Delta\omega_a$, ω_a is the atomic resonance frequency, f_m^i is essentially the field at the ith atom, and $\langle f_m^i f_n^i\rangle = \Sigma_i f_m^i f_n^i/N$ is an average over all atomic sites and is essentially an integration over spatial coordinates. Since the atomic sites are distributed randomly and the modes are orthogonal, $\langle f_m^i f_n^i\rangle$ is equal to zero and (4.39) becomes the uncoupled equation for a single mode. Therefore in this approximation, the material in the cavity does not couple the modes, and hence the admittance of each mode to the spontaneous dipole of the ith system is

$$\frac{q_m(\omega)}{\mu_s^i(\omega)} = -\frac{2\pi^{1/2}f_m^i}{z_m(\omega)} \,, \tag{4.40}$$

where to a good approximation

$$z_m(\omega) = 2(\omega - \omega_m) + i\gamma_m + i\omega_m 4\pi\mu^2 T\xi_m(N_1 - N_2)/\hbar V[1 - iT(\omega - \omega_a)]. \tag{4.41}$$

The total power per angular frequency interval in all the modes is

$$P_\omega = \sum_m \gamma_m\omega_m^2 \,|\, q_m(\omega)\,|^2 = \sum_m \frac{4\pi\,|\,\mu_s(\omega)\,|^2\,\gamma_m\omega_m^2\xi_m}{V\,|\,z_m(\omega)\,|^2} \,, \tag{4.42}$$

where $\xi_m = V\langle(f_m^i)^2\rangle$ is a geometrical factor and depends on the mode configuration, and the total fluctuating dipole squared is

$$|\,\mu_s(\omega)\,|^2 = 2\mu^2 N_2 \frac{T}{\pi[1 + T^2(\omega - \omega_a)^2]} \,. \tag{4.43}$$

From (4.42) specialized for a single mode, expressions may be obtained for the spectral width and frequency pulling, which have been derived by other methods in Section IV,B,1 and IV,B,2, respectively.

The power output, as a sum of the power contained in all the modes, is obtained by integrating (4.42), and may be put in the form,

$$P = \frac{N_2 \hbar \omega_a}{\tau_{21} p} \sum_m \frac{(3\xi_m)/\xi}{1 - K_m Q_m + T^2(\omega_m - \omega_a)^2}, \qquad (4.44)$$

where ξ is the average of $3\xi_m$ over all the modes and is of the order of unity,* p is the total number of modes contained within the atomic line width, and $K_m = [4\pi \mid \mu_{21} \mid^2 (N_2 - N_1) T\xi_m]/\hbar V$ is the reciprocal of the material Q. For a single mode (4.44) is identical with (4.18) except for the factors, $[1 + (\Delta\nu_c/\Delta\nu_a)]^{-1}$ and $(\omega_m - \omega_a)^2 T^2$. The latter factor measures the distance of the mode resonance from the atomic resonance in units of the atomic line width. Equation (4.44) has a simple meaning; namely, the total power output is the sum of the spontaneous emission power in each mode multiplied by the gain of that mode. However, the power output is a function of the population difference $N_2 - N_1$ and cannot be determined until the difference is evaluated. Alternatively, this difference is a function of the power output, i.e., the gain saturation effect which limits the amplitude of the oscillation. Given any spectrum of modes with arbitrary decay rates, the sum could in principle be evaluated on a machine to determine $N_2 - N_1$. However, it turns out to be sufficient to treat the modes as a continuum except for those modes having frequencies nearest resonance and with the lowest loss rates.

It is well known that any given cavity mode can be represented by a suitable superposition of plane waves. In particular, inside a rectangular cavity each mode can be represented as a superposition of eight plane waves with wave vector components

$$(k_x, k_y, k_z) = [\pm(\pi m/L), \pm(\pi p/L), \pm(\pi q/D)], \qquad (4.45)$$

where L is the width and D the length of the resonator. The plane waves move in a direction specified by the angles θ and ϕ, where the z-axis is parallel to the axis of the resonator. These angles are given by

$$\cos \theta = vk_z/\omega,$$

---

* When the material is isotropic, $\xi = 3\xi_m$.

and

$$\tan \phi = k_y/k_x. \tag{4.46}$$

The average time the plane wave lives in the box, neglecting the variation with ϕ, is

$$\gamma(\theta) = \gamma_0(1 + a \sin \theta) = \gamma_0/f(\theta), \tag{4.47}$$

where

$$\gamma_0 = \frac{2v}{D} \frac{1-R}{1+R},$$

and

$$a = \frac{D}{L} \frac{1+R}{1-R} \frac{1-R'}{1+R'}.$$

The power reflection coefficient of the sides perpendicular to the axial direction is denoted by R and that parallel to the axial direction by R'. For $R' = 0$, the rectangular cavity becomes the Fabry-Perot interferometer. By letting R' be finite and a function of θ, one could represent internal reflection effects at the dielectric-air boundary of a solid dielectric. Equation (4.47) agrees with a result of Kotik and Newstein (47) obtained from a derivation of the threshold condition for oscillation from an integral equation for the angular spectrum of the field. In any case, (4.47) is a convenient way to represent how the loss rate of the resonator modes might vary as a function of a single parameter for the purpose of calculating the radiated power spectrum.

By considering the ratio of the two terms in (4.44) which have the highest gain, G_1/G_2 where $G_1 > G_2$, it is readily seen that as $N_2 - N_1$ increases with increasing pumping power, G_1/G_2 rapidly becomes extremely large even if Q_1 is only very slightly larger than Q_2. In view of this behavior arising from the feedback in the system, (4.44) may be approximated by removing from the sum the term for the highest Q mode, assumed to be at the atomic resonance, and treating the rest of the modes as a continuum. The result is, by the method of Section IV, D,

$$P = \frac{N_2 \hbar \omega_a}{\tau_{21}} \left(\frac{1}{p(1-s)} + \int_0^1 \frac{dx}{[1 - sf(x)]^{1/2}} \right), \tag{4.48}$$

where $s = K\omega_a/\gamma_0$ is the ratio of the cavity Q for the most favored mode to the material Q, $x = \cos \theta = \omega_q/\omega$, and $f(x)$ expresses the way in which the mode Q varies with the angle θ. Since the power output equals P_{in}, the power input less lattice losses, (4.48) determines s as a function of P_{in}. Knowing $s(P_{in})$, we have essentially determined the degree of inversion as a function of the pumping rate from

$$N_2 - N_1 = \frac{\hbar\gamma_0 V s \Delta\omega_a}{4\pi\mu^2\omega_a\xi_m}.$$ (4.49)

It may be noted that the population increase in the upper level is limited by the requirement that s can be no larger than 1. The first term in (4.48) is the coherent power output, and the second term is the spontaneous emission power, P_s, which, as will be discussed in the next paragraph, is constant above threshold. We see from (4.48) that $(1 - s) = [p(P_{in}/P_s - 1)]^{-1}$, and even very slightly above threshold s is negligibly different from 1 since p, the total number of modes within the atomic line width, is such a large number.

A detailed analysis of (4.48) for the mode spectrum $f(x)$ described by (4.47) shows the following behavior illustrated in Fig. 2. When

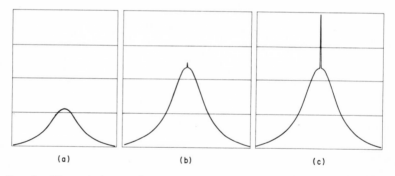

(a)   (b)   (c)

Fig. 2. Theoretical spectral output as a function of pumping power of an optical maser with an homogeneously broadened line: (a) below threshold; (b) slightly above threshold; (c) further above threshold.

$N_2 < N_1$, the output is distributed among the various modes within the spectrum of the atomic line. As the pumping rate increases and N_2 becomes greater than N_1, those modes near resonance with the lower loss rates deliver more of the output. Above a certain value of the pumping rate, when $N_2 - N_1$ reaches a critical value, the additional pumping power goes into one or a small number of modes. This transition is the exact analog of the condensation in the theory of an ideal Bose gas. At the other extreme, if all modes have the same losses, i.e., $f(x) = 1$, there would be no condensation and the spectrum would be Lorentzian with a width in units of $\Delta\omega_a$ equal to $(1 - s)^{1/2} = (N_2\hbar\omega/\tau_{21})/P_{\text{in}}$, a rather small spectral narrowing.

The effect of a much slower variation of γ with θ than that expressed by (4.47) was analyzed by W-B. It was found that when $f(x) = \cos^2\theta$, the pumping power needed to obtain oscillation in the highest Q mode is about three times greater than for the case where the discrimination of loss rates among the modes is stronger.

A situation intermediate between oscillation in a single mode and essentially participation of all modes was considered by W-B. Although a case not likely to be realized in practice, they suppose that some very small fraction of the modes have the same Q and oscillate with random phases, and all the rest of the modes have a smaller Q. An oscillation spike appears above threshold, which, although not as narrow as in the single mode case, also decreases in width with increasing pumping power.

The theoretical spectral emission characteristics of the optical maser illustrated in Fig. 2 show that below threshold there is little change in the spontaneous emission line shape. This result obtains when the quality of the resonator is high and $a \gg 1$ in (4.47). In this case the variation of loss rate with angle is high, i.e., the mode discrimination is good. For resonators of poor quality the mode discrimination is less and, as has been indicated, the oscillation threshold is higher. Below threshold one should expect a gradual narrowing of the emission resembling that for the case of equal loss rates for all the modes. This type of spectral narrowing implies that stimulated transitions are occurring but does not imply that the maser is actually oscillating. The onset of oscillation is marked by the appearance of a very sharp line superimposed on the spontaneous emission line. In practice, however, one often observes the appearance of many oscillation spikes. The reason for this will be discussed subsequently.

Above threshold the theory shows that the additional pumping power goes into one or a small number of modes, whereas the spontaneous emission power remains constant. However, measurements of the spontaneous radiation from the side of the rod of a $CaF_2 : Sm^{2+}$ maser (49) showed that contrary to theory the emission varied with the lamp intensity. A similar study on ruby (50) showed that the rate of side emission followed maser action, but that this effect was absent in a ruby rod with rough ground sides. However, this behavior was attributed to amplified spontaneous emission enhanced by the long path lengths resulting from internal reflection from the side of the rod. It should be noted that the sides of the rod may have greater population excess and consequently greater gain than the core of the rod where the cavity field is considerably stronger (see Section IV, E). Consequently, the spontaneous emission should be increased for the nonoscillating modes which can take advantage of the enhanced population inversion in the unsaturated medium. It is thought that the failure of the spontaneous radiation to saturate above threshold in masers where the atomic line is homogeneously broadened may be attributed to this effect.

2. Regenerative Amplifier

To treat the optical maser as a regenerative amplifier, we consider, following the analysis of W-B (51), that the modes are driven by an external force $C_m(\omega)$, where

$$C_m(\omega) = \gamma_m P_m^{\mathrm{in}}(\omega), \tag{4.50}$$

and $P_m^{\mathrm{in}}(\omega)$ is the input power per unit frequency range in the mth mode. It is assumed that the input signal can be represented by a suitable superposition of the normal modes of the resonant structure. $C_m(\omega)$ is the analog of $A_m(\omega)$, the spectral density of the forces on the mth mode due to noisy dipoles, viz.,

$$A_m(\omega) = \left| \sum_i 2\pi^{1/2} f_m^i \omega_m \mu_s^i(\omega) \right|^2. \tag{4.51}$$

Then the power contained in all the modes is given by

$$P = \sum_m \int d\omega \, \frac{\gamma_m}{|z_n(\omega)|^2} \, [A_m(\omega) + C_m(\omega)]. \tag{4.52}$$

The mode impedance $z_m(\omega)$ is well approximated by

$$|z_m(\omega)|^2 = 4(\omega - \omega_m)^2 + \gamma_m^2 [1 - K_m(\omega) Q_m]^2, \tag{4.53}$$

where

$$K_m(\omega) = K_m / [1 + (\omega - \omega_a)^2 / \Delta\omega_a^2]. \tag{4.54}$$

Since the gain is clearly

$$G_m(\omega) \simeq \{[1 - K_m(\omega) Q_m]^2 + 4(\omega - \omega_m)^2/\gamma_m^2\}^{-1}, \qquad (4.55)$$

(4.52) may be put in the form

$$P = \int d\omega \sum_m \frac{2}{\gamma_m} G_m(\omega) \left\{ \frac{N_2 \hbar \omega_a}{p\tau_{21}} \frac{1}{\pi} \left[1 + \left(\frac{\omega - \omega_a}{\Delta\omega_a} \right)^2 \right]^{-1} + \frac{\gamma_m}{2} P_m^{\text{in}}(\omega) \right\}. \qquad (4.56)$$

If the input power is small, the populations will not be appreciably affected and the device will act as a linear amplifier. For an input large enough to shift the populations, $N_2 - N_1$ must be determined as previously discussed for the oscillator.

For a monochromatic signal at the center of resonance the gain is $[1 - K_m(\omega_m) Q_m]^{-2}$. However, for an input whose spectral distribution is broad, it is the average power gain which is of interest. This gain depends on the input spectrum, and for a Lorentz distribution, one finds the gain to be $[1 - K_m Q_m]^{-1}$. This is the same as that for the oscillator, which is just a very high gain amplifier driven to saturation by its own noise.

D. OSCILLATION IN IMPERFECT CRYSTALS

A mode packet model has been presented for representing the effect of crystalline or resonator imperfections on the behavior of the optical maser (42). We wish to analyze another model here not only because it is believed to be more realistic, but also to illustrate the way in which the sum over modes in (4.44) is treated. Let us suppose that the maser is oscillating in one or a few axial modes, and that the radiation associated with these modes is scattered into many other modes by crystalline imperfections or irregularities in the mirrors. Then the power output may be represented by

$$P = \frac{N_2 \hbar \omega_a}{p\tau_{21}} \left\{ [1 - K_0 Q_0]^{-1} + \sum_{m \neq 0} [1 - K_m Q_m + T^2(\omega_m - \omega_a)^2]^{-1} \right. \qquad (4.57)$$

$$\left. + [1 - K_0 Q_0]^{-1} \sum_{n \neq 0} S_{0n}[(1 - K_n Q_n)^2 + 4(\omega_n - \omega_a)^2/\gamma_n^2]^{-1} \right\}.$$

The first term represents the coherent oscillation in the most favored mode, which is assumed to be at the atomic resonance. The second term represents the spontaneous emission background from all the other modes. These two terms are obtained from (4.44) by removing from the sum the term arising from the highest Q mode assumed to be at atomic resonance. The last term, whose form is suggested by (4.55) and (4.56), gives the output power from the amplified radiation scattered into the nth modes from the zeroth mode; S_{0n} is the scattering coefficient.

To evaluate the sums in (4.57), we treat the discrete but very dense mode spectrum as a continuum (42) and represent the mode frequency by

$$\omega = \omega_q \sec \theta, \tag{4.58}$$

where to a sufficient approximation

$$\omega_q = \pi v q / D. \tag{4.59}$$

Then with $T(\omega_m - \omega_a) = (\omega_a T / q_a)(q \sec \theta - q_a)$, and introducing the symbols $b = q_a / \omega_a T$, $K_0 \omega_a / \gamma_0 = s$, we arrive at the following equation for the power output,

$$P = \frac{N_2 \hbar \omega_a}{\tau_{21}} \left\{ \frac{G_0}{p} + \frac{1}{\pi b} \int_0^{\pi/2} \sum_{q=1}^{\infty} \frac{\tan \theta \, d\theta}{[1 - sf(\theta)] + b^{-2}[q \sec \theta - q_a]^2} \right.$$

$$\left. + \frac{G_0}{p} \int_0^{\pi/2} \sum_{q=1}^{\infty} \frac{S_q(\theta) \, d\theta}{[1 - sf(\theta)]^2 + \left(\frac{2\omega_a}{q_a \gamma(\theta)} \right)^2 (q \sec \theta - q_a)^2} \right\}, \tag{4.60}$$

where $G_0 = (1 - K_0 Q_0)^{-1}$. We have used the fact that the density of modes in the region of the spectrum which is important is $(L^2 \omega_a^2 / \pi c^2) \tan \theta = p(\theta)$, for a given q. $S_q(\theta) = p(\theta) S_{0n}$ is unknown but may be determined experimentally. For example, highly collimated light may be passed through a crystal, which is to be used in the optical maser, and the spatial distribution of the transmitted radiation is examined.

The second term in (4.60) may be shown to reduce to the bounded integral in (4.48) (42). The last term is sharply peaked when

$$\sec \theta = \frac{q_a}{q}. \tag{4.61}$$

The height of the peak per unit angle is

$$\frac{N_2 \hbar \omega_a G_0}{p\tau_{21}} \frac{S_q(\theta)}{[1 - sf(\theta)]^2} , \qquad (4.62)$$

and the angular half-width is

$$\delta = \frac{[1 - sf(\theta)] [\gamma(\theta)/\omega_a]}{2 \tan \theta} , \qquad (4.63)$$

for $\theta \neq 0$. When $\theta = 0$, $2 \tan \theta$ is replaced by δ and the width is the square root of the numerator in (4.63). The resonance condition (4.61) is easily put in the form $2nD \cos \theta = q\lambda$, which is the usual Fabry–Perot condition for the appearance of circular interference figures.

E. The Effect of Inhomogeneous Broadening

The complex analysis of maser oscillation in a multimode resonator when the atomic line is broadened by the Doppler effect has been treated by Lamb (46e). However, the important case where the inhomogeneous width is very much greater than the homogeneous or natural width, see Fig. 3, can be readily discussed in a qualitative way. If

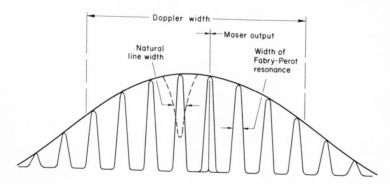

FIG. 3. The relation between the maser line, the Doppler broadened atomic line, the natural atomic line, and the regularly spaced axial modes ($\lambda = 2D/q$) of the resonator. [Herriott (94).]

the natural width of the atomic resonance is equal to or less than the width of a cavity mode, then the atoms contained within one cavity resonance cannot couple to the radiation field from atoms contained within another cavity resonance. Assuming that all modes have the same loss rate, that mode whose frequency is closest to the peak of the frequency distribution will break into oscillation first. As the pumping power is increased, the power in this mode continues to increase. However, at some value of the pumping power the next mode whose frequency is nearest the peak will reach threshold and start oscillating. Thus, when the atomic resonance is inhomogeneously broadened, the maser can simultaneously oscillate in a number of cavity modes. On the other hand, when the atomic resonance is homogeneously broadened, the gain saturates uniformly over the whole atomic distribution and the oscillation of one mode prevents the oscillation of less favored modes.

Figure 4 illustrates how the gain condition is satisfied for an

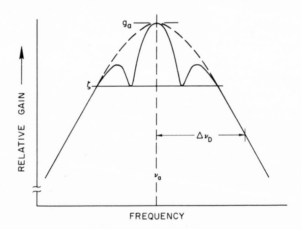

FIG. 4. Holes burned in the single pass gain curve of an inhomogeneously broadened line. [After Bennett (13).]

inhomogeneously broadened line by burning a hole (i.e., the absence of atoms) in the line. The dashed curve with a peak gain of g_a represents the gain in the absence of the mirrors, and the solid curve indicates the gain in the presence of two holes. The gain at the frequencies of oscillation saturates at ζ, the fractional energy loss per pass, whereas the gain over the rest of the line continues to increase with pumping rate. Thus the spontaneous radiation does not remain constant above threshold, as is theoretically the case for homogeneously broadened lines, but should continue to increase with the pumping rate.

In a gas, there are two holes burned in the Doppler line, and placed symmetrically about the line center for every oscillator resonance. However, it suffices for the following discussion to regard the two holes in Fig. 4 as belonging to two different oscillating modes as would be the case in a solid. Now the total gain at a given cavity resonance, ν_c, is determined primarily by those atoms whose resonance frequencies fall within ν_c by about one hole width, approximately the natural line width if the power in the mode is not too great. Thus the gain at one frequency is not appreciably affected by a non-overlapping hole burned at another frequency. However, the phase shifts introduced by the holes have large effects on the cavity resonances even when the holes are well separated. The phase shift of the hole represents the departure of the phase shift introduced by the original Gaussian by the absence of atoms. Like any phase shift or dispersion curve, that introduced by the holes have wings which extend far from the resonance frequency and are thus capable of having a relatively large effect on the phase shift of another resonance. Theory shows that the presence of a hole at one resonance reduces the frequency pulling at another resonance which would have existed in the absence of a hole, i.e., two holes repel each other (43).

The presence of two holes per oscillating frequency introduces new effects in the performance of gas masers. For example, as theoretically predicted by Lamb (46e) and qualitatively explained by Bennett (13), a dip is to be expected in the power output of a gaseous optical maser in single mode operation as the cavity is tuned through the line center. Such a power dip has been observed by McFarlane et al. (46g), and Szöke and Javan (46h).

F. Mode Coupling

Except for the two previous Sections, IV,D and IV,E, we have dealt thus far with maser oscillation in a single cavity mode uncoupled from any of the numerous other modes contained within the atomic line width. Section IV,D deals with the effect of scattering by crystal imperfections on the spatial distribution of the power. Section IV, E shows how an inhomogeneously broadened line leads to maser oscillation in a number of modes. In this section we will consider other mode coupling effects.

1. Imperfect Resonator

It is well known that in the presence of resistive losses, for example, the original unperturbed modes are no longer orthogonal nor is there any linear combination of these modes which can be made exactly orthogonal. Thus the excitation in a given mode will leak into all the modes to which it is coupled; in other words, the loss rate of the mode in question is increased by this coupling. Other and more important mode coupling mechanisms are scattering by crystal imperfections and aberrations in the geometry of the resonator. As an example of the latter may be mentioned the observation that in the He-Ne maser (43), the loss rate of the preferred mode was larger than the rate calculated from the measured mirror reflectivity by a factor of about two. This increased loss was attributed to mode coupling by geometrical imperfections in the mirrors.

2. Saturation

If saturation is important, i.e., the rate of induced transitions is not negligible compared with the relaxation rate, the emission processes at the different frequencies will not be independent of each other. Nonlinear effects due to saturation in the simultaneous stimulated emission of several fields in a low-pressure gas have been treated by Tang and Statz (52). They have shown, for example, that when a gas is irradiated by two oscillating linearly polarized fields of different frequencies well within the Doppler-broadened width of the same atomic line, maximum absorption of both fields occur when the two linear polarizations are perpendicular to each other.

3. Spatial Modulation of the Population Difference

The field distribution of an oscillating mode can produce a non-uniform spatial distribution of inverted population as illustrated in Fig. 5. Clearly, where the standing wave electric field is zero the population difference should be maximum, and where the electric intensity has its maximum value the population difference should have its minimum value. In terms of (4.39) it is easy to see that if

$N_2 - N_1 \to \varDelta N(\mathbf{x})$, then $\langle f_m^i f_n^i N(\mathbf{x}) \rangle$ is in general not equal to zero, if we remember that the angular brackets $\langle \rangle$ mean an integration over spatial coordinates, and the active material couples modes. If we note that the emissive power of the active material in the resonator is proportional to $\varDelta N(\mathbf{x})$, it is clear that the regions of high inversion should induce oscillation in modes which can take advantage of this situation. Should such additional modes arise, another distribution of $N_2 - N_1$ would prevail and would favor a

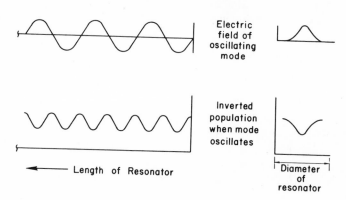

Electric field of oscillating mode

Inverted population when mode oscillates

⟵ Length of Resonator

Diameter of resonator

FIG. 5. The field distributions for one oscillating mode, and inverted population distribution when only that mode oscillates.

new or perhaps the original mode, a situation which would encourage mode jumping. In any case, it is clear that $\varDelta N(\mathbf{x})_{\max} - \varDelta N(\mathbf{x})_{\text{th}}$ is a function of the pumping power, and represents a mode excitation and coupling mechanism whose strength increases with the degree of excitation.

It is apparent that a spatial modulation of inverted population should occur in oscillating solid state masers where the atoms are fixed in space and are so well separated that the diffusion of excitation is very slow. In gas masers, the atomic motion would seem to prevent the development of a spatial modulation of inverted population, although the situation may be different in the axial and transverse directions. The inverted population will become spatially modulated if the time for diffusion between two adjacent node lines of the field is sufficiently less than the inverse of the induced transition rate. In the axial direction, the characteristic distance is of the order of one

half wavelength, whereas in the transverse direction for the fundamental or low order modes the characteristic distance is of the order
of the radius of the gas tube. Since the ratio of the characteristic
distance in the axial to the transverse directions is of the order of
10^{-4}, it is possible that the medium may be spatially modulated in the
transverse but not the axial directions.

Formulas which relate the number of unstable axial modes in solid
state masers to pump power when there is a mode-dependent spatial
distribution of excited atomic states have been derived by Tang
et al. (53). Their results show that the pump power must be kept
exceedingly close to threshold in order to achieve single mode excitation. The nonlinear interaction of two modes coupled by the spatially
modulated amplifying medium has been studied in detail by Haken
and Sauermann (46f). They have found that there is a repulsion of
the mode frequencies as function of power similar to that described
for the gas maser. Thus similar mode interaction effects have been
obtained for the case of fixed atoms with a homogeneously broadened
Lorentzian line and moving atoms in gases with a Doppler broadened
line. On the other hand, the power dipping effect in the gas maser has
no analogue in the solid state maser.

V.   Theory of the Transient Behavior of Optical Masers

A. Relaxation Oscillations

One of the simplest indications of maser action is the time dependent behavior of the power output when the pumping source is pulsed. If the pumping energy is less than the threshold value, the fluorescent output tends to follow the output of the pulsed light source, and decays in a characteristic time after the light source is turned off. Above threshold the system breaks into oscillation, at which point a sharp spike appears in the curve of power output vs. time. The interval between the time that the pumping lamp is turned on and oscillation begins is the time required to store the critical number of atoms in the excited state. The large power spike which appears above threshold is due to the fact that the coherent output is highly directional, whereas the spontaneous radiation is emitted in all directions. The oscillation rapidly decays when the lamp power has decreased to the point where it no longer pumps the critical number of atoms to the excited state. When the excited state has been so depleted that the system no longer oscillates, the remainder of the atoms decay at the spontaneous emission rate. Such a sequence of events, was first observed by Maiman (54) in his investigation of maser action in ruby. However, the oscillation spike was seen by Collins et al. (55) to be the envelope of a large number of much sharper spikes. It is the theoretical explanaton of spikes of this type that is the object of the following discussion.

Consider a three-level atomic system in which the following cycle of events occur: transitions between levels 1 and 3 are induced by a pumping signal, atoms in level 3 instantaneously relax by a non-radiative transition to level 2, and atoms in level 2 return to the ground state via spontaneous emission and emission induced by the radiation field of a single cavity mode. The rate equations governing the population difference between levels 2 and 1, $N = N_2 - N_1$, and the

51

number of photons in a given cavity mode J, are

$$\frac{dN}{dt} = W - \frac{N}{\tau_e} - 2NJB_J, \tag{5.1}$$

$$\frac{dJ}{dt} = -J\gamma + NJB_J + N_2B_J, \tag{5.2}$$

where $B_J = (\tau p)^{-1} = (\sigma v/V)$ is the Einstein B coefficient per quantum, γ is the cavity decay rate, and $N_0 = N_1 + N_2$. The quantity W, the net pumping rate to the metastable level, and τ_e, an effective lifetime, are defined respectively by

$$W = N_0(\Gamma_{13}^i - \Gamma_{21}^s),$$
$$\frac{1}{\tau_e} = \Gamma_{13}^i + \Gamma_{21}^s, \tag{5.3}$$

where Γ signifies a rate, and superscripts i and s mean, respectively, induced and spontaneous. Note that τ_e is an effective lifetime whereas τ is the usual lifetime, i.e. $(\Gamma_{21}^s)^{-1}$.

In an ideal four-level system, pumping takes place between levels 1 and 4, maser action occurs between levels 3 and 2, and instantaneous relaxation occurs between levels 4 and 3, and levels 2 and 1. Level 2, the ground state of the maser transition, is consequently empty, and $N = N_3 - N_2 \simeq N_3$. In this case the rate equations become

$$\frac{dN}{dt} = W - \frac{N}{\tau} - NJB_J, \tag{5.4}$$

$$\frac{dJ}{dt} = -J\gamma + NJB_J + NB_J, \tag{5.5}$$

where now

$$W = \Gamma_{14}^i N_0, \qquad \tau_e = \tau = (\Gamma_{32}^s)^{-1}. \tag{5.6}$$

The last term in (5.2) and (5.5) is negligible, but must be included to enable the induced emission to start.

In the steady state, (5.2) or (5.5) gives $N_{\text{th}} = \gamma/B_J$, which is the threshold condition (2.7), and (5.4), for example, gives

$$J = \frac{W}{\gamma} - p. \tag{5.7}$$

The case where J is negligible compared with p defines

$$W_{th} = p\gamma, \tag{5.8}$$

the threshold pumping rate which equals the loss rate of one photon for every mode. The photon density increases linearly with $W - W_{th}$ corresponding to the fact that for every additional photon absorbed at the pump transition one additional photon is emitted in the maser output.

Equations (5.4) and (5.5), describing the interaction between the resonant cavity and the population excess, are essentially the same as those presented by Statz and deMars (56,57). Although they formulated these equations to account for the undamped pulsations in the output of the ruby microwave and optical maser, Sinnett (57) and 'Makhov (58) have shown that these equations will not allow undamped solutions unless additional terms are added. Mechanisms leading to such term have been proposed, and the modified rate equations have been shown to give undamped pulsations (495).

Computer solutions for (5.4) and (5.5), shown in Fig. 6, have been obtained by Dunsmuir (59) for ruby using the following values of the parameters: $\tau = 5 \times 10^{-3}$ sec, $\Delta\nu = 8.3$ cm^{-1}, $\nu = 4.33 \times 10^{14}$ sec^{-1}, $W = 3.5 \times 10^{21}$ atoms/sec, $\tau_c = 1.6 \times 10^{-8}$ sec, $V = 1$ cm^3. The

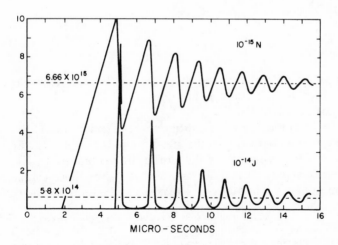

FIG. 6.   Relaxation oscillation in the ruby maser. [Dunsmuir (59).]

population excess is seen to rise linearly, overshooting the threshold or equilibrium value until the field building up in the cavity is large enough to start inducing transitions. Because the population excess is greater than the equilibrium value, the field rapidly builds up, and the excited state population begins to collapse. The population excess is brought below the equilibrium value by the large cavity field which now dies out. As the cycle repeats, the spiked output goes into a damped sinusoid.

Although (5.1) and (5.2), and (5.4) and (5.5) are nonlinear because of the product NJ and must in general be solved by machine, for small oscillations about the steady state values they may be solved by a perturbation method (59–62). Setting $\Delta N = N - N_s$ and $\Delta J = J - J_s$, we obtain from (5.1) and (5.2), or (5.4) and (5.5) the following equation for ΔJ:

$$\Delta \ddot{J} + \frac{W}{W_{\text{th}}} \frac{\Delta \dot{J}}{\tau_e} + \frac{\gamma}{\tau_e} \left(\frac{W}{W_{\text{th}}} - 1 \right) \Delta J = 0. \tag{5.9}$$

The solution to this equation is

$$\Delta J = Ae^{-(\lambda - i\mu)t} + Be^{-(\lambda + i\mu)t}, \tag{5.10}$$

where the damping time λ^{-1} is

$$\frac{1}{\lambda} = \frac{2W_{\text{th}}\tau_e}{W}, \tag{5.11}$$

and the relaxation frequency μ is

$$\mu = \left[-\frac{W^2}{4W_{\text{th}}^2 \tau_e^2} + \left(\frac{W}{W_{\text{th}}} - 1 \right) \frac{\gamma}{\tau_e} \right]^{1/2}. \tag{5.12}$$

These solutions apply to the three or four level systems depending on whether W, W_{th}, and τ_e are defined by (5.1) and (5.3), or (5.4) and (5.6), respectively.

It may be noted that the condition that the spikes should be damped out to give a smooth rise to the steady state is that $\lambda > \mu$. Equations (5.8) and (5.9) are essentially the same as those obtained by Kaiser (60) and Sorokin (61) but differ somewhat with those obtained by Dunsmuir (59).* The successive maxima and minima of the computer

---

* The equation for λ in Dunsmuir (59) agrees with (5.11) given here when $W \gg W$th, and the equation for μ agrees with (5.12) if $W^2/4W_{\text{th}}^2\tau_e^2$ is neglected. The signs of the two terms within the square root of Eq. (2) in Kaiser (60) should be multiplied by -1.

solutions in Fig. 6 compare well with the decay rate predicted by the approximate formula.

Although the solutions to the coupled equations were obtained on the assumption that the pumping power was suddenly turned on and remained constant thereafter, machine solutions to these equations may be obtained, of course, for any given time variation of the pumping rate $W(t)$. Conversely, it may be possible to shape the pumping power pulse to produce some desired modulation of the power output.

The origin of the pulsations in optical masers has been considered by a number of people (63–66). The theory of Hellwarth (63) does not seem applicable to the usual optical maser since he treats the case of noninterfering light rather than oscillation in cavity modes. In addition, his threshold for pulsations depends on the anisotropy of the propagation constant and consequently would not apply to isotropic media. Kaplan and Zier (65) treat the coupled system of resonator and homogeneously broadened atomic system by the density matrix formalism and include the off-diagonal elements. Their results reduce to the Statz-deMars equations under appropriate simplifications. They presented machine solutions for the case where the atomic line width, $\Delta\omega$, varies from $5 \times 10^6 \, \mathrm{sec}^{-1}$ to $5 \times 10^9 \, \mathrm{sec}^{-1}$ (for purposes of comparison, note that $\Delta\omega \sim 5 \times 10^{11}$ for the ruby fluorescent line at room temperature.) At the lower values of $\Delta\omega$, 5×10^6 and $5 \times 10^7 \, \mathrm{sec}^{-1}$, there is a large departure in the period of oscillation obtained from the machine solution with that obtained from the Statz-deMars equations. At the higher values of $\Delta\omega$, i.e., 5×10^8 and $5 \times 10^9 \, \mathrm{sec}^{-1}$, the agreement is good. This result shows that for small enough values of $\Delta\omega$, i.e. $\Delta\omega \lesssim E/\hbar$, the off-diagonal elements of the density matrix become important and the use of populations in treating the maser oscillation problem is incorrect. However, such small values of line width are not encountered in optical transitions.

Tang et al. (53) generalized the rate equations by taking into account the nonuniform spatial distribution of population inversion for pumping levels not too much above threshold. Computer solutions of these equations for the single mode case give results qualitatively similar to the case of uniform population inversion. Solutions for two modes show that the total intensity may exhibit regular damped oscillations although the two individual modes show irregular variations in their intensities. They found that in all cases for which numerical solutions were obtained, the transient oscillations always seemed to damp out and relax to the steady-state solutions.

We will see in Section XII,H that the coupled equations discussed in this section give a reasonably good account of some of the experimental results on spiking in masers. However, it is well to remember that these equations pertain to an homogeneously broadened atomic line coupled to a single mode, whereas in reality the atomic resonance is to a lesser or greater extent inhomogeneously broadened and is coupled to a resonator containing a great many modes, more than one of which may be oscillating. Although the real situation may be quite involved, the equations discussed here are apparently still useful in describing a number of the qualitative features of the transient behavior of masers.

B. The Q-Spoil Maser

This section is concerned with some aspects of maser behavior when the regeneration or feedback is controlled. Let us suppose that during the time that the pump is turned on the Q of the optical resonator is maintained at a value so low that the system cannot oscillate. After the excited state has been populated to some value N_0, the Q is very suddenly switched to some high value. Since $N_{th} \propto Q^{-1}$ and $N_0 > N_{th}$, it is apparent that after the switching there is a superabundance of excited atoms. This situation creates an enhanced regeneration with the result that the system will discharge its energy very quickly. This method of controlling the feedback, called Q spoiling, and known in connection with the problem of inverting spins in the microwave region (67, 68), has been proposed by Hellwarth for the optical maser (69). The behavior of a three level maser in the Q-spoil mode of operation may be described by (5.1) and (5.2), where the cavity damping $\gamma(t)$ is now a prescribed function of time. It is apparent that similar behavior may be expected if γ is fixed but the line width, for example, is controlled by the application of an inhomogeneous magnetic field.

Although (5.1) and (5.2) may be evaluated for arbitrary initial conditions and arbitrary time dependent functions $W(t)$ and $\gamma(t)$, it is instructive to integrate these equations in an approximate way to obtain some results in closed form. To do this we assume that $W(t)$ and $\gamma(t)$ are step functions, where the former is turned off at $t = 0$, while the latter is switched from a high value, γ_H, to a low value, γ_0. For the case $N_0 B_J \gg \gamma_0$, the damping during the build-up of the radiation pulse may be neglected in comparison with induced emission, and we have

$$\frac{dN}{dt} = -2NJB_J, \tag{5.13}$$

$$\frac{dJ}{dt} = NJB_J. \tag{5.14}$$

The solution to these equations is easily obtained in the form

$$N = \frac{N_0}{2} \left[1 - \tanh \frac{B_J N_0}{2} (t - t') \right], \tag{5.15}$$

$$J = \frac{N_0}{4} \left[1 + \tanh \frac{B_J N_0}{2} (t - t') \right], \tag{5.16}$$

where at $t = t'$, $N' = N_0/2$ and $J = N_0/4$. Note that N_0 means here the population difference at $t = 0$. We wish to find the time interval $\Delta t_1 = t' - t_0$, during which the number of photons in the cavity mode increases from its original value J_0 to its value at t'. Then since $\Delta t_1 > (B_J N_0)^{-1}$, and using the approximation $\tanh(-x) \simeq 2 \exp(-2x) - 1$ when $x > 1$, we obtain from (5.16)

$$\Delta t_1 = \frac{1}{B_J N_0} \ln \frac{N_0}{2J_0}, \tag{5.17}$$

where $B_J N_0 = \gamma_0 N_0 / N_{\text{th}}$. The number of photons in the given resonator mode at the time of switching is from (5.2) with γ replaced by γ_H,

$$J_0 = \frac{N_2/N_{\text{th}}}{\gamma_H/\gamma_0 - N_0/N_{\text{th}}}. \tag{5.18}$$

This equation shows that N_0/N_{th} must be less than γ_H/γ_0 before the time of switching, otherwise the maser would fire.

Now from (5.2) $\dot{J} = 0$ when $N = N_{\text{th}}$. Then by the same procedure as before, the time measured from t' required for N to decrease from $N_0/2$ to N_{th} where $N_0 \gg N_{\text{th}}$, is given by

$$\Delta t_2 = \frac{1}{B_J N_0} \ln \left(\frac{N_0}{N_{\text{th}}} \right). \tag{5.19}$$

The maximum value of J from (5.16) and (5.19) is $J_m = (N_0 - N_{th})/2$. The decay of J will be governed by the cavity damping, viz.,

$$J = J_m e^{-\gamma_0 t}. \tag{5.20}$$

The composite pulse calculated by this method is illustrated in Fig. 7. The delay in the start of the pulse is essentially Δt_1 given

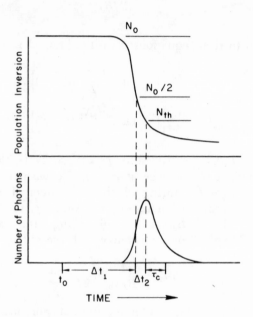

FIG. 7. Inversion and number of photons versus time in the Q-spoil maser. High Q switched on at t_0.

by (5.17) and the time to reach the peak is $\Delta t_1 + \Delta t_2$. The decay time γ_0^{-1} in the case considered is greater than Δt_2, and is the reason that the output pulse is given the asymmetrical shape in Fig. 7. The energy in the pulse is $E = \frac{1}{2}(N_0 - N_f)h\nu$, where N_f is the final value of the population difference and may be neglected in comparison with N_0 when $N_0/N_{th} \gg 1$.

This analysis of the Q-spoil maser serves to illustrate the principles and gives results useful for making rough estimates when $N_0/N_{th} \gg 1$. A treatment of this problem including damping has been given by Wagner and Lengyel (70), who have numerically integrated the coupled equations to obtain the time development of the pulse. The peak power output, however, was obtained in closed form with the result[*]

$$P_m = \tfrac{1}{2} h\nu\gamma_0 \left[N_0 - N_{\text{th}} \left(1 + \ln \frac{N_0}{N_{\text{th}}} \right) \right]. \tag{5.21}$$

C. RADIATION DAMPING EFFECTS

The preceding sections have dealt with the coupling between excited atoms and the resonator. However, circumstances may arise where the excited atoms interact with the electromagnetic field in unison, that is to say coherently, and instead of dealing with transitions of individual atoms, it is the interaction of the net polarization with the electromagnetic field that is pertinent. Behavior of this type has been observed in the microwave region in spin systems which after inversion may either give up their energy in a single pulse or in a succession of damped pulses. The entire magnetization, originally reversed with respect to an applied magnetic field (180° orientation), swings to the original orientation (0°), or swings back and forth through 0° until it comes to rest there. This phenomenon, sometimes referred to as radiation damping or super-radiation, is characterized by the fact that the power output is proportional to the square of the number of spins involved. Although radiation damping has not yet made its appearance in the optical region, it is instructive to understand its origin and its relation to the transient effects discussed earlier.

Bloembergen and Pound (B-P) (71) have discussed in a classical way the interaction of the magnetization and a resonant circuit for small departures of the magnetization from its equilibrium position. Provided that $\tau_R > \tau_C$ but $\tau_R < T_2$, where τ_R is the radiation damping time constant, τ_c is the cavity damping time, and $T_2 = \Delta\omega^{-1}$, the magnetization is rapidly damped with a characteristic time τ_R, defined by

$$\tau_R = (2\pi\chi\omega^2\tau_c)^{-1}, \tag{5.22}$$

where χ is the susceptibility. This damping, which may be regarded as an enhanced spontaneous radiation rate, has an appreciable magnitude

[*] The full width of the pulse at half amplitude given by $2.5(2J_m/N_{\text{th}})^{-1/2}$, where $2J_m/N_{\text{th}}$ is obtained from (5.21), is in excellent agreement with the computer solution of ref. 70 for the range $1.2 < J_m/N_{\text{th}} < 5$ (70a).

because of the phase coherence between the individual spins producing the magnetization. This phase coherence persists only for a time T_2, hence the requirement that $\tau_R < T_2$. Coherence effects of this type have been discussed from a quantum mechanical viewpoint by Dicke (72). It is interesting to note that the condition for the occurrence of coherent spontaneous decay, $\tau_R < T_2$, is also the condition for steady maser oscillation. The way in which the radiation pulse builds up for the case where $T_1 = \infty$ and T_2 is finite has been the subject of detailed analysis (73, 74).

When $\tau_R < \tau_C$ the field generated by the precessing magnetization is no longer in equilibrium with the resonator field, and B-P (71) find that for $T_1 = \infty$, $T_2 = \infty$, the energy in the circuit oscillates with a frequency given by $\omega = (\tau_C \tau_R)^{-1/2}$. This problem has been discussed in somewhat different but essentially equivalent ways by a number of people (75, 76, 77), for example, by Singer and Wang (76) whose equation, as shown by Kemp (77) can be put in the form,

$$\ddot{\theta} + \frac{\dot{\theta}}{\tau_c} + \frac{\sin \theta}{\tau_c \tau_R} = 0, \qquad (5.23)$$

where $\theta = 2\hbar^{-1} \int_0^t \mu E(t')\, dt'$, and μ is the dipole matrix element. This is the simple damped pendulum equation from which, according to Kemp (77), the field is given after the first cycle or two by $\exp(-t/2\tau_c) \sin t/(\tau_c \tau_R)^{1/2}$. Yariv (78) has given a machine solution for a homogeneously broadened line with T_2 finite, and Kemp (79) has discussed the case of an inhomogeneously broadened line.

Although the possibility of radiation damping in optical masers has been mentioned, or of inverting the population with a 180° pulse as in magnetic resonance, the fact that optical lines have values of $T_2 = \Delta\omega^{-1}$ orders of magnitude less than what obtains in magnetic resonance would appear to make the observation of such effects difficult in optical systems.

D. The Pulsed Traveling Wave Amplifier

Consider a slab of material containing atoms with a pair of energy levels whose occupation is prescribed as a function of the length of the material, x, at time $t = 0$. Imagine this slab illuminated with a beam of monochromatic light whose spatial intensity is also prescribed at $t = 0$. Then for times less than the relaxation time of the atoms in the upper level, the equations determining the population difference density, n, and photon density, j, are:

$$\frac{\partial n}{\partial t} = -2\sigma v j n, \qquad n_{t=0} = n(x), \qquad (5.24)$$

$$\frac{\partial j}{\partial t} = -v \frac{\partial j}{\partial x} + \sigma v j n, \qquad j_{t=0} = j(x). \qquad (5.25)$$

Equations (5.24) and (5.25) are similar to (5.13) and (5.14) except for the appearance of the term $-v(\partial j/\partial x)$ in (5.25) which allows for the fact that j depends, in general, not only on the number of transitions taking place but also on the net flow of photons out of a given volume.

As shown by Bellman et al. (80),* (5.24) and (5.25), although nonlinear, may be solved exactly in closed form, apart possibly from a final integration. We wish to examine the case where at $t = 0$

$$n(x) = n_0, \qquad D > x \geqslant 0,$$

$$j(x) = j_0, \qquad -D_p < x < 0,$$

and $n(x) = j(x) = 0$ everywhere else, which represents a square pulse of radiation of spatial extent D_p incident on a slab of material of length D. Outside the slab in the interval $x < vt < x + D_p$, the solution of (5.24) and (5.25) is

$$j(x, t) = j_0[1 - e^{2\sigma j_0(x-vt)} (1 - e^{-\sigma n_0 x})]^{-1}. \qquad (5.26)$$

The leading edge of the radiation pulse sees full gain as it travels through the material but drains off active atoms so that successive portions of the signal experience less gain. The amplified signal assumes the shape of a shock wave whose integrated energy is equal to the stored energy in the material. The output pulse half-width, is given by

$$\Delta t_{1/2} \simeq \frac{e^{-\sigma n_0 D}}{2\sigma j_0 v}, \qquad (5.27)$$

when $e^{\sigma n_0 D} \gg 1$. By using the pulse-sharpening property of the traveling wave pulsed amplifier, TWPA, it may be possible to produce light pulses shorter than by any other method.

* See also refs. 80a and 80b.

A TWPA is inherently unstable because the amplified spontaneous radiation depletes the number of excited atoms at an enhanced rate. The initial value of the reduced lifetime, τ', is given by (4.37). Although this equation gives the power output for a traveling wave oscillator which is continuously pumped to maintain a fixed number of excited atoms, it should apply to the transient case for times sufficiently less than τ' during which the number of excited atoms has not changed substantially from its initial value. It is for times less than τ' rather than τ that (5.24) and (5.25) are valid.

VI.   Optical Resonators

A. Introduction

Reasoning by analogy with the modes in a rectangular box with highly conducting walls, Schawlow and Townes (*1*) suggested the use of a plane-parallel Fabry-Perot (PPF-P) interferometer as a multimode resonator for optical masers. The use of two parallel plates for a maser resonator had also been suggested by Prokhorov (*81*) and Dicke (*82*), although they did not discuss the reduction of excess modes or spontaneous emission. However, it was the work of Fox and Li (*83*) who gave substance to the idea that modes, in the sense of a self-reproducing field pattern, exist for an open structure such as a Fabry-Perot interferometer. They obtained this result by self-consistent field calculations based on Huygens' principle. Using the same method, Boyd *et al.* (*84, 85*) investigated the modes in a resonator formed of two spherical reflectors. Goubau and Schwering (*86, 87*) and others (*47, 88, 89, 89a, 89b*), using various analytic techniques, have studied the modes of such resonators and have obtained results similar to those obtained by Fox and Li and Boyd *et al.* in common domains of validity. The discussion in the following sections on the plane and spherical end plate resonators is based on the work of the latter investigators (*83, 84, 85*).

In order for an open resonator without sides to be able to support high Q modes, it must satisfy two criteria (*14*). The first, which follows from geometrical optics, is that there must be a family of rays which, on being multiply reflected from the two reflectors, do not miss either reflector before making a reasonable number of crossings. This criteria is valid because the reflecting surfaces are large and have radii of curvature which are large compared to the wavelength. The second criteria, which follows from physical optics, is that the widths of the two reflectors, $2L_1$ and $2L_2$, must satisfy the relation*

$$\frac{L_1 L_2}{\lambda D} > 1,$$

* The parameter $N = L^2/\lambda D$, called the Fresnel number, is important in the theory of optical resonators. N is approximately equal to the number of Fresnel zones seen in one mirror from the center of the other mirror.

where D is the separation between the reflectors. This relation conforms to the requirement for low diffraction loss that the angle subtended by one reflector at the second be greater than the angle of the far field diffraction pattern of a nearly plane wave originating at and with the dimensions of the second reflector.

B. Fabry-Perot Resonator with Plane Parallel Reflectors

The electric field configuration of the dominant mode and a number of higher order modes for plane square and circular mirrors are shown in Fig. 8. The patterns in Fig. 8A have the cartesian mode designation

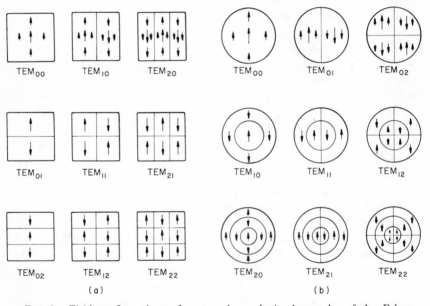

(a)   (b)

Fig. 8. Field configurations of rectangular and circular modes of the Fabry-Perot resonator with plane or spherical mirrors. [Fox and Li (83).] The 1st and 2nd subscripts of the circular modes are, respectively, the radial and angular integers (85).

TEM_{mnq}, a classification which applies to plane as well confocal mirrors. The designation TEM means transverse electric and magnetic fields, although it is clear that, in general, the field lines must have longitudinal components. However, provided the transverse variation is much greater than a half wavelength, the longitudinal field intensity should be negligible compared to the transverse intensity. This condition holds except for very high order modes. The individual modes of a Fabry-Perot interferometer, used as the resonator of a He-Ne maser, have been isolated, and the beam pattern photographed by Kogelnik and Rigrod (90). Their photographs, shown in Fig. 9, can clearly be identified as the mode patterns of Fig. 8a.

From the results on the two lowest order modes of the plane-parallel resonator, it appears that the mode spectrum of this resonator is similar to that of an enclosed rectangular box with highly conducting walls in the limit of large $L^2/\lambda D$. For the rectangular box of length D with two square end walls of dimension $L/2$, the resonant condition is

$$\left(\frac{2}{\lambda}\right)^2 = \left(\frac{q}{D}\right)^2 + \left[\frac{r^2 + s^2}{4L^2}\right], \tag{6.1}$$

where for the low order modes of interest q is a very large integer and r, s are small integers. Such modes can be thought of as consisting of waves reflecting predominantly back and forth between the reflecting end plates of the rectangular box. However, the actual field distribution of the lowest modes within the plane-parallel Fabry-Perot (PPF-P) and the rectangular box are different. In the former the field is always weak at the edge of the reflector, whereas in the latter the fields are periodically a maximum at the edge of the box.

The circular patterns in Fig. 8b have the mode designation TEM_{plq}, where p gives the number of nodes in the radial direction and l gives the number of nodes in the azimuthal direction. Such modes have been isolated and photographed by Rigrod using a He-Ne maser (91), and are shown in Fig. 10. The classification of modes in Fig. 8 applies to resonators with plane as well as spherical mirrors. The resonators used to obtain the mode patterns in Fig. 9 and 10 consisted, respectively, of two concave and a concave and flat mirror. Radiation patterns of pure modes have also been obtained by Polanyi and Watson using the He-Ne maser (91a).

The electric field patterns in Fig. 8 are all linearly polarized. However, by superimposing the two orthogonally polarized TEM_{01q} modes for circular plane mirrors, for example, one obtains a field configuration which is very similar to that of the circular electric (TE_{01}) mode of circular waveguide. Many other field configurations can be generated in this manner by the superposition of degenerate modes.

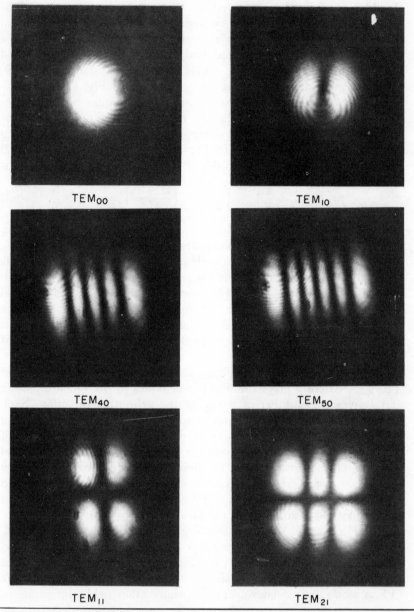

Fig. 9. Photographs of the radiation patterns of pure rectangular modes of a concave mirror interferometer. All the beams were polarized horizontally. The

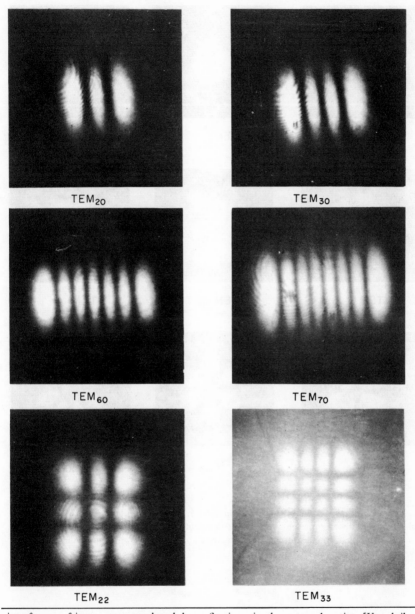

interference fringes were produced by reflections in the external optics. [Kogelnik and Rigrod (90).]

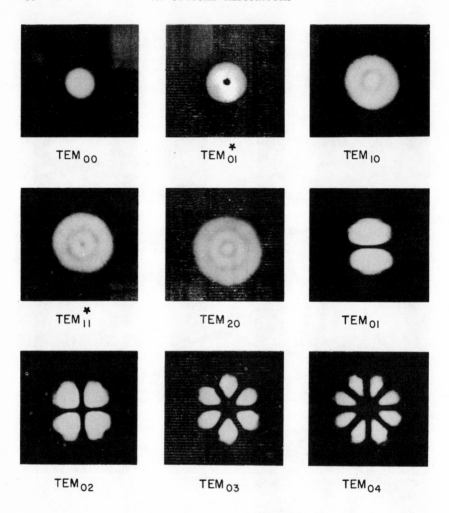

FIG. 10. Photographs of the radiation pattern of pure circular modes of a concave-plane mirror interferometer. An asterisk designates two degenerate modes combining in space and phase quadrature to form a composite circular-symmetric mode. All beams were polarized vertically. [Rigrod (91).]

The lowest order TEM_{mnq} of the PPF-P in the notation of Fox and Li (*83*) is the TE_{00q} mode. The field distribution in the transverse plane is approximately a half sine in each direction with the field strength falling off to zero approximately at the edges. This distribution is more closely represented by the TE_{11q} than by the TE_{01q} or TE_{10q} modes of the rectangular box. Thus in order to obtain the resonance frequency of the PPF-P resonator from (6.1) and the mode splitting from (6.2), it is necessary to let $r = m + 1$ and $s = n + 1$.

The mode separation is given by

$$\Delta \left(\frac{1}{\lambda}\right) = \frac{1}{2D} \left[\Delta q + \frac{1}{16}\left(\frac{D\lambda}{L^2}\right)(2r\Delta r + \Delta r^2 + 2s\Delta s + \Delta s^2)\right], \quad (6.2)$$

where for r, $s \ll q$, $q \simeq 2D/\lambda$. The mode separation due to $\Delta q = 1$, which corresponds to changing the number of half wavelengths between the mirrors by one, is given by

$$\Delta \lambda = \lambda/q, \quad (6.3)$$

which is also the spectral range for the PPF-P interferometer. The mode separation corresponding to $\Delta r = 1$ or $\Delta s = 1$ is much smaller and depends on the parameter $L^2/D\lambda$.

The diffraction losses for the fundamental and low order modes (*47, 83, 92, 92a*) are so low that for most practical geometries performance will be limited by reflection losses and scattering due to mirror misalignment and aberrations. The effect of simple mirror aberrations and misalignment on the power loss of a Fabry-Perot interferometer was calculated by Kotik and Newstein (*47*), and the effects of such departures from perfect geometry on the loss and phase shift of the modes were investigated by Fox and Li (*88*). According to an estimate by the former (*47*), a Fabry-Perot interferometer with mirrors tilted in opposite directions by the angle δ appears to have its power reflection coefficient decreased by the amount $(4\pi^2/3)(2L\delta/\lambda)^2$. This result shows that a very small amount of tilt causes a significant increase in the loss rate of the interferometer. Such an effect was quite likely the cause of the increasing threshold with increasing mirror tilt that was observed in a ruby maser (*93*). It was observed that tilting a mirror of the PPF-P resonator of a He-Ne maser caused a slight shift in its oscillation frequencies (*94*). This phenomenon was explained by the theory of Fox and Li (*88*).

C. RESONATORS WITH SPHERICAL REFLECTORS

A resonator formed by two spherical reflectors of equal curvature separated by their common radii of curvature is confocal since the focal points of the reflectors are coincident. The variation of the electric field with a given polarization over the surface of the reflector is approximately expressed by

$$\frac{E_{m,n}^{(x)}}{E_0} = H_m\left[x\left(\frac{2\pi}{\lambda D}\right)^{1/2}\right] H_n\left[y\left(\frac{2\pi}{\lambda D}\right)^{1/2}\right] \exp\left[-\pi\frac{x^2+y^2}{D\lambda}\right], \quad (6.4)$$

where H_m and H_n are Hermite polynomials. The approximation involved in (6.4) fails away from the center of the reflector. However, for reasonably large values of $L^2/D\lambda$ the field is weak at the edges of the reflector and of little interest. From (6.4) we see that the field in the lowest mode falls to $1/e$ of its value at a spot radius

$$w_s = (D\lambda/\pi)^{1/2}, \quad (6.5)$$

which is independent of the reflector aperture. As the quantity $L^2/D\lambda$ increases, the field at the edge of the reflector decreases, thus decreasing diffraction losses.

The field of the confocal resonator over the spherical surfaces of constant phase inside the confocal geometry as well as outside is approximately of the form, for large values of the Fresnel number,

$$\frac{E_{m,n}^{(x)}}{E_0} = \left(\frac{2}{1+\xi^2}\right)^{1/2} H_m\left(X\sqrt{\frac{2}{1+\xi^2}}\right) H_n\left(Y\sqrt{\frac{2}{1+\xi^2}}\right) \exp\left[-\frac{2\pi}{R\lambda}\frac{x^2+y^2}{(1+\xi^2)}\right],$$

$$(6.5a)$$

where $X = x(2\pi/R\lambda)^{1/2}$, $Y = y(2\pi/R\lambda)^{1/2}$, $\xi = 2z/R$, z being measured from the center of the resonator. R is the radius of curvature of the confocal reflectors, and is equal to their separation D. Omitted from this expression is a phase factor which describes the periodic variation of intensity in the z direction. Within the resonator the field will be a standing wave, whereas outside the resonator the field will be a travelling wave. For $\xi = 1$, i.e. at the surface of a reflector, (6.5a) reduces to (6.4).

The surfaces of constant phase of the confocal resonator are spherical with radii of curvature, R', given by

$$R' = \left|\frac{1+\xi^2}{2\xi}\right| R. \quad (6.5b)$$

Figure 11 shows the spherical surfaces of constant phase between the reflectors of a confocal resonator, and the Gaussian field variation over the surface of the reflector for the lowest order mode. Any two surfaces of constant phase may be replaced by reflectors to obtain a resonator with nonconfocal spacing. The field distribution in the lowest order mode falls to e^{-1} at the dashed curve, computed from the exponential term in (6.5a).

The resonant wavelength for a confocal system with reflectors of equal size is given by

$$\frac{4D}{\lambda} = 2q + (1 + m + n).$$ (6.6)

The mode spectrum contains a high degree of degeneracy; note that increasing $m + n$ by two and decreasing q by one gives the same resonant wavelength.

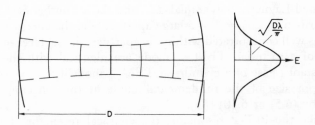

FIG. 11. Surfaces of constant phase and the transverse field variation at the reflector of the TEM_{00} mode of a confocal resonator. [After Boyd (*84*).]

This degeneracy is removed if the spacing is made nonconfocal. The resonance condition is now

$$\frac{2D}{\lambda} = q + \frac{1}{\pi}(1 + m + n)\cos^{-1}\left(1 - \frac{D}{R'}\right),$$ (6.7)

where R' is the radius of curvature of the two identical reflectors, and D is their separation. The confocal geometry of which this resonator is part has the spacing R, and from (6.5b) where $\xi = D/R$ is given by

$$D^2 - 2DR' + R^2 = 0.$$ (6.8)

The mode splitting is given by

$$\Delta \left(\frac{1}{\lambda}\right) = \frac{1}{2D}\left[\Delta q + \frac{\Delta(m+n)}{\pi}\cos^{-1}\left(1 - \frac{D}{R'}\right)\right].\qquad(6.9)$$

At the reflectors the spot size of the fundamental TEM_{00q} mode is given by

$$w'_s = \left(\frac{R'\lambda}{\pi}\right)^{1/2}\left(\frac{D}{2R' - D}\right)^{1/4},\qquad(6.10)$$

and is a minimum for a given spacing for the confocal condition $R' = D$. As the spherical resonator geometry is approached, i.e., $R' = D/2$, the spot size at the reflectors becomes very large.

The resonators discussed in this section have square or rectangular apertures and are given the cartesian mode designation TEM_{mnq}. When the modes have cylindrical symmetry, they are designated by TEM_{plq}, where the radial field variation is described in terms of the associated Laguerre polynomials L_p^l, and the azimuthal field variation is described by $\cos l\phi$. For a large aperture, i.e. the energy of a given mode is well concentrated within the aperture, the surfaces of constant phase of a cartesian TEM_{mnq} mode are identical with the surfaces of constant phase of a cylindrical TEM_{plq} mode if $m + n = 2p + 1$. The spot size of the fundamental mode at the reflectors is again given by (6.5) or 6.10) (85).

Unlike the PPF-P resonator, the confocal resonator is relatively easy to adjust because no strict parallelism is required between the reflectors. It is only necessary that the axis of the confocal resonator intersect each reflector sufficiently far from its edge so that the diffraction losses are not excessive.

Boyd and Kogelnik (85) have also obtained results for the following geometries: confocal resonator with unequal square and rectangular apertures; a confocal resonator with one reflector partially blocked; nonconfocal resonators of unequal radii of curvature; and the half nonconfocal resonator consisting of one curved and one plane reflector. Unequal apertures at the two reflectors have a large effect in determining mode patterns of the resonator, although the resonant condition is not changed. If the reflectors are larger than the spot size at the reflectors, the mode patterns of nonconfocal systems with reflectors of unequal size but equal radii of curvature are not significantly changed from the confocal case. For resonators formed of reflectors with unequal curvature, the system may be defocussed and unstable regions of high diffraction loss exist. The confocal system with reflectors of equal curvature is on the border of such unstable regions and certain deviations from the ideal dimensions will greatly increase the system losses. It may be advisable consequently to make the system slightly nonconfocal so that the operating point is at a safe distance from the unstable region. For resonators consisting of reflectors of unequal radii of curvature and/or aperture size, the spot size and shape on each reflector is not the same. When the system dimensions are such that it approaches a high loss region, one or both spots increase very rapidly in size.

As may be inferred from the diagram in Fig. 11 showing the spherical surfaces of constant phase in a confocal resonator, it should be possible to form a resonator by using a spherical mirror ($R_1 = 2D$) and a plane mirror ($R_2 = \infty$) located at the midway point ($D = R_1/2$) where the surface of constant phase is a plane. This system is in a stable region and like the confocal resonator does not require exact parallelism between the reflectors. The resonance condition for arbitrary spacing of the reflectors is

$$\frac{2D}{\lambda} = q + \frac{1}{2\pi}(1 + m + n)\cos^{-1}\left(1 - \frac{2D}{R_1}\right). \tag{6.11}$$

The spot size for the fundamental mode on the curved and plane reflectors are, respectively,

$$w_1 = \left(\frac{\lambda D}{\pi}\right)^{1/2}\left[\frac{R_1^2}{D(R_1 - D)}\right]^{1/4},$$

$$w_2 = \left(\frac{\lambda D}{\pi}\right)^{1/2}\left[\frac{R_1 - D}{D}\right]^{1/4}.$$

For $R_1 \gg D$, in which case essentially a plane wave propagates between the reflectors without spreading appreciably, both spot sizes are very nearly the same. On the other hand, as R_1 approaches D, w_2 decreases while w_1 increases, a result which indicates the focusing action of the spherical mirror.

The distribution of the energy stored within the interferometer with confocal mirrors is more concentrated on the axis than with plane parallel mirrors (84). Consequently, the confocal resonator has a smaller effective mode volume and requires a smaller volume of maser material than with the PPF-P. Assuming equal Q's, we see from the relation $P_{min} = n_2 h\nu V/\tau_{21}$ that less pump power is required for the confocal than for the plane parallel resonator.

The PPF-P and concave reflector resonators should find utility in the millimeter wavelength and even the microwave regions by virtue of their extremely low diffraction loss. A fair amount of work on the properties of such resonators in these regions has been reported. In particular may be mentioned that the stop band predicted for the resonator consisting of mirrors of unequal curvature (85) has been clearly shown by measurements at 4.7 mm of resonator Q as a function of reflector separation (95a). The near and far field radiation patterns of a PPF-P interferometer operating at 3.2 cm has been studied in some detail (96). The extensive work of Culshaw on the properties of resonators with open sides in the millimeter wavelength region is of importance (96a).

D. DIFFRACTION LOSS

The theoretical diffraction losses as a function of $L^2/D\lambda$ for confocal and plane parallel resonators are shown in Fig. 12. Diffraction losses for the confocal resonator are seen to be orders of magnitude less than those for the plane parallel resonator losses. The diffraction loss for an aperture assumed to be uniformly illuminated is, of course, considerably larger than that for the mode patterns where the field falls to a low value at the edges of the aperture. The diffraction losses computed for circular plane mirrors of various Fresnel numbers have been experimentally verified by Rigrod and Rustako (95).

The loss of a square nonconfocal resonator of dimension $2L'$ may be estimated on the assumption that this loss is equal to that of its equivalent confocal resonator with reflector dimensions L scaled up by the ratio of their spot sizes, viz. $L = L'w_s/w_s'$, where w_s and w_s' are given respectively by (6.5) and (6.10). This value of L fixes the Fresnel number which determines the diffraction loss.

To calculate the resonator Q due to diffraction and other losses we make use of a formula which is obtained from (4.3),

$$Q = \frac{(|\, r_1' r_2'\,|\, e^{-kD})^{1/2}}{1 - |\, r_1' r_2'\,|\, e^{-kD}} \frac{2\pi D}{\lambda}. \qquad (6.11a)$$

The amplitude reflection coefficients for the two reflectors are

$$|r_1'| = (1 - T_1 - F_1 - A_1)^{1/2},$$

and a similar expression for $|r_2'|$, where T_1, F_1, and A_1 are the fractional losses per bounce from reflector 1 due to, respectively, the power lost in transmission, diffraction, and absorption and scattering in the mirrors. Because of the losses in the mirrors, r' is complex and introduces a phase shift in the propagation constant of the waves in the resonator. kD is the single pass loss due to scattering and absorption in the medium. When the losses are small, the Q reduces to

$$\frac{1}{Q} = \frac{\lambda}{2\pi D}\,[kD + \tfrac{1}{2}(T_1 + T_2) + \tfrac{1}{2}(F_1 + F_2) + \tfrac{1}{2}(A_1 + A_2)].\quad (6.11b)$$

Consider the case $T_1 = T_2 = T$, $F_1 = F_2 = F$, $A_1 = A_2 = A$, and $k = 0$. If diffraction losses are small compared with the other losses, then the resonator Q is proportional to the spacing between the reflecting surfaces. For a given reflector aperture size, the resonator

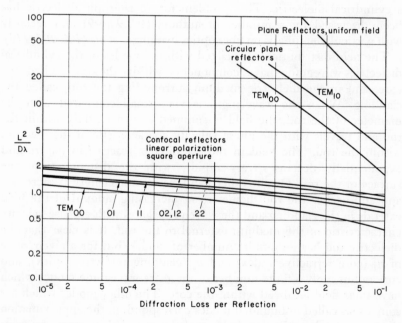

FIG. 12. Diffraction losses for confocal and plane-parallel resonators. [Boyd and Gordon (84).]

Q will continue to increase with D until diffraction losses become roughly comparable with the other losses. Further increase in spacing then decreases the Q because of increasing diffraction losses as shown in Fig. 12. Therefore an optimum length exists for which the Q is a maximum. If the diffraction loss curve is approximated by the function $F = A \times 10^{-B(L^2/4D\lambda)}$, then the maximum value of Q is obtained when $A + T = [2.30B(L^2/D\lambda) - 1] F$ (84).

E. Optical Dielectric Waveguides

The previous discussion of the modes in an open type resonator is applicable when the reflectors are immersed in a uniform isotropic dielectric medium with negligible loss and of infinite extent. When, however, the dielectric medium is in the form of a solid rod, the sides of the resonator may be regarded as partially enclosed because of reflection at the dielectric interface. In this case, it is appropriate to consider the system from the viewpoint of the waveguide modes in a cylindrical dielectric. This problem for an isotropic dielectric has been discussed by a number of authors (97, 98, 99) and recently with particular emphasis on fiber optics by Snitzer et al. (100-102, 115).

The field distributions associated with the modes of the cylindrical dielectric waveguide have components within the rod, called the core, and in the dielectric medium surrounding the rod, called the cladding. When the wavelength is very small compared with the diameter of the rod, the field is confined almost entirely within the rod and travels with the phase velocity characteristic of the medium within the rod. The field in the cladding is reactive in nature and exponentially decreases very rapidly with the distance from the surface of the rod. On the other hand, as the wavelength is increased and approaches the rod diameter, an increasing amount of the field extends in the cladding and the wave propagates with a phase velocity characteristic of the medium external to the rod. It is clear that the dielectric rod has an infinite number of modes, but for a given value of n_1 (core refractive index) and n_2 (cladding refractive index), and core radius, only a finite number of these are waveguide modes which have their field localized within the core. The other modes which are sometimes called unbounded modes correspond, in the approximation of geometrical optics, to light striking the dielectric interface at angles less than the critical angle.

For cylindrical metallic waveguides the modes are designated TE_{nm} or TM_{nm}. In the dielectric waveguide only the cylindrically symmetric $n = 0$ modes are either transverse electric (TE_{0m}) or transverse magnetic (TM_{0m}). The other modes have nonzero values for both E_z and H_z and are called hybrid modes, EH or HE. The transverse components of the field depend on the radius through J_{n+1} for the EH modes and J_{n-1} for the HE modes, where $J_{n\pm1}$ are Bessel functions. The HE_{1m} modes are the only ones with light intensity at the center of the guide and with an on-axis lobe in the radiation pattern.

Snitzer (100, 101, 102), on whose work this discussion is based, has described the lower-order modes for wavelengths far from cutoff for the case $0 < n_1 - n_2 \ll 1$. This case of small difference in the indices of refraction of core and cladding is of interest first of all because the field equations simplify considerably since the indices of refraction of optical materials are rather small. In addition, some physical insight may be obtained from the simpler description which applies for this case. Finally, if a length of such a guide is terminated by plane-parallel reflectors, then in the limit of large core diameter and $n_1 - n_2 \simeq 0$, Snitzer (102) has asserted that the modes discussed by Fox and Li (83) are obtained, apart from some detail near the outer boundary of the reflectors.

For wavelengths far from cutoff, the cutoff parameters u are solutions of

$$J_{n+1}(u) = 0, \tag{6.12}$$

for the TE_{0m}, TM_{0m}, and EH_{nm} modes, and are solutions of

$$J_{n-1}(u) = 0, \tag{6.13}$$

for the HE_{nm} modes. By considering a waveguide mode as a properly phased array of plane waves whose normals make the angle θ with respect to the guide axis, the following relation is obtained between θ and u:

$$\sin \theta = \frac{u}{2\pi n_1} \frac{\lambda}{a}, \tag{6.14}$$

where a is the radius. The parameter u depends on how far the wavelength is from cutoff but remains in fact within narrow limits for a given mode. For the HE_{11} mode $u = 2.405$, for the TE_{01},

TM_{01}, HE_{21} modes $u = 3.832$. The successively higher-order modes have increasing values of u and consequently increasing values of θ. Since the guide wavelength is $\lambda/n_1 \cos \theta$, the resonance condition is

$$\nu \cos \theta = \nu_q = qc/2n_1 D, \tag{6.15}$$

which is identical in form with that used in describing the resonance condition for the modes of the rectangular box or PPF-P resonator. The frequency difference between two modes specified by θ and θ' is given by

$$\Delta\nu = \frac{\nu}{2} (\theta^2 - \theta'^2). \tag{6.16}$$

Snitzer has succeeded in selectively exciting and observing in the visible region of the spectrum a given mode or a combination of modes in dielectric fibers whose core diameter is several microns. Photographs of the mode patterns were found to correlate with schematic drawings of the modes constructed from solutions of the field equations. With an increase of fiber diameter, patterns appeared which could not be true bound modes, since they were beyond cutoff for the given diameter, but which could be considered to arise from rays that spiral around the outer portion of the core. These are called leaky or quasibound modes, although for fibers with diameters greater than 0.001 in. the attenuation for the quasibound mode was not found to be noticeably greater than that for the true bound modes. Because of the penetration of the field in the cladding, energy can be transferred between two fibers if they are placed close to each other. It is thought that the resulting interference between the waveguide modes can be used to good advantage as a mode selecting scheme (*102*).

Optical maser action has been reported in a cylindrical fiber, 32μ in diameter, of Nd^{3+} in barium crown glass clad with ordinary glass (*179*), and in rectangular fibers of ruby and $CaWO_4:Nd^{3+}$, with cross sectional dimensions of the order of 100μ (*102a*).

Another type of optical dielectric waveguide is the dielectric slab or sandwich configuration. Mode patterns have been obtained in such a waveguide, constructed of two glass plates separated by 10 to 100μ with a suitable liquid between them, by excitation with a He-Ne maser (*102b*). The dielectric sandwich formed in p–n junctions by having a depletion layer bounded by the p and n regions can act as a dielectric waveguide. This configuration, of importance for maser action in p–n junctions, is discussed in Chapter XI.

We conclude this section with some remarks on the nature of modes in a large diameter dielectric rod terminated with plane mirrors. It will be seen in Section VIII,B that in the optical excitation of solids, the intensity of the pumping light may be greater at the center of the rod than at the sides, in which case the oscillation will be confined to the central region of the rod. Since in this circumstance the core and cladding have essentially the same refractive index, as mentioned earlier, the modes of the dielectric rod with plane-parallel reflectors are expected to be those discussed by Fox and Li (83). On the other hand, it has been suggested that to the propagating wavefront in the crystal the reflectors are not optically parallel due to variations in the refractive index and may even appear to be spherical as in a resonator with spherical reflectors (103).

F. Various Configurations for Optical Resonators

Although the open type resonator and the dielectric rod terminated by reflecting surfaces have played central roles in optical masers thus far, modifications of these resonators and a number of other configurations have been investigated. Among these is a ruby crystal in the shape of a rectangular parallelepiped. Stimulated emission characteristics quite different from that of the usual cylindrical rod was obtained. Emission was observed in directions given by (4.46), which are the geometrical optical ray directions in which a ray is superimposed on itself after a given number of reflections (104). The frequencies and field distributions of rectangular parallelepiped microwave resonators made of an anisotropic dielectric have been obtained by Okaya and Barash (105). These results may be readily applied to the optical region.

The spacing of the axial modes, or the spectral range, of a PPF-P interferometer is given by $(2nD)^{-1}$ in wavenumbers. Since the optical resonances usually cover a band greater than $(2nD)^{-1}$, it is evident, as illustrated in Fig. 3, that there may be many orders or axial modes within the atomic bandwidth. For example, in the He-Ne gas maser the axial mode separation is typically 0.005 cm^{-1}, whereas the atomic line width is approximately 0.03 cm^{-1}. In the ruby optical maser the axial mode spacing is typically 0.1 cm⁻¹, whereas the atomic width at room temperature is roughly 5 cm⁻¹. It may not be always feasible to reduce the number of orders by shortening the resonator, for then it may not be possible to realize sufficient gain to achieve oscillation. In this circumstance, it may be desirable to modify the original Fabry-Perot resonator to provide discrimination against unwanted modes.

It is well known that constructing an interferometer with each mirror replaced by a plate with two surfaces of high reflectivity has the advantage of greater spectral range for a given resolving power (*106*). Kleinman and Kisliuk (*107*) have discussed the discrimination against unwanted modes by a similar method. The composite resonator is illustrated in Fig. 13a, and the calculated Q of each mode for the composite and original interferometer is shown in Fig. 13b and 13c. Except for the extra modes in the region of high loss, the general effect of the extra surfaces is to impose a modulation of the original mode Q's. Greatest discrimination against unwanted Fabry-Perot orders is said to be obtained by setting $(b - a) \sim (2\Delta\nu)^{-1}$,

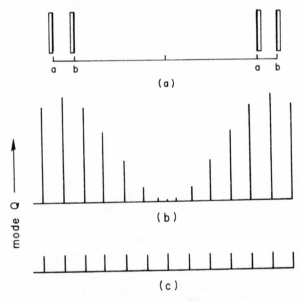

FIG. 13.   (a) The composite Fabry-Perot interferometer. (b) The Q's of the axial modes of the composite interferometer. (c) The Q's of the axial modes of the interferometer without the outer mirrors. [Kleinman and Kisliuk (*107*).]

where $\Delta\nu$ is the halfwidth of the atomic resonance. In practice good mode discrimination has been obtained by using as reflectors only one rather than two double mirrors.*

Resonators using corner cube reflectors instead of plane or curved mirrors are illustrated in Figs. 14a and 14b (*108*). The polarization

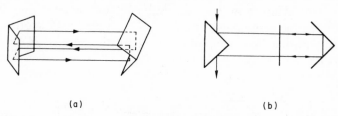

(a)   (b)

Fig. 14.   Resonators using (a) crossed 90° corner reflectors, and (b) a partially transmitting plane mirror and a corner reflector. The prism is used to direct radiation into and out of the interferometer. [Gould *et al.* (*108*).]

properties of cube corner reflectors have been analyzed theoretically by Peck (*109*) and investigated experimentally by the observation of polarized interference fringes by Rabinowitz *et al.* (*110*). The reflection losses in corner reflectors are virtually eliminated by employing total internal reflection in a prism (Fig. 15a) (*111*).

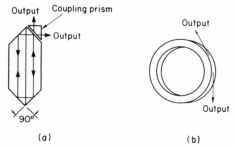

(a)   (b)

Fig. 15.   Dielectric resonators using total internal reflection: (a) prism; (b) ring. The radiation leaves the ring tangential to the surface.

Maser operation by internal reflection of fluorescent light has been observed in a ruby ring, Fig. 15b (*113, 113a*) and in a sphere of $CaF_2 : Sm^{2+}$ (*114*). In these dielectric resonators one expects that

* Further discussion of mode discrimination especially for the off-axial or transverse modes (i.e., modes where m and n are greater than zero) may be found in Section XII, H.

some of the fluorescent light will be totally reflected and so remain trapped. However, reflection is not quite total for any angle of incidence if the reflection surface is not plane, and the light traveling roughly circumferentially just inside the surface will leak out very slowly tangentially to the surface. In other words, there are surface modes, in the case of spheres called whispering modes by analogy with a related situation in acoustics, which are modes of very high Q.

A ring type resonator using four mirrors set at 45 degrees to the optical path has been proposed (*112*), and the analysis of the conditions for stable operation of such a configuration has been given (*112a*). The ring resonator shown in Fig. 16 has been developed by Macek

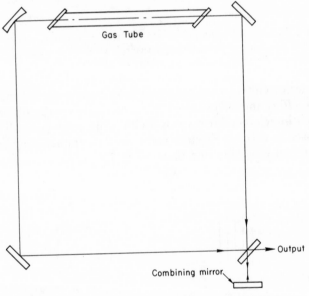

Fig. 16.   Ring resonator. [Macek and Davis (*112b*).]

and Davis (*112b*) for the sensing of rotation rates. Although only one gas tube is shown, one to four such tubes containing He and Ne may be distributed along the path. One mirror is slightly concave to reduce diffraction losses and make alignment less critical. Output is obtained from clockwise and counterclockwise traveling waves in a superimposed colinear fashion by the use of a combining mirror. In ring type resonators (Figs. 14, 15, and 16), the clockwise and counterclockwise waves are independent unless coupled by the medium or some perturbation in the system. By inserting an optical isolator in the path of the beam of the resonator shown in Fig. 16, one of the traveling waves was eliminated (53).

G. SPATIAL DISTRIBUTION OF OUTPUT RADIATION

The spatial distribution of the radiation leaving an optical maser depends on the field distribution excited within the resonator. Consequently, we may expect the spatial characteristics of the output radiation to depend on the type of resonator and the nature of the modes which are participating in the oscillation.

If many modes are excited in a resonator, the individual diffraction patterns will be washed out, and what may be observed is a beam of approximately uniform intensity or perhaps with structure, but in either case, with a divergence considerably larger than what would be obtained if only the lowest order mode were present. In certain cases, the output may be distributed among several rings whose angular separation is given by the usual expression for the spacing of Fabry-Perot interference fringes or rings.

Although the coherent radiation leaving the optical maser is highly collimated, the background spontaneous emission will, of course, be distributed over all angles. There may be an enhancement of the radiation in certain directions corresponding to the radiation in those cavity modes which while not oscillating still have substantial gain. In principle, a careful analysis of the background spontaneous radiation from optical masers could yield information concerning the distribution of excitation among the modes.

1. Plane-Parallel Fabry-Perot Resonator

It follows from the picture of a wave reflected between the mirrors of the Fabry-Perot resonator that the coherent output radiation should be highly collimated with a beam divergence limited by diffraction. Schawlow and Townes (1) have considered the nature of the output beam for field distributions along the end mirror appropriate for the modes of a rectangular resonator. When $q \gg m, n$, the Fraunhofer or far field diffraction pattern of the radiation has an intensity distribution in the x direction, for example, given by

$$I \propto (2\pi m)^2 \sin^2 \left(\frac{2\pi L \sin \theta}{\lambda} + \frac{\pi m}{2} \right) \Big/ \left(\pi m + \frac{4\pi L \sin \theta}{\lambda} \right)^2 \left(\pi m - \frac{4\pi L \sin \theta}{\lambda} \right)^2,$$

$$(6.17)$$

where θ is the angle between the direction of observation and the perpendicular to the mirrors. The direction of radiation is thus critically dependent on m, and also, of course, on n. For a given value of m, the strongest diffraction maxima occur at

$$\sin \theta = \pm m\lambda/4L, \tag{6.18}$$

and the first minima on either side of the maxima at

$$\sin \theta = \pm m\lambda/4L \pm \lambda/2L. \tag{6.19}$$

It may be seen that this value of the diffraction maxima agrees with that obtained from $\cos \theta = ck_z/\omega$ where θ is the direction of propagation in a rectangular box of those plane waves whose superposition represents the mode in question. The size of the radiation pattern at a large distance from the maser, or the far field pattern, depends on the angular spread of the beam. The angular spread of the strongest diffraction maxima is from (6.18) and (6.19) for small values of θ, $\lambda/2L$. The near field radiation has a pattern containing m and n maxima in the x and y directions, respectively. On the other hand the far field pattern contains only four lobes or strongest diffraction maxima for $m, n > 0$ (96). Thus the near and far field patterns are not alike, in general, for the field distributions of a rectangular box resonator.

The field on the mirrors of a PPF-P resonator, however, decays toward zero more like a Gaussian function than the sinusoidal distribution of the rectangular box. If the intensity of illumination is assumed to follow a Gaussian, falling off to zero at the edge of the reflector, then according to Fraunhofer diffraction theory no secondary maxima would be expected. This result also applies for a field distribution which is a product of a Gaussian and a Hermite polynomial. However, as may be deduced from the much greater diffraction losses of plane as compared with spherical mirrors, the field is not zero at the edges of the plane mirrors. To the extent that this is true, one would expect some modification of the far field as compared with the near field pattern.

Standard diffraction theory shows that if the illumination on the mirror is ellipsoidal or rectangular in shape, the far field pattern will be rotated by 90°. Such an effect has been observed by Birnbaum et al. (114a) with a ruby maser employing detached plane parallel mirrors.

2. Confocal Resonator

We see from (6.5a) that the far field pattern should be similar to the direct image since the principal effect of the light leaving the resonator is a spreading of the pattern. The field distribution of the TEM_{00q} mode for the confocal geometry $R = D$ is from (6.5a) seen to fall to e^{-1} at a radius

$$w = \left[\frac{R\lambda}{2\pi} (1 + \xi^2) \right]^{1/2}, \tag{6.20}$$

where $\xi = 2z/D$ (84). At the reflector $\xi = 1$ and (6.5) is obtained, whereas at $\xi = 0$ $w = w_s/\sqrt{2}$. To obtain the angular beam width of the spherical wave of the TEM_{00q} mode, we take the ratio of the spot diameter from (6.20) as $\xi \to \infty$ to the distance from the center of the resonator. Then the beam width between the half-power points is given by

$$\theta_B = 2 \left(\frac{\ln 2}{\pi} \right)^{1/2} \left(\frac{\lambda}{D} \right)^{1/2} = 0.939 \left(\frac{\lambda}{D} \right)^{1/2}. \tag{6.21}$$

The beam width of the confocal resonator is larger than that of the PPF-P resonator approximately by the factor $L(\lambda/D)^{-1/2}$.

VII.   Optical Maser Systems

In this section we shall consider several topics of importance to the design and operation of masers. In particular, we consider the question of minimum pumping power and the requirements for maser media, and the problem of optimum cavity coupling for maximum power output. The many factors contributing to the cavity loss, upon which the minimum pumping power depends, are summarized. Methods of population inversion are summarized, and optical maser systems are briefly surveyed.

A. Minimum Pumping Power—Requirements for Maser Media

On the threshold of oscillation, the minimum power which must be supplied in order to maintain the critical number of atoms in the excited state, N_2, is for homogeneously and inhomogeneously broadened lines,*

$$P_{\min} = \frac{N_2 h\nu}{\tau_{21}}, \tag{7.1}$$

provided the atoms relax from the excited state only by spontaneous emission. The power $P_{\min}$ is also the incoherent power given off as fluorescence by N_2 atoms in the excited state. Using (2.27), we may put (7.1) in the form

$$P_{\min} = h\nu \, \frac{p}{\tau_c} \, \frac{N_2}{N_2 - N_1(g_2/g_1)}, \tag{7.1a}$$

which shows that $P_{\min}$ is greater in three than four level systems where $N_1 = 0$.

Should atoms relax from the excited state by nonradiative processes or by emission to states other than the terminal maser state, the

---

* The actual pumping power at threshold is given by (8.13). The frequency ν in (7.1) to (7.3) refers to the maser transition.

correct rate is obtained by dividing (7.1) by the factor ϕ, which will be defined shortly. Doing this, and substituting (2.27) for N_2, we obtain for the minimum pumping power

$$P_{\min} = \frac{N_1(g_2/g_1)\,h\nu}{\phi\tau_{21}} + \frac{8\pi^2\nu^2\varDelta\nu V}{\nu^3}\frac{h\nu}{\phi\tau_c}. \tag{7.2}$$

The first term in (7.2) gives the power required to depopulate the ground state. This term is absent in maser systems where the terminal maser state is not the ground state and is sufficiently higher than the ground state to be depopulated at the operating temperature. In this case $P_{\min}$ given by

$$P_{\min} = \frac{8\pi^2\nu^2\varDelta\nu V}{\nu^3}\frac{h\nu}{\phi\tau_c} = \frac{ph\nu}{\phi\tau_c} \tag{7.3}$$

is essentially independent of the radiative lifetime τ_{21}. The ν^3 frequency dependence shows that the pumping requirement will be more difficult to satisfy as the frequency is increased.

The factor ϕ, defined as the fraction of excited atoms which decay by spontaneously emitting the desired radiation, is given by

$$\phi = \frac{\tau_2}{\tau_2 + \tau_{21}}, \tag{7.4}$$

where $1/\tau_2$ is the rate of nonradiative transitions from state 2 to 1 plus the rate of radiative and nonradiative transitions from state 2 to any state other than 1. If every photon absorbed in some pump transition results in putting an atom into level 2 from which fluorescent emission occurs, then ϕ is the same as the quantum efficiency (per absorbed photon).

In three level systems, maser action ensues with $N_2 \approx N_1$, in which case the first term in (7.2) is considerably greater than the second. The minimum pumping power is then quite insensitive to the atomic line width or the cavity damping rate, but directly proportional to the relaxation rate from level 2. Thus a long lifetime is advantageous for three level operation. Should ϕ decrease due to crystal heating, greater pumping power will be required to reach threshold (see Section IX,B,2). In four level systems where the first term in (7.2) is absent, $P_{\min}$ is independent of the spontaneous emission rate but depends directly on the atomic line width and inversely on the product of ϕ and the cavity damping time. The use of a low loss resonator is clearly important in reducing the pumping power required to reach threshold in four-level systems.

It follows from (7.1a) and (7.3) that the minimum pumping power of a four-level maser is smaller than that of a three-level maser, all other factors being equal, by the factor $\Delta N_{th}/N_2$, where N_{th} is the threshold population difference, and N_2 is approximately one-half the total number of active atoms in the crystal. The degeneracy factors which will not substantially change the following conclusion are neglected. For some typical solid state systems $\Delta N_{th} \sim 10^{16}$ and $N_2 \sim 10^{18}$, in which case 100-fold more pumping power would be required in the three level maser as compared with the four-level maser. If the maser is operated on a pulsed rather than a continuous basis, the minimum energy that must be supplied for the maser to reach threshold is $N_2 h\nu$, provided the excitation of atoms to level 2 occurs in a time which is less than the relaxation time of that level. The minimum energy for four level operation is smaller than that for three-level operation by the same factor as for continuous operation, viz., $\Delta N_{th}/N_2$.

With the aid of (7.2), we can summarize the requirements for a maser medium, which as we have noted above, will differ in some of the requirements depending on whether a three- or four-level system is used. The following are the main requirements for four level masers.

(1) The medium must of course have energy level separations appropriate for the spectral region of interest.

(2) The atomic line width should be as small as possible for the maser transition.

(3) There should be no strong absorption bands in the maser atoms at the frequency $2\nu_{21}$ which would cause the excited atoms to absorb rather than emit.

(4) The terminal maser level should be far enough above the ground level so that four-level operation is possible.

(5) The lifetime of the metastable state should be radiative, i.e., $\phi = 1$.

(6) Excitation must be possible. The lifetime of the terminal maser level must be smaller than the lifetime of the excited maser level.

(7) For optically pumped systems the medium should possess broad pumping bands with an appreciable absorption coefficient and

a high quantum efficiency. The medium should be optically thin at the pumping frequency, however, to obtain uniform pumping.

(8) The total cavity losses should be small to obtain a long photon lifetime.

(9) In solid state masers, the maser atom should be incorporated into a host with suitable mechanical and optical properties.

The mechanisms which damp the cavity field and consequently increase the oscillation threshold are summarized below.

(1) Transmission and absorption in the mirrors (Section IV,B).

(2) Diffraction by the mirrors (Section VI,A).

(3) Absorption in the maser medium due to mechanisms other than the 1-2 transition (Section II,B).

(4) Geometrical imperfections in the mirrors (Section VI,A).

(5) Misaligned mirrors (Section VI,A).

(6) Scattering by crystal imperfections (Sections IV,D and XII,F).

These loss mechanisms are discussed in the sections as noted.

Mechanisms (4), (5), and (6) all give rise to mode conversion. If as a result of the various losses the loss rates of the axial and off axial modes become more alike, then, as explained in Section IV,C,1 greater pumping power would be required to bring the maser to threshold.

B. Power Output and Optimum Output Coupling
of Maser Oscillators

1. *Homogeneously Broadened Lines*

We have shown previously that for a homogeneously broadened atomic system the power output above threshold consists of coherent power in an oscillating mode and incoherent power in all the modes contained within the bandwidth of the atomic resonance [see Eq. (4.48)]. Because the populations of the maser levels are clamped by the threshold condition, the incoherent power is constant with increasing excitation. The coherent power expressed as the spontaneous emission in the oscillating mode multiplied by the gain of the mode increases with increasing excitation because the gain increases.

The coherent power output P_i may be evaluated directly from the expression for conservation of power, viz.,

$$P_p = P_l + P'_l + P_s + P_i \,,$$

where the subscripts p, l, s, and i mean, respectively, pump, lattice, spontaneous, and induced, and P'_l is the power lost to the lattice at the maser transition.* This relation may be put in the form

$$P_i = (P_p - P_l) - P_{\text{min}} = P_{\text{min}}(P_r - 1), \qquad (7.5)$$

where $P_{\text{min}} = P'_l + P_s$ is given by (7.1) and, P_r, defined by

$$P_r = \frac{P_p - P_l}{P_{\text{min}}}, \qquad (7.6)$$

is the factor by which the threshold pumping is exceeded. Equation (7.5) should be independent of the number of modes which oscillate. If all the modes but one are suppressed, the total coherent power can be made to appear in a single mode. Since P_l is proportional to P_p, (7.6) implies that P_r is proportional to the pumping power, provided of course that the radiation at the pumping transition is not intense enough to cause saturation. In energy level systems which can be described by only two population variables, a case which applies for almost all practical maser systems, it is easy to show that P_l is proportional to P_p. In a four-level system, for example, where relaxation is assumed to be instantaneous from levels 4 to 3 and 2 to 1, there is population in only levels 3 and 1, and consequently $\Gamma^i_{14}N_1 = \Gamma^l_{43}N_4$, and $\Gamma^i_{14}N_1 = \Gamma^l_{21}N_2$. Thus $P_l = P_p(\nu_{43} + \nu_{21})/\nu_{14}$.

If the atomic line is inhomogeneously broadened, the population in the excited maser level not at the frequency of the oscillating mode continues to increase with increasing pumping above threshold, and the linear relation between the coherent power output and the pumping power implied by (7.5) does not hold.

The linear relationship between coherent power output and pump power predicted by (7.5) has been observed by Yariv (116) using a cw $CaF_2:U^{3+}$ maser oscillating at 2.61μ, and by Kaiser et al. (49) using a pulsed $CaF_2:Sm^{2+}$ maser. In the latter system, the relaxation time is so much less than the duration of the pumping pulse that the maser operation may be regarded as quasi cw.

---

* P_l is the total power lost in radiationless transitions originating from levels other than the fluorescent level.

As may be seen from (7.2), P_{min} depends on the total cavity damping rate γ_c, which is given by

$$\gamma_c = \gamma_c' + \gamma_t. \tag{7.7}$$

The rate γ_c' is the contribution to the photon decay rate due to all resonator losses excluding γ_t, the loss rate due to the finite transmission of the end reflectors, i.e., to the power delivered externally. The available power leaving the resonator is clearly

$$P_0 = P_i \frac{\rho}{1 + \rho}, \tag{7.8}$$

where the cavity coupling ratio is defined by

$$\rho = \gamma_t/\gamma_c'. \tag{7.9}$$

This quantity is the ratio of the power leaving the resonator to that lost within the resonator. It is evident that increasing γ_t increases the power coupled out of the resonator but increases P_{min}, and consequently decreases the available power in the resonator.

The optimum coupling, ρ_{op}, for which the power output is a maximum has been obtained by Yariv (*116*) as follows. For the four level system, the coherent power output is, from (8.6) and (8.7a),

$$P_i = (N_0 - \Delta N)\, \Gamma_{14}^i\, h\nu_{32} - \Delta N\, \Gamma_3 h\nu_{32}, \tag{7.9a}$$

where the first term is $P_p - P_l$ and the second term is P_{min}. In terms of ρ and $\Delta N'$, the threshold population for zero coupling, ΔN is given by $\Delta N = \Delta N'(1 + \rho)$. Then the result obtained by maximizing (7.8) with respect to ρ is

$$\rho_{op} = -1 + \left[\frac{P_r'}{xP_r' + (1 - x)}\right]^{1/2}, \tag{7.10}$$

where $x = \Delta N'/N_0$, and P_r' is the ratio of the pump power to that at threshold for zero coupling. For the three level system the optimum coupling is

$$\rho_{op} = -1 + \left[\frac{1}{x}\frac{P_r' - (1 - x)/(1 + x)}{P_r' + (1 - x)/(1 + x)}\right]^{1/2}. \tag{7.11}$$

In practical maser oscillators $x \ll 1$, and may be neglected in comparison with unity. The optimum cavity coupling is seen to depend on the amount by which threshold is exceeded, and in a different way for the three and four level systems. When $P_r' > 4$, ρ_{op} for the four level system is greater than 1, in which case the power given by (7.8) is more than 1/2 the power available in the cavity. In the three-level system for $P_r' > 1.5$, for example $\rho \gg 1$, and most of the power in the cavity is available as output power. This result may of course be anticipated from the fact that in three-level masers the threshold pumping is relatively insensitive to the cavity loss rate.

The preceding treatment of cavity coupling and power output is based on the circuit viewpoint. It is useful to consider this problem also from the wave viewpoint as formulated by Rigrod (116a). It follows from (4.25), and (4.34b), which is shown in Section VIII, A, 1 and 2 to represent the saturated negative absorption per pass of the maser oscillator, that oscillations stabilize at internal energy densities such that

$$\alpha D = \frac{\alpha_0 D}{(1 + w/w_0)^n} = k'D + \tfrac{1}{2}(T_1 + T_2),\qquad (7.11a)$$

where T_1 and T_2 are the power transmission coefficients of mirrors 1 and 2, and all other resonator losses are represented by $k'D$. Now when the atoms are homogeneously broadened, i.e., $n = 1$, both the forward and backward waves in the resonator are amplified by interacting with the same atoms. Thus when the power levels in both directions are nearly equal, and the standing wave is replaced by an average field intensity, the normalized one way power density or power is approximately $w/2w_0$. Then the output power at each end is given by

$$w_1/T_1 = w_2/T_2 = \tfrac{1}{2} w_0 \left[\frac{\alpha_0 D}{k'D + T} - 1 \right],\qquad (7.11b)$$

where $T = \tfrac{1}{2}(T_1 + T_2)$. The value of T obtained by optimizing the total power coupled out of the resonator is

$$\frac{T_{op}}{k'D} = \left(\frac{\alpha_0}{k'} \right)^{1/2} - 1.\qquad (7.11c)$$

This result may be shown to be the same as (7.10) or (7.11) by noting that $\alpha_0 D$ is proportional to the inverted population when the mirrors are removed, $k'D$ is proportional to the threshold population for zero cavity coupling, $\gamma_t = (v/D)T$, and $\gamma_c' = vk'$. The optimum power coupled through each mirror is $w_1/w_0 = T_1 T_{op}/2k'D$ and $w_2/w_0 = T_2 T_{op}/2k'D$, where $\tfrac{1}{2}(T_1 + T_2) = T_{op}$.

2. *Inhomogeneously Broadened Lines*

In a Doppler broadened line, the forward and backward waves for a single oscillating mode burn two holes in the Gaussian gain curve, which saturate independently (*13*). Thus the normalized one way power of a uniform beam is w/w_0. According to Rigrod (*116a*), the output power is from (7.11a) with $n = \frac{1}{2}$,

$$w_1/T_1 = w_2/T_2 = w_0 \left[\left(\frac{\alpha_0 D}{k' + T} \right)^2 - 1 \right]. \tag{7.11d}$$

The optimum transmission coefficient and power output may be evaluated from (7.11d) as before.

The power output may be computed when oscillations occur simultaneously in more than one axial mode by assuming that the holes do not overlap, and the gain saturates independently at each frequency. Then the power output at each resonant frequency ν_m is given by (7.11d) where $\alpha_0(\nu_a - \nu_m)$ has the Gaussian shape taken to be the same for both directions. The total power output may be obtained by summing over all oscillating modes, viz.

$$w_1/T_1 = w_2/T_2 = w_0 \sum_m \left\{ X^2 \exp \left[-2 \ln 2 \left(\frac{\nu_a - \nu_m}{\Delta \nu_D} \right)^2 \right] - 1 \right\} \tag{7.11e}$$

where

$$X = \alpha_0(\nu_a)\, D/(k'D + T).$$

Power measurements by Rigrod (*116a*) on He–Ne masers at 1.15μ in a semiconcave resonator 1.75 meters long, restricted to oscillate in the TEM_{00q} modes, were found to be in good agreement with (7.11e), with the summation approximated by an integration for the case where the number of oscillating modes are large. The measurements of small signal or unsaturated gain, $\alpha_0 D$, were made with a probe beam generated by another He–Ne maser, also restricted to oscillate in the TEM_{00q} mode, and with low level excitation. The power measurements somewhat surprisingly were found to agree with theory even when oscillations occurred simultaneously in several transverse modes whose frequency spacing is so small that the modes overlap. However, as a possible explanation, it should be borne in mind that the peak fields of higher order modes are located at greater distances from the resonator axis than lower order modes and tend to interact with different atoms. These measurements are considered to provide indirect confirmation of (4.34b), which describes gain saturation in inhomogeneously broadened systems, and permit an estimate to be made of the saturation parameter w_0 for the maser medium.

White *et al.* (*116b*) have dealt with the case where the spacing between mirrors is made sufficiently large so that the mode spacing is smaller than the natural line width and the population inversion will be reduced over the entire range of oscillating frequencies. A theoretical expression developed for this case was found to be in agreement with the power output of a gas maser. On the other hand this same data was found to be reasonably well represented by an expression for the power output when many noninteracting modes oscillate (*116c*).

C. Quantum Mechanical Amplifiers

The spontaneous noise power given by (7.1a) is emitted into p modes and corresponds to an equivalent excitation of the black body modes with an average number of photons per mode given by $\langle J \rangle = N_2/[N_2 - (g_2/g_1)N_1]$.* From the equation for equilibrium black body radiation,

$$\langle J \rangle = [e^{h\nu/kT} - 1]^{-1}, \qquad (7.12)$$

we find that the mode excitation given by (7.1a) implies an effective input noise temperature T_n given by

$$kT_n = \frac{h\nu}{\ln [2 - (g_2 N_1/g_1 N_2)]}, \qquad (7.13)$$

which for $N_1 = 0$ reduces to $h\nu/\ln 2$. The noise performance of an amplifier is often described by the noise factor, F, which is related to the noise temperature T_n by

$$F = 1 + (T_n/290). \qquad (7.14)$$

---

* The populations in the case of the resonator amplifier will be only slightly less than the values for the oscillation threshold. Equation (7.13) also applies for the traveling wave amplifier.

For the four-level system $N_1 = 0$, and $\langle J \rangle = 1$. Thus the noise temperature for three-level amplifiers is greater than that for four-level amplifiers by $\ln [2 - (g_2 N_1 / g_1 N_2)]$. At a wavelength of 1μ and a temperature of $290°K$, T_n is about $15,000°K$ for the case $N_1 = 0$. Since this noise temperature corresponds to an average of one photon per mode, the optical maser as the microwave maser is capable of detecting in the limit a power per unit bandwidth of one or a few quanta.

It is well known that other photon detectors such as the photo-electric tube have a theoretical capability of detecting a single quantum. However, although the optical maser amplifier has no great advantage over other devices for detecting small numbers of quanta, it does offer for the first time a method for coherent optical amplification. Only a small amount of work has been reported thus far on the use of the optical maser as an amplifier. This work, which includes the use of the He-Ne, xenon, and ruby masers as amplifiers, will be discussed in later sections.

Since a great many modes exist within the bandwidth of the atomic system, a large background noise can occur if care is not taken to isolate only those modes used for amplification. On the other hand, the fact that the maser amplifier at optical frequencies can support a large number of modes can be turned to advantage, as discussed by Geusic and Scovil (46), since image information can be sent through the amplifier. Used this way, the amplifier can be considered as a limited aperture, infinite focal length lens with gain. The usual electronic amplifier has a spatial width of only one mode and information is conveyed in the frequency and time domain. On the other hand, the optical maser amplifier can coherently amplify images and preserve the frequency, phase, and direction of a signal.

In addition to the use of a maser system as a coherent amplifier, it may also be used as a quantum counter in the manner proposed by Bloembergen (117). Consider a four-level system, $E_4 > E_3 > E_2 > E_1$, with a pump signal between levels 2 and 4 strong enough to saturate this transition. If a signal photon is absorbed causing a transition from level 1 to 2, the atom will be immediately pumped from level 2 to 4. From level 4, the atom decays spontaneously to level 3 emitting a photon which may be detected by a photomultiplier. Because the quantum mechanical system may be kept in the lowest energy state by lowering the temperature as required, the maser quantum detector is free of noise. By this method, the sensitivity of the photomultiplier whose spectral range is limited to wavelengths below roughly 1μ may be translated to longer wavelengths. The possibility of using maser systems as photon detectors has been reviewed by Basov *et al.* (*281a*). In addition, infrared quantum counters using rare earth salts (*118, 119*) and diatomic gases (*120*) have been discussed.

D. OPTICAL MASER OSCILLATORS

The number of gases and solids that exhibit maser action has been rapidly increasing. One may confidently expect the list of maser substances to continue its vigorous growth, in view of the interest in obtaining maser devices throughout the electromagnetic spectrum, and the ability to accomplish this by virtue of the numerous methods of achieving an emissive state that have been developed. These methods, which will be discussed in detail in subsequent sections, include:

(1) Optical pumping in gases and solids.
(2) Optical pumping of one atom followed by energy transfer to another.
(3) Inelastic electron-atom collisions.
(4) Inelastic electron-atom collision followed by inelastic atom-atom collision.
(5) Inelastic electron-atom collision followed by dissociation in excited atom-molecule collision.
(6) Excitation by photodissociation.
(7) Vibrational excitation in chemical reactions.
(8) Pulsed and steady electric fields in semiconductors.

In addition to these methods may be mentioned the possibility of pumping solids in the form of thin wafers by electrons (*117a*). Maser action has been obtained to-date with excitation methods (1) to (5), and (8).

It may be remarked that state selection of atomic or molecular beams by electric or magnetic fields, although important in the microwave region, has not played any role in the optical region. The reason for this is not hard to find. In the optical region, it would be very difficult to eliminate Doppler broadening with beams, in which case there is little point in accepting the low density of atoms in the beam as compared with the gas.

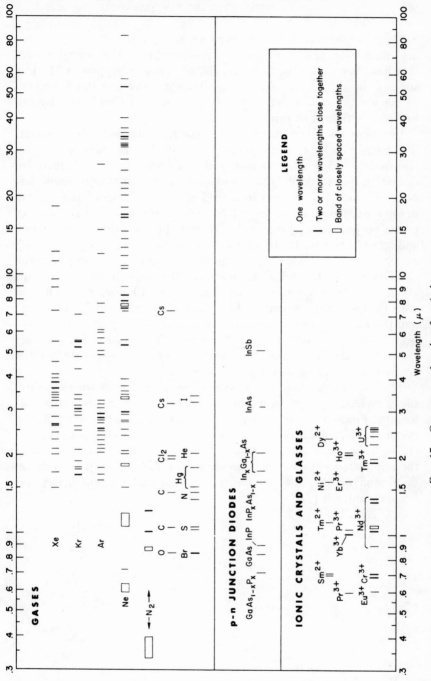

FIG. 17. Output wavelengths of optical masers.

97

Maser action has been observed in gases, ionic crystals, glasses, organic glasses, and semiconductor p–n junctions. The optical masers that have been reported thus far, are tabulated in Appendix II. The state of the art is advancing so rapidly that many new developments in the way of new maser materials may be anticipated even by the time this article is in print.

Let us see in broad outline where the field stands at the moment. The longest and shortest wavelengths at which maser action has been reported is 85μ in neon and 0.33μ in nitrogen, limits which are certain to be extended. The wavelengths at which masers action has been obtained are summarized in Fig. 17. Because of the greater density of maser atoms in solids, solid state masers have greater power output than gas masers but do not approach the latter in mode and spectral purity. However, advances in the technology of growing maser crystals of high optical quality is expected to improve the characteristics of solid state masers. The highest power output, about 50MW in a pulse whose duration is 10 nsec, was achieved with the Q-spoil ruby maser. The smallest beamwidth, 3 min of arc, and the highest spectral purity, of the order of one part in 10^{14}, have been established with the He–Ne maser. The beamwidth is in fact the theoretical limit, but the spectral width is apparently limited by mechanical instability.

There is much interest in devising maser oscillators for extending the wavelength range from the ultraviolet region to shorter wavelengths. Proposals have been put forward for an ultraviolet exciton maser (*117b*), solid state X-ray masers (*117c*), induced γ-ray emission (*117d, 117e*), and maser action without population inversion using the stimulated emission of bremsstrahlung (*117f, 117g*). In addition to photon masers, the possibility of an optical phonon maser has been considered (*117h*).

VIII. Optical Pumping

One of the most important techniques for population inversion is optical pumping, which is universally applicable to solids, liquids, and gases. Optical pumping has been used in the Cs vapor maser, and in all glass and solid state masers with the exception of the *p-n* diode. Although this device uses electron hole injection, optical pumping is feasible, in principle, in other semiconductor systems. In this section we will discuss the kinetics and techniques of optical excitation, leaving to later sections the discussion of the characteristics of optically pumped solid state masers.

Optical pumping described in terms of populations is closely related to the technique proposed by Bloembergen (*121*) for paramagnetic solids and Basov and Prokhorov for gases (*122*) in the microwave region. Pumping with monochromatic radiation at intensities so great that higher order quantum processes occur will be discussed in Chapter XIII.

A. The Rate Equations

1. *Homogeneously Broadened Lines*

The rate equations considered in this section are general and not necessarily restricted to the case of optical pumping. Consider a system of atoms with 4 states, represented by the energy level diagram shown in Fig. 18. Level 4 is shown as a band, but could be a sharp line. Atoms in an excited state relax either by photon emission, or by collisions with the lattice in the case of solids (phonon emission) or by atomic and wall collisions in the case of gases. The rate equations for the system under discussion are (*123*):

$$\frac{dN_4}{dt} = N_1 \Gamma^i_{14} - N_4 \Gamma^l_{43} , \tag{8.1}$$

$$\frac{dN_3}{dt} = N_2 \Gamma^i_{23} - N_3(\Gamma_3 + \Gamma^i_{32}) + N_4 \Gamma^l_{43} , \tag{8.2}$$

$$\frac{dN_2}{dt} = N_1 \Gamma_{12}^l - N_2 (\Gamma_{21}^l + \Gamma_{23}^i) + N_3 (\Gamma_{32}^i + \Gamma_{32}), \qquad (8.3)$$

$$N_1 + N_2 + N_3 = N_0, \qquad (8.4)$$

where the symbol Γ signifies a rate, the superscripts i, s, and l mean respectively, induced, spontaneous, and lattice or collision, and where $\Gamma_{32} = \Gamma_{32}^s + \Gamma_{32}^l$, and $\Gamma_3 = \Gamma_{32}^s + \Gamma_{31}^s + \Gamma_{32}^l + \Gamma_{31}^l$. As is often the case, we have taken $h\nu_{43} \gg kT$, and Γ_{43}^l much larger than all other rates from level 4; consequently, $N_4 \simeq 0$. In addition, we assume that Γ_{21}^l is much larger than all other rates from level 2,

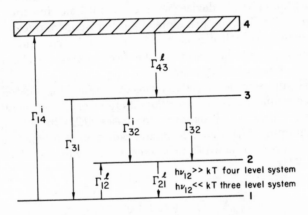

FIG. 18.   Three and four level systems.

and use the equilibrium relation between the lattice rates, viz., $\Gamma_{12}^l = \Gamma_{21}^l \exp(-h\nu_{21}/kT)$. Then the steady state solution of the rate equations is

$$\frac{N_3 - N_2}{N_0} = \frac{\Gamma_{14}^i - \Gamma_3 e^{-h\nu_{21}/kT}}{\Gamma_{14}^i + \Gamma_3 + \Gamma_{32}^i + (2\Gamma_{32}^i + \Gamma_3) e^{-h\nu_{21}/kT}}. \qquad (8.5)$$

Assuming, as we have done, that all atoms are subjected simultaneously to the same driving field limits the analysis to the case of homogeneous broadening.

If level 2 is sufficiently higher than the ground level, i.e., $h\nu_{21} \gg kT$, then level 2 is essentially empty, and (8.5) reduces to

$$\frac{N_3}{N_0} = \frac{\Gamma_{14}^i}{\Gamma_{14}^i + \Gamma_3 + \Gamma_{32}^i}. \qquad (8.6)$$

On the other hand, when $h\nu_{21}$ becomes comparable with kT, the four-level system behaves essentially like a three-level system. The rate equations for this case give

$$\frac{N_2 - N_1}{N_0} = \frac{\Gamma_{13}^i - \Gamma_{21}}{\Gamma_{13}^i + \Gamma_{21} + 2\Gamma_{21}^i}, \tag{8.7}$$

and N_2 does not become greater than N_1 unless Γ_{13}^i is greater than Γ_{21}. Since we assumed that $\Gamma_{14}^i \ll \Gamma_{43}^l$, these equations apply for pumping rates below the saturation value, a condition not likely to be violated for practical maser materials and broad band pumping sources. In any case, the solution of the rate equations for the case of saturation may be found in refs. *123a* and *123b*. For a given pumping rate, the population difference between the excited and ground maser levels, can be increased by increasing the number of atoms N_0, provided the substance does not become so optically dense that the pumping is not uniform over the volume of the sample.

When there are more levels and/or more transitions connecting any given state, obtaining the steady state populations by solving the rate equations may become tedious. In such cases, it should prove advantageous to use a computational scheme for obtaining the populations which has the advantage of speed (*124*).

Below threshold the induced rate is zero, and the excited population difference increases with the pumping rate. Above threshold, the population difference is fixed by the oscillation condition, in which case (8.5), (8.6), and (8.7) give the relation between the pumping rate and the induced emission rate. Then the total stimulated power may be calculated from

$$P_i = \Delta N_{\text{th}} h\nu_{21} \Gamma_{21}^i. \tag{8.7a}$$

The pumping rate required to reach threshold is from (8.6), for the four-level system,

$$(\Gamma_{14}^i)_{\text{th}} = \Gamma_3 \frac{\Delta N_{\text{th}}}{N_0 - \Delta N_{\text{th}}}, \tag{8.8}$$

and from (8.7), for the three-level system,

$$(\Gamma_{13}^i)_{\text{th}} = \Gamma_2 \frac{N_0 + \Delta N_{\text{th}}}{N_0 - \Delta N_{\text{th}}}. \tag{8.9}$$

All other things being equal, the ratio of the threshold pumping rate of the four- to the three-level system is $\Delta N_{th}/(N_0 + \Delta N_{th})$. Multiplying (8.8) by $N_1 h\nu_{32}$ and (8.9) by $N_1 h\nu_{21}$, we obtain the minimum pumping powers discussed in Section VII,A.

When levels 1 and 2 do not have the same degeneracy, $\Delta N_{th} = [N_2 - (g_2/g_1)N_1]_{th}$, and (8.9) must be modified by multiplying N_0 in the numerator by (g_2/g_1).

When the relaxation rate from the pumping level to the ground level is not negligible compared with that to the metastable level, then the previous solutions of the rate equations must be corrected by multiplying the pumping rate, wherever it appears, by the branching ratio η'. η' is the fraction of absorbed quanta that transfers its energy to the metastable level, and is, for example, given by $\Gamma_{41}^s/(\Gamma_{41}^s + \Gamma_{43}^l)$.

From (2.31) and the expression for the steady state population difference, e.g. (8.7), one may obtain an equation for the saturated negative absorption or gain per unit length. If Γ_{21}^i is due to an applied signal as in an amplifier, then $\Gamma_{21}^i = wBS(\nu)$, and the expression for the negative absorption is given by

$$\alpha(\nu) = n_0 h\nu B_{21} S(\nu)(\Gamma_{13}^i - \Gamma_{21})\tau/\nu[1 + 2\tau w B_{21} S(\nu)] \,,$$

where $\tau^{-1} = \Gamma_{13}^i + \Gamma_{21}$. This expression also applies for the maser oscillator where $S(\nu)$ is replaced by $S(\nu_m)$. As shown by (III.32), Γ_{12}^i for the oscillator is equal to $wB_{21}S(\nu_m)$, where ν_m is the frequency of the oscillating mode.

The efficiency of an idealized three-level maser has been discussed in terms of its performance as a heat engine (125). The efficiency of the maser defined as the ratio of the coherent power output to the pump power absorbed is for the three-level system

$$E_{\text{eff}} = \left(1 - \frac{N_2(\Gamma_{21}^s + \Gamma_{21}^l)}{N_1\Gamma_{13}^i}\right)\frac{\nu_{21}}{\nu_{31}} \,, \qquad (8.10)$$

which in the limit of high pumping rates is simply ν_{21}/ν_{31}. It may be noted, however, that the efficiency defined as the ratio of the power output to the total incident power contained within the atomic bandwidth is less than (8.11) because of the assumption of optical thinness. Furthermore, if the spectral output of the pumping source is greater than the atomic line width, as is likely to be the case, then the actual efficiency is poorer still.

2. Inhomogeneously Broadened Lines

When the atomic system is inhomogeneously broadened, the populations in (8.1) and (8.2) should be replaced by the population per unit frequency interval. The steady state solution to these equations for the four level case may be written in the form

$$N_2(\nu_0) = N_0 \Gamma_{14}^i \tau \frac{H(\nu_a - \nu_0)}{1 + w B_{32} \tau \, S(\nu_0 - \nu)}, \qquad (8.10a)$$

where the induced rate is given by $\Gamma_{32}^i = w B_{32} S(\nu_0 - \nu)$ and $\tau^{-1} = \Gamma_{14}^i + \Gamma_3$. The distribution of atomic frequencies is represented by $H(\nu_a - \nu_0)$, and the response of an atom to monochromatic radiation at frequency ν is given by the Lorentzian shape, $S(\nu_0 - \nu)$. The saturation term clearly produces a hole in the population distribution at ν. The negative absorption at ν due to an externally applied signal has the same form as (3.10), and may be written as (4.34b) with $n = \frac{1}{2}$. The spontaneous emission power obtained by integrating (8.10a) and multiplying the result by $h\nu\Gamma_{32}^s$ is equal to the pumping power less the coherent power.

Let us now suppose that Γ_{32}^i is due to an oscillating mode at ν_m. The negative absorption at some other frequency ν is then

$$\alpha(\nu) = \frac{n_0 h\nu B_{21}}{\nu} \Gamma_{14}^i \tau \int_{-\infty}^{\infty} \frac{S(\nu_a - \nu - \nu_D) \, H(\nu_D) \, d\nu_D}{1 + w B_{32} \tau \, S'(\nu_a - \nu_m - \nu_D)}, \qquad (8.10b)$$

where S' is the shape of the hole burned in the inhomogeneous line.

When $\nu - \nu_m$ is greater than the hole width, the saturation term in the denominator is very small at $\nu_D = \nu_a - \nu$ where $S(\nu_a - \nu - \nu_D)$ has its maximum value. Thus $\alpha(\nu)$ at these frequencies is unaffected by the coherent signal and increases with pumping. On the other hand when $\nu = \nu_m$, the value of $\alpha(\nu_m)$ above threshold is fixed by the threshold condition. This behavior of the fractional gain $\alpha(\nu)D$ for inhomogeneously broadened lines is illustrated in Fig. 4. When $\nu = \nu_m$, and assuming that $S' = S$, the integral in (8.10b) may be evaluated as in (3.10). The resulting expression set equal to the total loss per pass is (7.11a) with $n = \frac{1}{2}$.

This treatment of population inversion in inhomogeneously broadened lines is limited by the following assumptions: (1) one oscillating mode burns only one hole in the atomic line; (2) the shape of the hole is Lorentzian; and (3) the width of the hole is not substantially increased because of a reduction in lifetime of the atomic levels by the coherent radiation field.

B. Optical Excitation

To obtain an expression for the light intensities required to sustain continuous maser action, we use a method employed in ref. *145*. The number of excited atoms being pumped may be estimated from the quantum efficiency, η, defined by*

$$\eta = \frac{N_2/\tau_{21}}{N_0\Gamma^p},$$ (8.11)

where the numerator is the rate of emission of fluorescent photons, and the denominator is the rate of absorption of pump photons. N_2 is the number of excited atoms and, in a four-level system, N_2 is also the population excess. The pumping rate is from (2.2) and (2.31)

$$N\Gamma^p = V\alpha S/h\nu,$$ (8.12)

where S is the monochromatic power per unit area. Since there is a power loss on reflection at the crystal surface, S should be taken as the power flow in the crystal. The number of excited atoms being pumped by radiation which is not monochromatic is then

$$\frac{N_2}{\tau_{21}V} = \frac{1}{hc} \int \lambda k(\lambda)\, S(\lambda)\, \eta(\lambda)\, d\lambda,$$

$$= \frac{1}{hc} \lambda \langle k \rangle \langle S \rangle \langle \eta \rangle\, \Delta\lambda,$$ (8.13)

where $S(\lambda)\, d\lambda$ is the pump power per unit area for wavelengths between λ and $\lambda + d\lambda$. The second form of (8.13) is obtained by replacing $k(\lambda)$, $S(\lambda)$, and $\eta(\lambda)$ by their average values in the useful absorption range $\Delta\lambda$. The critical pumping power obtained from (8.13) differs from that given by (7.2) in that the former gives the critical power flowing in the crystal whereas the latter gives the power lost in spontaneous and lattice transitions from the fluorescent level.

Let us next illustrate the roles played by the lamp brightness or temperature and its power output, assuming that the lamp has the spectral character of a black body. The pumping rate, Γ^p, is related to the energy density, $w(\nu)$, by

$$\Gamma^p = B_p \int S(\nu)\, w(\nu)\, d\nu.$$ (8.14)

---

* For atomic systems which can be described by only two population variables, $\eta = \eta'\phi$, where η' is defined on page 102, and ϕ is defined by (7.4).

For blackbody radiation, the energy density is given by the Planck radiation formula,

$$w(\nu) = \frac{8\pi h\nu^3}{v^3} \frac{1}{e^{h\nu/kT} - 1}.$$ (8.15)

Since the radiation is essentially uniform over the bandwidth of the optical transition, $\Gamma^p = w(\nu) B_p$. These relations immediately fix the temperature of the black body radiation (or the equivalent blackbody temperature to produce a radiation density $w(\nu)$ for frequency components within the atomic bandwidth) required to obtain a given pumping rate. In a three-level system, for the pumping rate Γ^p to equal the total relaxation rate from the excited maser level, $(\phi\tau_{21})^{-1}$, where τ_{21} is the spontaneous emission rate and ϕ is the fraction of atoms which decay by spontaneously emitting the desired radiation, the radiation temperature required is

$$T_p = \frac{h\nu_p}{k \ln \left[1 + (g_3/g_1)\Gamma^s_{31}\phi\tau_{21}\right]},$$ (8.16)

where Γ^s_{31} is the spontaneous emission rate from the pumping level. For the four-level system, the bracketed term in (8.16) is replaced by $[1 + (g_4/g_1)(\Gamma^s_{41}\phi\tau_c N_1/p)]$. At a given temperature, T, the total power per unit area (watts/cm²) radiated by a blackbody is given by the Stefan-Boltzmann equation,

$$P_B = 5.67 \times 10^{-12} T^4.$$ (8.17)

Instead of the blackbody temperature required for threshold, one could specify the brightness, $K(\nu)$, which is the power radiated per unit area per unit solid angle per unit frequency interval. For unpolarized radiation that is uniform in all directions, $K(\nu) = vw(\nu)/4\pi$.

Using the parameters appropriate for ruby, for example, we obtain $T \approx 5 \times 10^3\,°K$. By way of comparison, we give the effective temperature of the maser radiation computed on the basis of the output power per unit area, cone angle, and bandwidth, viz., about $10^{13}\,°K$, for 10^3 watts/cm², $\theta \sim 2 \times 10^{-3}$ rad., and $\Delta\nu_{os} \sim 0.05$A.

Not only must the source have a minimum effective temperature, but it must also have the minimum power output $N_2\tau^{-1}h\nu_p$, where N_2 is the number of excited atoms needed for oscillation. In effect, these requirements determine the source brilliance and effective radiating surface, or total power output. When the pumping source is pulsed, the energy absorbed by the maser material in time T is

$$W = B_p h\nu_p \int_0^T N_1(t)\, w_{av}(t)\, dt, \qquad (8.18)$$

where $w_{av}(t)$ is the frequency averaged value in the useful absorption bandwidth. Provided $T \ll \tau$, W must be equal to $N_2 h\nu_p$ for the system to reach threshold.

C. OPTICAL PUMPING TECHNIQUES

Since the rate of optical pumping is directly proportional to the radiation density, it is important to have an efficient transfer of energy from the lamp to the maser substance. We consider in this section a number of schemes for accomplishing this and discuss some of their characteristics.

Although we do not propose to discuss optical sources (the much used xenon flash lamp has been discussed in refs. *126–128a*), in the category of novel techniques may be mentioned the use of exploding wires (*129, 129a*), radiation from the sun (*130, 130a*), and the possibility of using optical radiation from a plasma, the dynamic pinch (*131*). The use of X-rays for exciting fluorescence in crystalline solids has received some attention (*131a*).

Many of the optical pumping arrangements that have been used thus far are summarized in Figs. 19–22. Consider the helical lamp and reflecting cylinder configuration shown in Fig. 19 (*150*). The performance of this system may be analyzed by regarding the enclosure as a nonresonant reflecting box with a high Q (*132*) whose walls

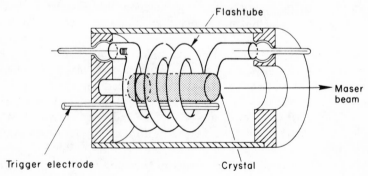

FIG. 19. Maser with helical flashlamp and reflector arrangement. [Maiman *et al.* (*150*).]

are kept at some fixed temperature by cooling. The lamp is considered to be a blackbody with some effective surface area. It may be shown that the energy density in the box $w_C(\nu)$ is related to the energy density radiated by the lamp $w_R(\nu)$ by an equation of the form $w_C(\nu) \propto w_R(\nu)A_R/(A_R + A_C T)$. T is a constant of the order $(1 - R)$, where R is the wall reflectivity, and A_R and A_C are the areas of the radiator and box, respectively. (We have neglected the lowering of the box Q by the holes in the enclosure and the absorption of the maser substance.) To achieve $w_C(\nu)/w_R(\nu) \sim 1$, it is necessary that $A_R \gg A_C T$. In view of this result, it is not surprising that considerably higher efficiency than the helical lamp and shield arrangement has been obtained by using straight flash tubes whose geometry conformed to that of the sample which is in close proximity, and which were wrapped with either aluminum foil or an MgO shield (133).

In the photon box scheme, the photons travel uniformly in all directions, and apart from variations in the dielectric medium within the box, the energy density is uniform. This is not the case when the radiation is focussed on the maser substance as, for example, by the elliptical reflector shown in Fig. 20a (134, 135). If the lamp were a

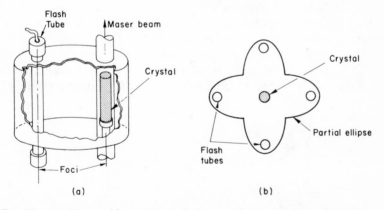

FIG. 20. (a) Maser with straight flash lamp and elliptical focuser. (b) Cross-section view of a maser with 4 straight flash tubes in 4 partial elliptical focusers.

line source, and the focusing perfect, a line image would be formed with the same energy density as the source. However, since the lamp has a finite cross section, the focusing will not be perfect, and the energy density will vary along the diameter of the image. Another source of energy density variation is the fact that the lamp brightness is not uniform. In any case, the elliptical system gives a considerably lower threshold than the helical lamp arrangement. In comparing these pumping systems as applied to the pulsed ruby maser, it is found that the threshold energy with the elliptical arrangement is lower by a factor of at least 10. A simplified (*136*) and more complete (*136a*) analysis of radiation transfer to cylindrical rods by elliptical cylinder reflectors have been developed.

If it is desired to obtain a more uniform energy distribution over a greater area than possible with the single lamp and elliptical focuser, then the multiple lamp and multiple ellipse configuration shown in Fig. 20b (*137*) may be used. However, it is clear from fundamental principles that the energy density in image space can be no greater than that determined by the brightness of the lamps, apart from variations due to different dielectric media. The efficiency of coupling light into the crystal was found to decrease as the number of elliptical sections were increased because of the removal of the wall in the region common to the ellipses. Increasing the number of elliptical sections does not improve the ability to concentrate light but does spread the image (*138-139a*).

In the light gathering schemes shown in Fig. 21 and 22, the radiation density in the crystal is enhanced by choosing crystal geometries which act as radiation condensers. When rays of pumping light strike the side surface of the composite dielectric cylinder, Fig. 21, they are refracted toward the normal. The result of this refraction, analyzed by Devlin (*140*), Svelto(*141*), and McKenna(*141a*)

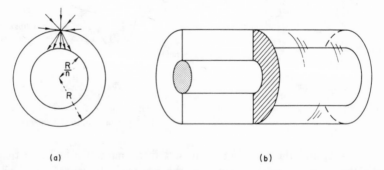

(a)   (b)

Fɪɢ. 21. (a) Rays of light incident on the side wall of a dielectric cylinder (of refractive index *n*) are refracted toward the axis. (b) Composite rod structure. The core section is doped, as for ruby, while the outer sheath is clear (e.g., sapphire). [After Devlin (*140*).]

is that all the light that penetrates the surface of the cylinder of radius R essentially passes through a smaller internal cylinder of radius R/n. Advantage may be taken of this by doping the core with the required metal ion, while the sheath merely contains the host material. That light is concentrated by such a scheme was verified experimentally (140). In all cases it was found that threshold energies for a ruby-sapphire clad rod were appreciably lower (by a factor of roughly 1/2) than for solid ruby rods. A considerably lower threshold for all rods was obtained with the straight lamp and elliptic cylinder as compared with the helical lamp and reflector configuration. Instead of a cylindrical dielectric sheath, a spherical sheath composite rod may be used. It has been shown experimentally and theoretically that the latter gives a lower threshold than the former (141b).

In the trumpet rod configuration, Fig. 22a, energy density enhancement is obtained by internal reflection and reflection from a mirror

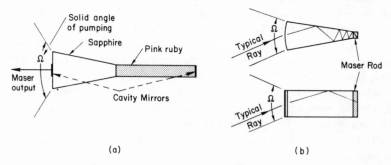

(a)   (b)

FIG. 22. Radiation concentration by dielectric condensers: (a) trumpet-shaped rod (142); (b) chisel-shaped rod (142a).

on the end of the rod. Light is focused into the collecting cone by a system of spherical mirrors, rather than by entering the rod through the side as in all the other pumping schemes. For equations giving the dimensions of the cone and the expected intensity within the shank, consult Nelson and Boyle (142). In the chisel-shaped dielectric for gathering and concentrating the pumping light shown in Fig. 22b, pumping is from the side of the active material rather than end-on as in Fig. 22a.

In addition to the pumping arrangements discussed, it is obvious that the more usual arrangement of reflectors and mirrors may be used to concentrate light in a maser crystal. A pair of parabolic mirrors where the lamp is at one focus and the crystal at the other is a possible arrangement (143).

Optical pumping and cooling geometries for experiments at liquid hydrogen and helium temperatures are given in Sorokin (144), Kaiser (145), and Yariv (146).

Observations on the effect of different pumping schemes on the output of the pulsed ruby maser have been reported by Li (147). In particular, he used the two schemes which have found wide usage, the helical lamp and cylindrical shield, and the straight lamp and elliptical reflector. As was discussed earlier in this section, in the former system the pumping light fills the cavity containing the ruby rod more or less uniformly, while in the latter system the reflector images the flash lamp onto the ruby rod. Photographs were taken of the maser light distribution at the end of the rod. With the helical lamp system, a very small spot was found to grow in diameter, remaining circular, until its diameter was about 0.6 of the radius of the rod. This result is in harmony with the light concentration effect computed for the composite rod by Devlin et al. (140). Subsequent increase in input energy produced a relatively slower growth of the extent of maser action, which eventually spread over the entire rod. Similar observations have been reported (148) and, in addition, it was found that for ruby with rough, diffusely reflecting sides, the dielectric focusing disappeared, and the output occurred fairly uniformly over the end of the rod suggesting that the pumping light intensity was fairly uniformly distributed with respect to the crystal axis.

With the elliptical pumping configuration, the central spot at threshold became oval in shape with increasing pumping intensity, thereby illustrating a nonuniform distribution of light with respect to the axis of the cylinder (147). It was also shown that because of the focussing action of the elliptical reflector, maser action could be induced in different parts of the ruby by simply displacing either the flash lamp or the ruby off the focal lines of the ellipse.

An interesting possibility for attaining highly efficient pumping is suggested by the observation of fluorescence in $CaWO_4:Nd^{3+}$ produced by the recombination radiation from a GaAs $p-n$ junction (149). Such diodes are highly efficient sources of radiation which is concentrated into a relatively narrow band. The small size and simple structure of the diodes could make possible a direct coupling of the pumping radiation to the maser substance without any complex optics.

IX. Ionic Crystal and Glass Masers

A. INTRODUCTION AND SURVEY

Digests of ionic crystal and glass masers, including some of their characteristics, and spectral properties of the active material are given in Tables I.1 to I.3 in Appendix I. The materials which have been used include:

(1) $3d$, transition metal ions in crystals.
(2) $4f$, rare earth, ions in crystals and glasses.
(3) Actinide $(5f)$ series ions in crystals. Only thorium and uranium occur naturally as long-lived isotopes. Maser action has been obtained with U^{3+} in ionic hosts.
(4) Rare earth-organic compounds (chelates).

Of the many materials which have shown pulsed maser action, only the following have been operated continuously: $Al_2O_3 : Cr^{3+}$, $CaF_2 : U^{3+}$, $CaWO_4 : Nd^{3+}$, glass: Nd^{3+}, and $CaF_2 : Dy^{2+}$.

Although an extensive literature on the optical properties of ions in solids has developed ($187–195a$), much of the spectral information that has been needed on the use of specific substances as the active medium in masers was not available and had to be obtained for the substance of interest. Tables I.1, 2, 3 and Figs. 26–29 summarize the pertinent spectral data. It is clear from the expression for the oscillation condition that to assess the maser potential of a given substance a complete spectroscopic analysis is hardly required, since only certain parameters need to be evaluated. A method for directly obtaining a figure of merit for maser potentiality for a given material and pumping scheme has been proposed (198).

Although the question of material preparation and crystal growth is not considered here, it may be noted that the need for new materials ($196a$) and for crystals of high optical perfection has encouraged a great deal of activity in these areas. Techniques have been developed for making crystal rods for masers with the ends parallel to better than 10 sec, and flat to better than 1/10 the wavelength of visible light.

From the applications point of view, high energy and high peak power optical masers are of considerable importance.* The current leader in the high energy race is a neodymium glass maser, using a clad rod 1/4 in. diameter and 18 in. long with 6 wt per cent Nd_2O_3 in barium crown glass. An output energy of 113 joules at an efficiency in excess of 1.5 per cent was obtained in a pulse lasting 1.6 msec; the beam divergence was somewhat less than 10° (197). Peak powers in the neighborhood of 50 megawatts lasting for 10^{-8} sec have been obtained with a Q-spoil ruby maser. This device, and related methods for generating large, controlled pulses of optical radiation, are dealt with at the end of this chapter.

B. THE RUBY OPTICAL MASER

Of the many solid state masers which have appeared since successful operation in ruby was reported by Maiman (150), the ruby maser still continues to attract considerable attention, and a profuse literature on this subject has been developing. Among the reasons for this position of importance are possibly the following: (1) the output radiation is in the visible part of the spectrum, (2) the crystal does not require cooling, (3) it gives high power output, (4) and relatively high quality ruby crystals can be readily obtained.

1. Spectroscopic Considerations

The available optical data of the 3d series is summarized by McClure (188). Since the 3d electrons are exposed to the crystal field, the position and nature of the energy levels are markedly different from the free ion. This is the principle reason why a different nomenclature is used for the spectra of these ions in crystals (188, 195).

The experimental aspects of the fine structure and properties of chromium in aluminum oxide has been reviewed by Schawlow (199), and discussed by Maiman et al. (150), and Wieder and Sarles (200). A detailed energy level diagram for ruby illustrating the optical and microwave levels are shown in Figs. 23 and 24. The theory of the Zeeman effect and the selection rules of the R lines have been discussed by Sugano et al. (201, 202) and Varsanyi et al. (203). Although for

---

* It appears that energies in the neighborhood of 10^3 joules and peak powers in the neighborhood of 10^9 watts can be obtained, respectively, with a Nd^{3+} glass maser, and by cascading a Q-switched ruby maser with a ruby amplifier.

maser purposes ruby may be approximately represented by three energy levels, it is in fact a considerably more complicated system. What is usually designated as level 3 includes the green $^4F_2$ and blue $^4F_1$ pumping bands, both of which are important in the excitation of the $\bar{E}$ and $2\bar{A}$ levels. The latter levels, which have a statistical weight of 2, are connected by a very fast lattice relaxation rate. The ground state at room temperature may be treated as a single level with degeneracy $g_1 = 4$. This is a valid assumption since the widths of the R_1 and R_2 transitions are large compared to the separation of the $\pm 1/2$ and $\pm 3/2$ levels of the ground state. Because $g(^4A_2) = 2g(\bar{E})$, maser action occurs when $N_2 < N_1$, where $N_2 = N(\bar{E})$ and $N_1 = N(^4A_2)$. At approximately 80°K, the line widths of the R_1 and R_2 transitions become sufficiently small so that two zero field levels of the ground

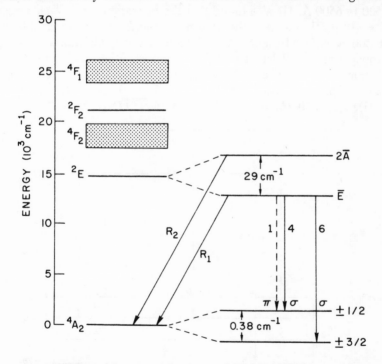

FIG. 23. Energy level diagram of $Al_2O_3 : Cr^{3+}$ showing the splitting of the ^2E and $^4A_2$ levels [d'Haenens and Asawa (204)]. The $^4F_2$ and $^4F_1$ bands are, respectively, the green and blue pumping bands. The relative transition probabilities for R_1 fluorescence are shown. π signifies radiation polarized parallel to the optic axis (c-axis) and σ signifies radiation polarized perpendicularly to the optic axis.

state, each with a degeneracy of 2, are resolved. The $2\bar{A}$ and $\bar{E}$ levels are connected to each other and the $^4F_2$ level by lattice transitions which are very rapid at room temperature. It is known that the lattice rates of the $^4A_2$ levels vary from about 10^7 sec at 300°K to about 10 sec^{-1} at 4.2°K. At about 80°K and below, the relaxation rate is sufficiently slow so that the $\pm 1/2(^4A_2)$ and $\pm 3/2(^4A_2)$ levels may be regarded as uncoupled. When this situation obtains, the transitions to these levels from the $\bar{E}(^2E)$ level each exhibit its own oscillation threshold (204).

A parameter of particular interest in the study of fluorescent solids is the quantum efficiency. Working with a 0.05 weight per cent of Cr_2O_3 in Al_2O_3 (1.62×10^{19} Cr^{3+} per cm³, a concentration typical of ruby crystals), Maiman (205) obtained an average value of the quantum efficiency of about 70% for excitation wavelengths from 3500 to 6500 Å. He also found that the relaxation rate, Γ_{32}^l, is roughly 2×10^7 sec^{-1}, and that the lifetime of the $\bar{E}$ level is about 3.0 msec at 300°K (150). In a crystal with 0.05 weight % Cr^{3+}, and with light propagating parallel to the c axis, the absorption coefficient for the R_1 line is 0.4 cm^{-1}, and the cross section is 2.5×10^{-20} cm². Other values of parameters for ruby are: $f = 7.5 \times 10^{-7}$, $\mu^2 = 1.1 \times 10^{-40}$esu (203), $\sigma_{13} = 10^{-19}$ cm² and $\Gamma_{21}^s = 330$ sec^{-1} (150).

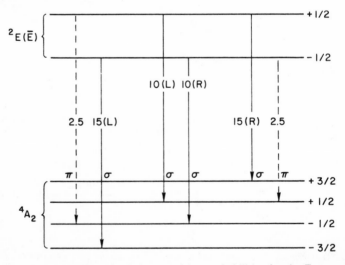

FIG. 24.   Energy levels and relative transition probabilities for the Zeeman levels of the R_1 line in $Al_2O_3 : Cr^{3+}$ [Varsanyi et al. (203)]. The magnetic field is parallel to the optic axis. L signifies left circularly polarized light, and R signifies right circularly polarized light.

2. Temperature Dependence of Line Width, Wavelength, and Quantum Efficiency

The width of the R_1 line of a typical pink synthetic ruby varies with temperature from about 21 cm^{-1} at 380°K to about 0.3 cm^{-1} at 77°K, and slowly decreases by about 0.07 cm^{-1} as the temperature is reduced to 2°K (199). In a relatively unstrained dilute crystal at 4.2°K the width is only 0.12 cm^{-1}, which corresponds to an atomic Q of about 1.2 × 10^5. At temperatures below the Debye temperature, no optical modes of vibration are excited, and one would expect to find extremely sharp lines. However, the observed widths are quite variable suggesting that inhomogeneous internal strains in the crystal is the dominant factor determining the low temperature line width. This idea was tested by Schawlow et al. (206) by compressing crystals of MgO containing small amounts of chromium. The compression reduced the purely cubic symmetry of MgO, thereby lifting the twofold orbital degeneracy of the ^2E level and causing line splitting and shifts. In unstressed ruby, the symmetry is not quite cubic and the degeneracy is already lifted, but the lines can still shift. These considerations were borne out by compressing a ruby crystal (206).

The temperature dependence of the fluorescent lines has been known for some time, but has recently been studied by measurements on fluorescence (207, 208), and as it appears in the output of the maser (209). As in the case of the temperature variation of the line width, there is not much change in the wavelength below 77°K. As may be expected, the temperature dependence of the wavelength as it appears in the output of the maser closely follows that observed in fluorescence. From 25° to 80°C, the slope of the curve is 0.065 Å/deg. Although the slope decreases with temperature, the average value 0.045 Å/deg. may be used for the interval −180 to 0°C.

Wittke (208) has measured the wavelengths, linewidths, and fluorescent efficiencies of the R_1 and R_2 lines in the temperature range 300–500°K and has also summarized previous results. With regard to the quantum efficiency, he found that the value dropped from 0.7 at room temperature to about 0.1 at 220°C. Further investigation has shown that the fluorescent efficiency to +240°C is independent of temperature if one is careful to accept all of the radiation coming out of ruby in the red region. It is the fraction of the red radiation that is emitted in the R lines themselves that decreases rapidly at high temperature (210). The point is that although the total amount of radiation in the red is independent of temperature, the spectral distribution of the radiation changes very much with temperature.* These results have a direct bearing on the threshold power that is required at various temperatures. Indeed, it may be seen from (8.9) that the threshold pumping rate for $\Delta N \ll N_0$ is directly proportional to Γ_{21}^s/ϕ, where ϕ, the fluorescent efficiency for radiation emitted in the R lines, is the major factor in raising the threshold with increasing temperature.

3. Concentration Effects

Whereas the lifetime of the $\bar{E}$ level for a 0.05% ruby crystal is 3.0 msec at room temperature, the lifetime at 77°K was found to be 15 msec by Varsanyi et al. (203). However, in a very dilute crystal (10^{-6} Cr per Al) and in finely divided and dispersed 0.05% ruby the value at 77°K decreased to 4.3 msec. The increased lifetime in the concentrated crystal was thus demonstrated to arise from radiation trapping, the first time observed in a solid.

Even at chromium ion concentrations as low as 0.05%, there are other lines in the neighborhood of the R lines whose relative intensity increases rapidly as the chromium concentration is increased. These lines were studied by Schawlow et al. (211, 211a) who proposed that their origin is due to exchange-coupled ion pairs. Two of the strongest fluorescent lines, at 7009 and 7041Å, end on levels which are above their ground states and are consequently empty at low temperatures. Optical maser action was observed in these lines in a 0.5% Cr_2O_3 sample cooled to 77°K (152, 153).

4. The Effect of Magnetic and Electric Fields

The Zeeman effect in ruby is well known and has been discussed by a number of authors (201, 202, 203). As shown in Fig. 24, the magnetic field splits the $\bar{E}$ level into a doublet and the $^4A_2$ level into a quartet. The levels of this quartet are used to obtain maser action in the microwave region.

A splitting and shifting of the emission lines of ruby in an external electric field has been observed (212). The splitting, which is much larger than possible from the normal Stark effect, is directly proportional to the electric field and reaches a value of 3×10^{10} cps at a field of 1.7×10^5 volts/cm. It is clear from these results that the application of an ac magnetic or electric field to the maser crystal

---

* Similar behavior in the fluorescent emission of Sm^{2+} has been observed (223).

should allow frequency modulation of the maser. By passing the maser beam through an absorber of the same material, the intensity of the transmitted beam can be amplitude modulated by applying an alternating electric or magnetic field to the absorber if this material exhibits a Stark or Zeeman effect (213).

5. The Pulsed Ruby Optical Maser

The ruby maser has been made with rods of various dimensions (214), silver and multilayer dielectric mirrors with different degrees of parallelism and flatness and located either on the ends of the rod or detached from the rod, various pumping configurations, and crystals in different conditions of strain. In view of the diversity of possibilities and the consequent diversity in performance, it may not be very meaningful to present typical operating characteristics of the pulsed ruby maser. Instead, we shall summarize the results of Maiman et al. (150) and Collins et al. (151), who have conducted the most comprehensive study of the characteristics of a given device. Maiman et al. (150) used a 0.05 % ruby shaped in the form of a rod with dimensions 3/8 in. by 3/4 in. and with ends flat and parallel to within $\lambda/3$ at 6943Å. The mirrors were formed by evaporating silver on the ends, one of which was opaque and the other partially transmitting. The ruby was supported inside the helical, xenon-filled flash tube, GE FT-506, which were enclosed in a polished aluminum cylinder as shown in Fig. 19. The following performance data were obtained: threshold energy about 700 joules, peak power output approximately 5 kW, total output energy nearly 1 joule per 1700 joule input to flash lamp, beam divergence less than 10^{-2} rad, and a spectral width of individual components in the output radiation of about 6×10^{-4} Å. These sharp components were superimposed on background radiation about 10^{-2} Å wide. Threshold energies smaller by an order of magnitude have since been obtained with crystals of superior quality and improved pumping schemes (140).

Although the crystal used by Collins et al. (151) was somewhat smaller than that used by Maiman (150), the threshold power obtained by the former group was in the vicinity of 1700 joules as compared with 700 joules obtained by the latter. However, as pointed out by Schawlow (199), the crystal used by Collins was so badly strained that the R lines were about 1 cm^{-1} wide at 77°K. The orientation of the c-axis of this crystal was found to vary down the length of the rod by as much as $\pm 1°$ (199).

The polarization of the output from the ruby maser has been studied by Nelson and Collins (215), in the temperature range 100° to 300°K. For rods where the optic axes is oriented at 60° and 90° to the rod axis, the maser light in every spike had a linear polarization of 100%, with the electric vector in a direction perpendicular to the plane containing the rod and optic axes. In fluorescence below threshold, the component of the R_1 line having its electric vector perpendicular to the plane containing the optic axis was much stronger than the component parallel to this plane. Therefore, it is not surprising that the maser would select the perpendicular polarization for amplification in the 60° and 90° rods. No polarization was found for the 0° oriented rods, as expected, since R_1 fluorescence when viewed along the optic axis is unpolarized.

The normal optical maser transition in ruby is between the $\bar{E}$ level and the ground level $^4A_2$. Located 29 cm^{-1} above the $\bar{E}$ level is the $2\bar{A}$ level whose population at room temperature is only slightly lower than that of the $\bar{E}$ level. For any significant amount of inversion there is considerable gain at the R_2 transition ($2\bar{A} \rightarrow {}^4A_2$). By using frequency sensitive reflectors to make the losses at the R_1 transition greater than that at R_2, oscillations at the R_2 transition were observed (154).

Other work on the pulsed ruby maser includes studies of the factors effecting threshold (216-216b) and their optimization (217), determination of performance with detached reflectors (218), and γ-irradiation of the crystal (219).

6. The CW Oscillator

A continuously operating ruby optical maser using the novel pumping arrangement shown in Fig. 25 was developed by Nelson and Boyle (142). The resonator portion of the crystal was 0.061 cm in diameter and 1.15 cm long and contained 1.6×10^{18} Cr atoms cm^{-3}. The crystal was cooled to 77°K where each component of the R_1 emission line was about 0.2 cm^{-1} wide. At an input power of 930 watts to a high pressure mercury lamp, the maser beam had a power of about 4 mW. Since about 0.3 watt of green and violet light is absorbed to reach threshold, no more than 16 mW could be expected at this input power. The beam divergence was about 9.7°. A striking feature of the output radiation was the continual presence of relaxation oscillations. Measurements of the factors affecting the threshold and comparison with the results of a mathematical model have been made by Nelson and McCumber (*219a*).

7. The Pulsed Traveling Wave Amplifier

The difficulty of observing gain in an optical maser is that of distinguishing the signal from the very large noise background arising from spontaneously emitted radiation. By using a ruby maser oscillator as the source, the signal is made so large that the signal to noise ratio becomes favorable. In this way, a gain of 2 in a traveling wave amplifier was observed (*220*). An extensive study of a pulsed, unidirectional ruby amplifier with a gain of about 12 db has been made by Geusic and Scovil (*46*), who also discussed the basic ideas leading to this device.

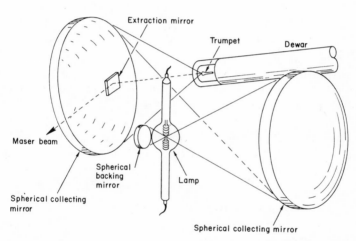

FIG. 25. Schematic drawing showing the geometrical arrangement of mirrors to image the arc of the lamp on the end of the trumpet-shaped maser rod [Nelson and Boyle (*142*)]. See Fig. 22a for an enlarged drawing of the trumpet-shaped rod.

It is evident that to achieve high stable gain, regeneration must be reduced to a very low level. A source of feedback arises from reflections at the dielectric interface. For ruby with an air interface $R \simeq 0.07$, and from the stability requirement $GR < 1$, where G is the single pass gain, a stable gain less than 14 may be obtained. On the other hand, if a gain of 30 db is required, then R must be less than 0.001, which is very difficult to achieve even with dielectric coatings. This problem may be solved by using a succession of isolated amplifying sections, each of which has a gain of 6 db for the figures given above, an arrangement which also serves to reduce the amount of power wasted by amplification of the spontaneous radiation. A Faraday rotation isolator was designed by Geusic and Scovil (46) which was found to have a reverse loss of about 16 db and an insertion loss of about 3 db at the R_1 line. Experimental data on the gain of a two section amplifier as a function of pumping power was found to be in good agreement with theory.

Inasmuch as the optical maser is a multimode device, it may be said to have spatial vision and image information can be sent through the amplifier. Image amplification with a gain of 5 db was observed in the amplifier under discussion.

8. Optical Maser Oscillation in $MgF_2:Ni^{2+}$

Until the very recent report of maser oscillation in $MgF_2:Ni^{2+}$ by Johnson et al. (164a), Cr^{3+} was the only representative of the $3d$ transition ions with which maser action had been obtained. The maser transition in $MgF_2:Ni^{2+}$ is unique in that it involves a transition of Ni^{2+} from the excited $^3T_2$ state to the ground $^3A_2$ state plus a simultaneous excitation of 340 cm^{-1} by the MgF_2 lattice. Therefore the terminal state for the maser is an excited state of the lattice-impurity system 340 cm^{-1} above the ground electronic state. The maser oscillation at 6164 Å was characterized by the familiar spiking phenomena.

C. Optical Masers Using $4f$ Rare Earth Ions

1. Trivalent Ions

a. General Spectroscopic Considerations.   The unpaired electrons of the $4f$ shell ($n = 4$, $l = 3$) which are involved in the optical transitions, are well shielded from the crystal field by two $5s$ and six $5p$ electrons. Consequently the crystal field is small relative to the spin-orbit interaction and can generally be regarded as a perturbation on the system. In this case it is appropriate to use the energy level designation of the free ion, the LS or Russell-Saunders coupling scheme, to describe the spectra of the solids (189).

The pump and maser transitions in trivalent ions are due to the very weakly allowed $4f \rightarrow 4f$ transitions ($f \sim 10^{-6}$) which are generally radiative and possess narrow line widths (*221*). The $4f \rightarrow 5d$ transitions occur in the ultraviolet region and are far less suitable for pumping. Optical maser action has been reported thus far in seven trivalent rare-earth ions in various host materials: erbium, europium, holmium, neodymium, praesodymium, thulium, and ytterbium. Energy level diagrams of the trivalent rare earth ions which have exhibited maser action are shown in Figs. 26 and 27.

b. *$CaWO_4 : Er^{3+}$.* Pulsed maser action in this material cooled to liquid N_2 at 1.612μ was observed by Kiss and Duncan (*157*). The pumping takes place in the weak absorption lines of the forbidden $4f \rightarrow 4f$ transition. In view of the few pumping lines and poor fluorescent quantum efficiency of this material, it was not considered as a promising candidate for continuous operation.

c. *Gd^{3+} in Glass.* Gandy and Ginther (*177*) have reported stimulated emission from Gd^{3+} in activated silicate glass at 3125Å, the shortest maser wavelength reported for a rare earth ion. They tentatively assigned this radiation to a transition from the $^6P_{7/2}$ state to the $^8S_{7/2}$ ground state of the $4f^7$ electronic configuration of Gd^{3+}. No subsequent work confirming maser action in this system has appeared.

d. *$CaWO_4 : Ho^{3+}$.* Pulsed maser action at 77°K was observed in this material by Johnson et al. (*158*) at 2.046μ, corresponding to a transition from the $^5I_7 \rightarrow {}^5I_8$ states of the free ion. No maser action was found at room temperature.

e. *Nd^{3+} in Various Crystals.* As may be seen from Tables I.1 and I.2, maser action has been observed in 11 materials containing Nd^{3+}. Of the many host materials containing neodymium, eight are divalent lattices and present complications in interpreting the details of absorption and emission spectra. The local unbalance of charge at the site of a given neodymium ion can be neutralized in a variety of ways, vacancies of the host anion, interstitial ions, pairing of Nd^{3+}, etc. The spectrum of each Nd^{3+} is then characteristic of the local crystal field in which it finds itself. The problem of charge compensation is partially relieved by the addition of a monovalent alkali metal ion, Na^+, K^+, or Li^+. In this case the emission spectrum due to the transition, $^4F_{3/2} \rightarrow {}^4I_{11/2}$ which is responsible for the maser action, simplifies considerably. In addition the oscillation threshold is lowered by a factor of 3 relative to uncompensated crystals of the same Nd^{3+} concentration (*158a*). The problem of charge compensation is completely solved by using a trivalent lattice. LaF_3 is the first trivalent lattice in which maser action has been observed from a trivalent rare earth ion (*158a*).

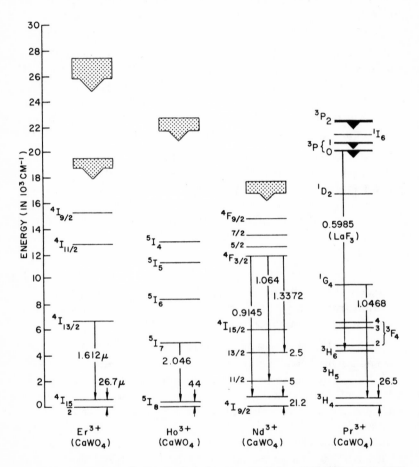

FIG. 26.   Energy level diagrams of trivalent rare earth ions in $CaWO_4$: Er^{3+} (*157*), Ho^{3+} (*158, 158a*), Nd^{3+} (*158a, 161*), and Pr^{3+} (*165, 166*). The following comments apply to this figure as well as Figs. 27, 28, and 29. The dark or shaded triangles indicate useful absorption bands for optical excitation, which are often known only approximately. The maser transitions are indicated by downward pointing arrows. Energy level separations are given in microns.

Nd^{3+} operates successfully at both room temperature and 77°K in all crystals except CaF$_2$, BaF$_2$, and Y$_2$O$_3$, where operation only at the lower temperature was observed. The infrared fluorescence of Nd^{3+} originates from the $^4F_{3/2}$ level and terminates in the various ground ^4I multiplets, the strongest component of which is the

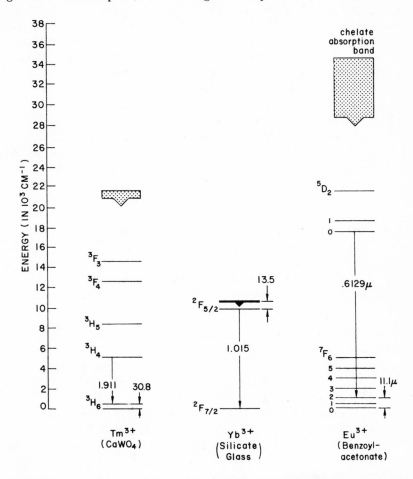

FIG. 27.   Energy level diagrams of trivalent rare earth ions: CaWO$_4$: Tm^{3+} (*168*, *158a*), Yb^{3+} in silicate glass (*181*), Eu^{3+} benzoylacetonate (*183*, *184a*). The chelate absorption band is so intense, 10^4 cm^{-1}, that excitation arising from the long wavelength tail extending up to 4500 Å where the absorption has fallen to ~10 cm^{-1} is more likely to penetrate the center of the material. Which of these regions is primarily responsible for pumping has not yet been established.

$^4F_{3/2} \rightarrow \, ^4I_{11/2}$ group at 1.065μ. In accordance with the fact that the terminal level is about 2000 cm^{-1} above the ground level, no marked rise in the threshold was observed at room temperature as compared with 77°K. Johnson (158a) has attempted to increase the effective pumping range of Nd^{3+} by incorporating in the host ions which might behave as excitation transfer agents. No enhancement of Nd^{3+} emission was noted on adding uranium, niobium, and all the rare earths except Pm^{3+}, Eu^{3+}, Gd^{3+}, and Lu^{3+} in equal concentration with Nd^{3+}. Since the added ions apparently behave as independent agents, simultaneous maser action from two trivalent ions within the same crystal should be possible. This was confirmed for the combinations Nd^{3+} − Tm^{3+}, and Nd^{3+} − Ho^{3+}.

Experiments demonstrating continuous maser action in CaWO$_4$: Nd^{3+} at 1.065μ operating at about 85°K have been performed by Johnson et al. (161). A schematic of the equipment is shown in Fig. 30. The rod was 2 in. long, 0.079 in. in diameter, and one end was left partially transmitting ($\sim$1 %). Further work has resulted in continuous operation at room temperature at 1.058μ by water cooling the crystal. A power output of about 10 mW was obtained at an input power to the lamp of 1.5 kW. The principal factor making this possible was the use of a charge compensated crystal which lowered the threshold for oscillation by a factor of 3. Continuous operation at room temperature has been obtained also by focusing the output of a high pressure xenon arc lamp onto the end of the dielectric condenser shown in Fig. 22b (142a).

f. *Pr^{3+} in CaWO$_4$ and LaF$_3$*.   Pulsed maser action has been observed in Pr^{3+} in CaWO$_4$ by Yariv et al. (165) at 20°K, 77°K, and 90°K, but not at room temperature. The emission occurs at 1.0468μ corresponding to the transition $^1G_4 \rightarrow \, ^3H_4$. Since the terminal state terminates only 377 cm^{-1} above the ground state, it may be expected that threshold for maser action at room temperature will be significantly greater as compared with 77°K [see Eqs. (8.5) and (8.6)]. Stimulated emission at 77°K in LaF$_3$: Pr^{3+} was observed at 5985 Å, corresponding to the $^3P_0 \rightarrow \, ^3H_6$ transition (166). However, there was no evidence of stimulated emission at 1.04μ as reported in CaWO$_4$: Pr^{3+}.

g. *CaWO$_4$: Tm^{3+}*.   Pulsed optical maser action at 1.911μ was first reported in this material cooled to 77°K by Johnson et al. (168). Stimulated emission has also been observed in a second line at 1.916μ (158a). That maser action has been obtained at all in this ion is rather surprising since there are fewer lines for pumping than in Nd^{3+} or Ho^{3+}. Furthermore, these lines are weak, $f \sim 10^{-7}$, compared with $f \sim 10^{-6}$ for Nd^{3+}, for example. However, pumping is aided because of the near coincidence of the lines of the xenon lamp and Tm^{3+} absorption lines. The fluorescence intensity of Tm^{3+} in SrF_2 is comparable with that in $CaWO_4$, but the threshold for stimulated emission is very high.

h. *Yb³⁺ in Silicate Glass.*   Stimulated emission of this material at 1.015μ at liquid nitrogen temperature and lower was observed by Etzel *et al.* (*181*). The overall bandwidth of the emission is about 6mμ, and, according to the authors, there are at least 29 lines present, the shortest wavelength line being at 1.0125μ and the longest at 1.0184μ. It is thought that the stimulated emission corresponds to transitions from the $^2F_{5/2}$ excited state multiplet to the $^2F_{7/2}$ ground state multiplet in the $4f^{13}$ electronic configuration of Yb^{3+}.

2. Divalent Ions

a. *General Spectroscopic Considerations.*   There is much less information available on the spectral properties of divalent than on the trivalent ions. It is therefore useful to recognize that divalent rare-earth ions should bear some resemblance to their isoelectronic counterparts among the trivalent rare earths. The divalent rare earth ions possess relatively strong $4f \rightarrow 5d$ bands ($f \sim 10^{-4} - 10^{-3}$) in the visible region which are eminently suited for optical pumping. In addition, they possess $4f \rightarrow 4f$ transitions which preserve the sharp-line fluorescence characteristics of the trivalent rare earths. Despite such obvious virtues only four systems incorporating rare-earth ions have been found to exhibit maser action: $CaF_2 : Sm^{2+}$, $SrF_2 : Sm^{2+}$, $CaF_2 : Tm^{2+}$, and $CaF_2 : Dy^{2+}$. The problem of the divalent ions has been considered by Johnson (*158a*). Although he observed sharp lines in the strong infrared fluorescence of Er^{2+} (isoelectronic with Tm^{3+}), Pr^{2+} (isoelectronic with Nd^{3+}), and Ho^{2+} (isoelectronic with Nd^{3+}) incorporated in CaF_2, he was not successful in obtaining stimulated emission in these systems. The explanation that was offered as being most likely is that the fluorescent radiation is absorbed in upward transitions from the excited state to a $5d$ band. In addition, the divalent form of the ion is often not the most stable valence state for the ion. Energy level diagrams for the divalent rare earth ions which have exhibited maser action are shown in Fig. 28. The spectroscopy of divalent rare earths in CaF_2 has been reviewed by Kiss (*190*).

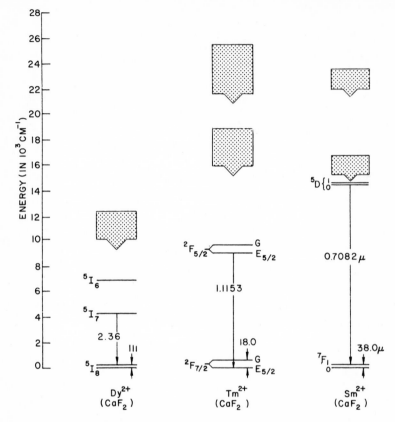

FIG. 28.   Energy level diagrams of divalent rare earth ions in CaF_2 : Dy^{2+} (*155, 156a*), Tm^{2+} (*169*), and Sm^{2+} (*49*).

b. CaF_2 : Sm^{2+}.   Optical maser action of Sm^{2+} in CaF_2 has been investigated in some detail by Kaiser *et al.* (*49, 222*) and Sorokin *et al.* (*167*). The main emission line at 7082 Å (14,118 cm^{-1}) narrows strongly with decreasing temperature and exhibits a line width of 1.6 cm^{-1} at 20°K, the temperature where most of the experiments were performed. The quantum efficiency for emission in this line is 0.2, and the fluorescence lifetime is 2×10^{-6} sec. In a typical size sample (3-mm diameter and 20-mm length) the threshold was calculated to be 5 watts/cm^2 whereas the observed value was 21 watts/cm^2.* The output power was not given but was probably in the milliwatt range. The maser beam was confined to an angle of about $\frac{1}{2}°$ ($\sim$3.6 $\times$ 10^{-2} rad). In one sample, five discrete frequencies appeared covering a range of 0.5 cm^{-1} and each with a width of about 0.1 cm^{-1}. The CaF$_2$: Sm^{2+} maser has greater beam divergence, and less spectral narrowing than the Al$_2$O$_3$: Cr^{3+} maser. Wood and Kaiser (223) have made a detailed study of absorption and fluorescence of Sm^{2+} in CaF$_2$, SrF$_2$, and BaF$_2$ and have presented data on intensity, line width, and quantum efficiency which are relevant to experiments on stimulated emission on all three systems. Sorokin et al. (167) have obtained spectroscopic results on SrF$_2$: Sm^{2+} and maser action at 6969Å. The crystal was operated as a pulsed optical maser at temperatures close to 4.2°K. The maser output, in contrast to what prevails in CaF$_2$: Sm^{2+} systems, was characterized by strong relaxation oscillations.

c. *CaF$_2$: Dy^{2+}.* The strong infrared emission at 2.36μ found by Kiss and Duncan (155) is due to a $^5I_7 \rightarrow {}^5I_6$ transition terminating about 35 cm^{-1} above the ground state. Continuous maser action was observed by Kiss and Duncan (155), Johnson (156), and Yariv (156a). The very efficient pumping of this maser is due principally to a $4f - 5d$ band near 0.9μ, which coincides with a strong emission region of the xenon discharge. The threshold for continuous operation, 100 watts, is the lowest threshold reported for a solid system, (156a). A power output of 0.3 watt was measured with 800 watts input to the lamp.

The natural fluorescent linewidth of the maser transition in CaF$_2$: Dy^{2+} as well as in CaF$_2$: Tm^{2+} ($<$0.08 cm^{-1} at 77°K and 0.03 cm^{-1} at 27°K, respectively) are smaller than the axial cavity mode spacings of the Fabry-Perot resonators. The CaF$_2$: Dy^{2+} maser has been Zeeman tuned over a range of 5 cm^{-1} and modulated with a bandwidth of $\frac{1}{2}$ Mc (156b).

d. *CaF$_2$: Tm^{2+}.* This system exhibits two strong fluorescing lines at 1.116μ and 1.189μ arising from transitions from the $^2F_{5/2}$ level to two of the crystal field split components of the $^2F_{7/2}$ ground state (See Fig. 28). Kiss and Duncan (169) found that the 1.116μ line

---

* Since the lifetime is less than the duration of the pumping light pulse, it is appropriate to give the threshold in power rather than energy.

went into oscillation as a three-level maser, a surprising result since the 1.189μ line terminates 556 cm^{-1} above the ground state and could provide a suitable four level system with a depopulated terminal state even at room temperature. This result was attributed to the absorption of the 1.189μ radiation by transitions from the excited $^2F_{5/2}$ level to the 5d bands. Kiss (224) has demonstrated the tuning of this maser over the range of 1.5 cm^{-1} with a magnetic field.

D. THE CaF$_2$: U^{3+} OPTICAL MASER

The actinide (5f) series is similar to the 4f series in having its unpaired 5f electrons partially shielded (by 6s and 6p electrons). However, this shielding is not as effective as that of the rare earth ions and the departures of the energy levels from the free ion levels is more pronounced.

The spectroscopy and stimulated emission characteristics of CaF$_2$: U^{3+} have been reviewed by Wittke et al. (172). Spectroscopic studies have shown that apart from a set of absorption lines due to U^{4+}, CaF$_2$: U^{3+} crystals exhibit two types of U^{3+} sites. One type which is found in dilute crystals corresponds to isolated ions which give rise to a maser oscillation at 2.51μ due to a transition between the lowest crystal-field component of the $^4I_{11/2}$ state and the highest component of the $^4I_{9/2}$ ground state (Fig. 29). Since this terminal state is 515 cm^{-1} above the ground state, it is essentially depopulated at liquid N$_2$ temperatures and below, although it has appreciable population at 300°K. Thus as long as the terminal maser level remains in thermal equilibrium with the other levels of the $^4I_{9/2}$ state, at low temperatures the 2.51μ transition should oscillate as a four-level system. The second type of site appears only in more highly doped crystals and is associated with masers lines at 2.61μ and 2.57μ. The fact that the fluorescent intensity of the 2.57μ line was observed to rapidly decrease with reduced temperature may be taken as evidence that this transition arises from a level of the upper ion-pair state that is not lowest and hence is depopulated as the crystal is cooled. This explains why the 2.57μ line oscillated at room temperature but failed to oscillate at 77°K.

Paramagnetic resonance studies indicate that the local symmetry of the dominant U^{3+} sites is tetragonal for ground state ions. However, in crystals where the U^{3+} sites are apparently trigonal, Porto and

Yariv (*173*) have observed stimulated emission at 2.24μ. Wittke *et al.* (*172*) did not observe maser action at this wavelength although they observed a line at 2.24μ in highly doped crystals in both absorption and fluorescence. In view of this result, they suggested that the 2.24μ oscillation corresponds to a three level maser.

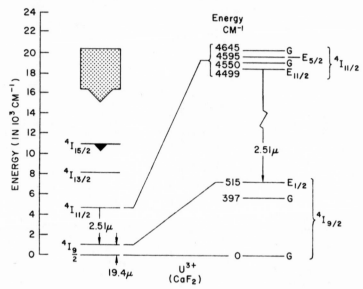

FIG. 29. Energy level diagram of CaF_2 : U^{3+} (*171, 172*). In concentrated crystals the wavelength of the $^4I_{11/2} \rightarrow \,^4I_{9/2}$ transition is 2.61μ and the terminal state is 16.4μ above the ground state.

Pulsed optical maser action of U^{3+} in CaF_2 was first reported by Sorokin and Stevenson (*144, 171*) and continuous maser action was achieved by Boyd *et al.* (*170*). The experimental arrangement used to obtain continuous maser action in CaF_2 : U^{3+} (*170*), as well as $CaWO_4$: Nd^{3+} (*160*) and CaF_2 : Dy^{2+} (*156*) is shown in Fig. 30. An elliptic cylinder is used to concentrate the radiation from a mercury or xenon arc lamp, which is placed along one focus, onto the maser rod, which is placed along the other focus. The crystal is surrounded by a double dewar in which a suitable coolant flows through the inner dewar space, and a liquid filter flows through the outer annular region. The coolant keeps the crystal at the proper operating temperature, and the liquid filter absorbs pump radiation which is not useful in exciting the desired transitions. The xenon

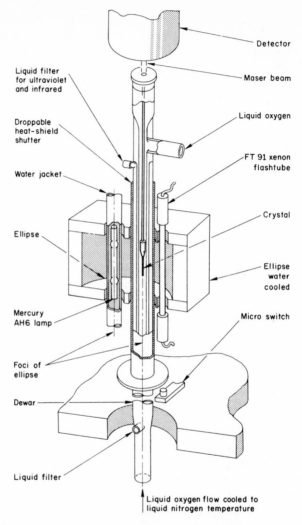

Detector

Liquid filter
for ultraviolet
and infrared

Maser beam

Droppable
heat-shield
shutter

Liquid oxygen

Water jacket

FT 91 xenon
flashtube

Crystal

Ellipse

Ellipse
water
cooled

Mercury
AH6 lamp

Micro switch

Foci of
ellipse

Dewar

Liquid filter

↑ Liquid oxygen flow cooled to
| liquid nitrogen temperature

FIG. 30. Experimental arrangement for continuous maser operation of crystals [Boyd *et al.* (*170*)].

flash tube GE FT91 was incorporated within the ellipse to determine the threshold for pulse operation of the crystal *in situ*. The lamp is located in a nonfocusing position behind the crystal, where it blocks as little light as possible of the light from the mercury lamp. A continuous power output of around 10 mW was obtained.

The threshold for pulsed operation increased from 2.0 joules at 20°K to 3.78 joules at 77°K. This increase was attributed to the depopulation of the metastable state at the higher temperatures by the thermalization of a number of levels whose separation from the metastable state is smaller than 20 cm^{-1} (Fig. 29) (*170*). The much greater increase in threshold from 3.28 joules at 77°K to 1200 joules at 300°K may be accounted for in a qualitative way by (8.5) by the fact that the decay rate of the excited state increases tenfold, and the fact that the terminal maser state while empty at 77°K has some population at 300°K.

In addition to maser oscillation in $CaF_2 : U^{3+}$, pulsed maser action has been observed in $Sr : U^{3+}$ at 2.407μ and $BaF_2 : U^{3+}$ at 2.556μ.

E. Optical Maser Action in Metallo-Organic Compounds

The possibility of obtaining maser action with rare-earth chelates in liquid or solid solutions was suggested by several authors (*182c, 184*). However, optical maser action was first observed in the metallo-organic complex, Eu-benzoylacetonate (EuB_3) contained in a frozen solution of ethyl and methyl alcohols, by Lempicki and Samelson (*182a*). Benzoyl-acetone is known to absorb in the ultraviolet region as a result of a transition from the ground state to an excited singlet state. It then relaxes to a triplet state from which it returns to the ground state with the emission of its characteristic phophorescence. When the EuB_3 chelate is formed, the phosphorescence is suppressed and, instead, the line emission characteristic of the intra $4f$ transitions of Eu^{3+} is found. This occurs as a result of the transfer of energy from the triplet state of the chelating agent principally to the $^5D_0$ level of Eu^{3+}, and the subsequent decay to the ground multiplet, as shown in Fig. 27.

The metallo-organic compound EuB_3 was studied in solution with methyl and ethyl alcohol made to a glass by operating at temperatures below 120°C. Because the low-temperature glass has a large coefficient of expansion, a special type of cavity had to be used. It consisted of a quartz cylinder, 0.4 cm inside diameter, fitted with two accurately ground quartz pistons, the inside surfaces of which were fabricated as spherical mirrors. Maser oscillation was observed at 6130Å. At 30% above threshold the line width decreased from 8Å to less than 0.3Å.

Perhaps the chief attraction of the metallo-organic system as compared with inorganic hosts for the metal ion lies in the broad absorption associated with the ligands. In addition, the quantum efficiency is high, approximately 0.85 for EuB_3. Absorption measurements show that the long-wavelength pumping band has a peak at 3200Å, a width at half maximum of 600Å, and for a concentration of 5.2×10^{18} molecules/cm³, a peak absorption coefficient of 850 cm⁻¹. However, with such large absorption, it is difficult to excite a large volume of the sample. To alleviate this difficulty, Schimitschek (*184*) used a quartz tube 0.08 cm in diameter, and 5 cm long with nearly confocal movable mirrors in contact with the liquid, to obtain maser action in EuB_3. The output exhibited irregular spiking similar to that in ruby and well defined mode patterns. The different characteristics obtained with the 0.08 cm tube (*184*) compared with the 0.4 cm tube (*182a*) may be that the very high absorption coefficient for pump light of EuB_3 prevented effective excitation of the larger volume.

Stimulated emission in a coiled fiber of Eu^{3+}-tris[4,4,4-trifluoro-1-(2-thiemyl)-1,3 butanedione] in polymethyl methacrylate (Eu TTA) has been reported (*183*), but never confirmed.

Evidence of stimulated emission in Eu-dibenzoylmethide (EuD_3) has been reported by Lempicki and Samelson (*182b*). However, unlike EuB_3, with EuD_3 no sharp threshold or relaxation oscillation was present. There is an abrupt decrease of fluorescence following an initial peak resulting in a decrease of total light output with increasing excitation energy. This quenching can be explained (*182b*) by the existence of an excited state with a reasonable lifetime situated at twice the fluorescence emission energy above the terminal state of the fluorescence ($^7F_2$). Then the emitting state ($^5D_0$) can be depopulated by absorption as well as by stimulated emission. Depending on the lifetime of the postulated excited state, which has not been as yet identified, an accumulation of systems there may tend to depopulate the ground state during the flash and cause a decrease in the total fluorescent output. An analogous process of absorption from the excited state may be encountered in benzophenone where there are suitably situated excited triplet states above the lowest triplet state.

In studying the time dependence of the fluorescence from benzophenone, Lempicki and Samelson (*182b*) did not observe the spiking which was reported previously and attributed to stimulated emission

(*186*). The possibility of using organic molecular crystals in optical masers has been proposed (*185, 186*), although success in this area has not been realized.

F. Control of the Oscillation in Pulsed Masers

For many applications, it is desirable to operate a maser in such a fashion that one or more pulses of controlled amplitude, duration, and timing are produced. It was suggested by Hellwarth (*69*) that materials which can be made to exhibit normal maser action can also be made to emit short pulses of high amplitude by controlling the regenerative action in the following way. The maser substance is pumped while the regeneration is kept low thereby storing a superabundance of atoms in the excited state; the regeneration is then suddenly switched on. In this way, McClung and Hellwarth (*225, 226*) obtained one giant pulse per light flash which was orders of magnitude more intense and shorter in duration than the repeating pulsations observed in ruby when operated in the normal way.

A schematic diagram of their apparatus is shown in Fig. 31. The

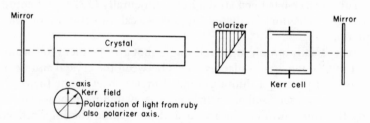

FIG. 31. Schematic diagram of a *Q*-spoil maser using a Kerr cell and polarizer as the optical shutter.

polarizer is a quartz Wollaston, optically contacted prism. The 60° oriented ruby was pumped by a GE FT506 helical flash lamp. The ruby employed was a 0.05% concentration, unclad rod 2.84 cm long and 0.9 cm in diameter. The mirrors were multilayer dielectric coated optical flats with reflectivities of about 98%. The nitrobenzene Kerr cell could be discharged as fast as 5×10^{-9} sec causing the effective transmission of the Kerr-cell polarizer to go from 0.1 to 0.9 in that time. This rapid switching resulted in pulses of about 15 megawatts peak power and less than 3×10^{-8} sec in duration. The beam divergence was about 2 mrad. The original population inversion of perhaps 25% was found to decrease at about eight times the spontaneous rate, but the reason for this shortening of the lifetime under heavy inversion was not determined. The original population inversion that can be obtained in practice is less than the theoretically attainable value (226a).

The arrangement shown in Fig. 31, modified by directing a portion of the maser output onto a photodiode which drives the Kerr cell, was used to stabilize the output of the ruby maser (227). By controlling the regeneration this way, the irregular spiking output changed to essentially steady emission which generally followed the intensity of the pumping light.

Instead of a Kerr cell, a Faraday cell or magneto-optic shutter may be used for Q-switching. With the latter arrangement, a peak power output of approximately 600 kW in a pulse 60 nsec wide at the base was obtained from ruby, 0.39 in. in diameter by $2\frac{7}{8}$ in. long (227a).

An important method of obtaining giant pulses is to replace one of the reflectors by a rapidly rotating mirror. In this arrangement, regeneration is high only during the very short time the rotating mirror is parallel with the fixed mirror. This and the Kerr-cell method for Q switching the ruby maser has been studied experimentally (227b) and compared with the behavior predicted by numerical integration of the rate equations.

An especially simple although single shot arrangement for producing giant pulses consists in placing a lens between the crystal and detached mirror and placing a thin aluminized mylar sheet at the focus (227d). The initial maser oscillation triggers the switching process by vaporizing the aluminum off the mylar and presenting the high reflectivity surface through the transparent mylar film. By using a piece of extremely thin foil (3×10^{-5} in.) the focusing lens was not necessary. With either arrangement bursts of approximately 1-MW peak power with a duration of 1 μsec were achieved.*

Giant pulses have been obtained from a ruby optical maser by utilizing the refraction resulting from the passage of the maser beam through an ultrasonic cell located within the cavity (227e). In addition, the ultrasonic shutter can be utilized to synchronize the randomly occurring pulses of the ruby optical maser with the ultrasonic frequency (227f), or to amplitude modulate the output (227g).

* A related but repeatable method uses a cell containing phthalocyanine molecules in solution, which is bleached as the maser light is absorbed (227c).

In the following methods of controlling the regeneration of optical masers, a smaller enhancement of the power output is obtained, and a train of pulses rather than a single giant pulse is usually observed. In one method, the feedback is controlled by the use of a rotating disc as a shutter between the crystal and the reflector (*228, 229*). In another method, an inhomogeneous magnetic field was used to break up the active volume of the material into smaller volumes through Zeeman detuning (*230*). The magnetic field was obtained by passing a current through a single loop of a copper bar, which encircled the center of a ruby rod. The application of a homogeneous electric field, 4kV/cm at 10^5 cps, changed the irregular spiking output of a ruby maser into regularly spaced spikes with a substantially enhanced amplitude (*231*).

Finally, the output of one Nd^{3+} glass maser has been used to switch off the oscillation in a second Nd^{3+} maser, provided the radiation from the first maser was sufficiently intense to reduce the excited population in the second below the value required for oscillation (*232*).

X. Gaseous Optical Masers

A. METHODS OF POPULATION INVERSION

1. *Pumping by Collisions in a Gas Discharge*

This section includes a discussion of excitation by electron-atom collisions, and excitation of an atom of one species by collision with an electron followed by the transfer of this excitation to an atom of another species by an inelastic atom-atom collision. Because these techniques have proven to be so fruitful in producing maser action, they are discussed more fully than the other methods for producing population inversion in gases.

Whereas the subject of negative absorption for optical transitions in solids is of recent origin, this is apparently not the case for atoms in gas discharges. The use of a gas discharge to obtain a negative absorption coefficient was evidently proposed by Fabrikant (*233*) in 1939 in a system in which the relaxation of the lower level was to be obtained by collisions of the second kind with atoms or molecules in a buffer gas. Lamb (*234*) in 1950 mentioned the possibility of obtaining negative temperatures between the $2\,{}^2S_{1/2}$ and $2\,{}^2P_{3/2}$ levels of hydrogen in a Woods discharge. Methods for obtaining population inversion in single component gas discharges for the purpose of obtaining maser action were proposed recently by Sanders (*235*) and Javan (*236*). The latter also proposed the use of two component systems in which the upper state of the atoms of one gas is populated by collisional transfer of energy from a metastable level of the atoms of a second gas, a technique in the case of helium-neon mixtures which led Javan, Bennett, and Herriott to the first successful gaseous optical maser (*237*).

Theoretical studies of population inversions in gas discharge systems have been conducted for a number of limiting cases (*236, 238, 239, 239a*). A gaseous discharge represents, in general, a highly complicated nonequilibrium situation involving radiative transitions and nonradiative transitions due to electron-atom and atom-atom collisions between the numerous energy levels of the atomic system.

In many instances the relevant transition probabilities and cross sections are poorly known, if at all. Hence it is not surprising that theoretical analysis of the populations in a gas discharge, although undoubtedly valuable in planning experiments, has not apparently permitted the prediction of which transitions could be made to oscillate.

Although resort to experiment has proven to be necessary in evaluating gas discharge systems, much may be said about the types of levels suitable for maser action through a discussion of the excitation processes involved. Surveys of theoretical and experimental work in this field may be found in books by Mitchell and Zemansky (22), Massey and Burhop (240), and in a review article by Bennett(241). In the following discussion of population inversion in gas discharges, we will restrict ourselves to dominant mechanisms that have actually been used to produce oscillations in gas systems. To illustrate the nature of the problems involved, we will apply, in a qualitative way, the kinetic equations for the system.

Consider a two component gas system whose energy levels are represented by the diagram in Fig. 32. The maser atoms, designated

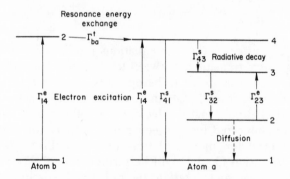

FIG. 32. Schematic energy level diagram illustrating pumping by electron excitation and resonance collision between atoms of different species.

by a, are shown with four energy levels, and the auxiliary atoms, designated by b, are shown with two energy levels. The horizontal arrow indicates the resonance or nearly resonance transfer of energy in a collision between atoms a and b according to the reaction,

$$a(E_1) + b(E_2) \rightarrow b(E_1) + a(E_4) + \Delta E, \tag{10.1}$$

where ΔE is the energy difference between initial and final states. In the manner of Basov and Krokhin (238), the rate of change of the number of atoms of type a in level 4 is given by

$$\frac{dN_4^a}{dt} = N_1^a(\Gamma_{14}^e + \Gamma_{ba}^t) - N_4^a(\Gamma_{ab}^t + \Gamma_4^s + \Gamma_4^e), \qquad (10.2)$$

where Γ_4^s is the total radiative decay rate from level 4, $\Gamma_{14}^e = n_e\langle\sigma_{14}v\rangle$ is the excitation rate by electron collisions of the first kind, $\Gamma_4^e = n_e\langle\sigma_4 v\rangle$ is the total transition rate from level 4 by electron collisions of the second kind, $\Gamma_{ba}^t = n_2^b\langle\sigma_{ba}v\rangle$ is the rate of energy transfer from atom b to a, and $\Gamma_{ab}^t = n_1^b\langle\sigma_{ab}v\rangle$ is the reverse process. n_e is the density of electrons, σ is the cross section, and v is the relative velocity of the colliding particles. An average is taken over σv because, in general, σ is a function of velocity. Omitted from (10.2) is a term which corresponds to electron excitation from level 3 to 4 since it is considered that $N_3^a \ll N_1^a$ always holds. The rate of change of population in level 3 is given by

$$\frac{dN_3^a}{dt} = N_2^a\Gamma_{23}^e - N_3^a(\Gamma_{32}^e + \Gamma_{32}^s) + N_4^a(\Gamma_{43}^s + \Gamma_{43}^e). \qquad (10.3)$$

We have omitted in the rate equations (10.2) and (10.3) radiative and nonradiative transitions between levels 1 and 3, for the following reason. Level 4 is assumed to be optically connected to level 3 and the ground state, level 1. On the basis of the symmetry properties of the electric dipole matrix elements, it follows that if two levels $(4 \leftrightarrow 1)$ are connected by an electric dipole transition and if one of these is allowed for an optical transition to a third level $(4 \leftrightarrow 3)$, the other transition $(3 \leftrightarrow 1)$ will be forbidden, and vice versa. Thus for the case under consideration, the radiative lifetime for the $4 \leftrightarrow 1$ transition should be extremely short compared with the radiative lifetime for the $3 \leftrightarrow 1$ transition. In practice, this difference may not be so drastic because the atomic states may not be pure states and the transition $3 \leftrightarrow 1$ only partially forbidden. The previous remarks apply for transitions induced by electron impact as well as for radiative transitions, since it may be shown that for electron energies above excitation threshold, the largest cross sections are obtained for optically allowed transitions. The cross section for electron excitation above excitation threshold is related to the spontaneous emission rate by

$\sigma_{m1} \propto A_{m1}$, where m represents some excited state, and 1 represents the ground state. The atomic system under discussion, where the lower maser level acquires its fast decay by radiation to a set of levels other than the ground state and where the upper maser level is optically connected to the ground state, is ideally suited for excitation by electron impact. Such a scheme has been used successfully in masers utilizing pure neon, argon, krypton, and xenon.

Let us take atom a to be neon, in which case level 4 is one of the 3s or 2s levels,* level 3 is one of the 2p levels, and level 2 is one of the 1s levels (see Fig. 33). The 2s states are known to be optically connected to the ground state and hence should have a very large

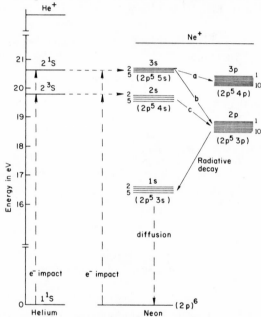

FIG. 33. Energy levels of helium and neon illustrating the dominant excitation cycle for the visible red and infrared maser transitions (258). The helium levels are designated by Russell-Saunders notation. The neon levels are designated by Paschen notation; the configuration designation is enclosed by parenthesis. The maser transitions designated by a, b, and c are in the wavelength ranges: a, 2.8–4.0μ; b, 0.59–0.73μ; and c, 1.1–1.5μ.

* This is the semiempirical notation of Paschen, which, although now obsolete, has been extensively used in the literature for rare gas spectra. The modified Racah notation (241a) has been adopted for designating these energy levels, although Russell-Saunders notation is sometimes used.

cross section for electron excitation compared with that for excitation to the $2p$ states. The $1s$ level is metastable and its population tends to build up as the pumping continues. If the $1s$ level population becomes too high, photons emitted by decaying $2p$ atoms have a finite chance of re-exciting $1s$ atoms before they escape from the gas. This process of radiation trapping has the effect of increasing the lifetime of the $2p$ states. If the gas mixture is free from other impurities, then the only way $1s$ state atoms can decay to the ground state is by colliding with the walls of the gas container. For this reason, the gain or power output of the helium-neon maser as well as that of the other gas discharge masers, which have energy level schemes related to that in neon, have been found to vary inversely with the tube diameter.

Another factor which increases the lifetime of the $2p$ level is due to collisions of the type

$$e + Ne(1s) \rightarrow Ne(2p) + e. \tag{10.4}$$

When the electron density is so high that reaction (10.4) is important, collisions of the type

$$e + Ne(2s) \rightarrow Ne + e \tag{10.5}$$

should also be considered. Reactions (10.4) and (10.5) indicate the need to limit the electron density, and in practice $\Gamma_{mn}^e \ll \Gamma_{mn}^s$, i.e., decay from excited states is by radiative transitions. Then from (10.3), provided $N_2 \Gamma_{23}^e \ll N_4 \Gamma_{43}^s$, we have

$$N_4 \Gamma_{43}^s = N_3 \Gamma_{32}^s. \tag{10.3a}$$

In order for the system to have gain, it is necessary that $N_4 g_3 > N_3 g_4$, in which case the decay rates must obey the relation

$$\Gamma_{32}^s > \Gamma_{43}^s (g_4/g_3).$$

This inequality shows that in principle gain may be obtained when the decay rate from the upper level is greater than that from the lower level.

Neglecting the Γ^t terms in (10.2) as is appropriate for a single gas system, we have for the equilibrium population difference between the maser levels, provided $N_2 \Gamma_{23}^e \ll N_4 N_{43}^s$ and decay is by radiative transitions,

$$\frac{N_4 - N_3}{N_0} = \left[\frac{\Gamma_{32}^s}{\Gamma_{43}^s} - 1 \right] \left[\frac{\Gamma_{14}^e}{\Gamma_{14}^e + (\Gamma_{14}^e + \Gamma_4^s)(\Gamma_{32}^s/\Gamma_{43}^s)} \right], \tag{10.6}$$

To obtain a large inverted population, not only should $\Gamma_{32}^s \gg \Gamma_{43}^s$, but also the ratio of the pumping rate to the radiative decay rates from level 4 should be as large as possible. However, we have already seen that if Γ_{14}^e is large, then Γ_{41}^s will also be large. The solution to this dilemma is to make the gas pressure high enough to insure complete trapping of the ultraviolet photons resulting from the $2s$ to ground state transitions. On the other hand higher gas pressures favor trapping of the $2p \rightarrow 1s$ photons, and collisions of the type (10.4) which would tend to destroy the population inversion. Noble gas pressures of the order of 0.01–0.1 mm Hg have been found in practice to satisfy these conflicting requirements and to give maser oscillations when the gas system is placed in a suitable resonator.

The question of photon trapping or imprisonment of resonance radiation is of sufficient importance in the attainment of negative temperatures in gas discharges to warrant further discussion. The radiative transition rate from the mth excited state to the ground state may be expressed as $\Gamma_{m1}^s = FA_{m1}$, where F is the trapping factor which varies from 0 to 1, and A_{m1} is the usual spontaneous radiation rate. The trapping factor is a function of the line shape, pressure, temperature, and geometry of the gas vessel and may be estimated from Holstein's theory (242). For most strong ultraviolet transitions and typical geometries, trapping generally becomes complete, i.e., $F \sim 0$, for pressures in excess of a few tens of microns. Hence the pressures used in the gas masers correspond to the limit of complete trapping for vacuum ultraviolet transitions involving the upper maser level. In this case Γ_{41}^s may be neglected in comparison with Γ_{43}^s.

Consider next a two component gas system where the energy of an excited state of atom a does not differ by more than roughly kT from the energy of an excited state of atom b. Then a large inelastic cross section is expected for the transfer of excitation from one atom to another by a collision of the type described by (10.1). This cross section is weighted by the factor $\exp \Delta E/kT$ in favor of the transfer of a given amount of energy to the atom whose excited energy is less. There is considerable practical advantage in making use of a reaction such as (10.1), as is exemplified by the He-Ne system. Since the He (2^3S) level is the first excited state of helium, the many mechanisms by which it can be formed lead to an exceptionally high effective excitation cross section. In addition, its metastable character permits these large formation rates to be transferred selectively through a reaction such as (10.1) to an excited level of another species. It is quite apparent that excitation via (10.1) is considerably more selective than excitation by electron impact.

In addition to (10.2) and (10.3), the following equation is required to describe the kinetics of a two component system, namely

$$\frac{dN_2^b}{dt} = N_1^b \Gamma_{12}^e(b) - N_1^a \Gamma_{ba}^t , \qquad (10.7)$$

where the second term gives the loss rate from the excited state of atom b due to resonant collisions with atom a in the ground state. The equilibrium solution of (10.2), (10.3), and (10.7) is the same as (10.6) provided Γ_{14}^e is replaced by Γ_{14}' where,

$$\Gamma_{14}' = \Gamma_{14}^e(a) + (N_1^b/N_1^a) \Gamma_{12}^e(b). \qquad (10.8)$$

If one makes the reasonable assumption that $\Gamma_{14}^e(a) \approx \Gamma_{12}^e(b)$, and as is the case in practice, $N_1^b \gg N_1^a$, then (10.8) clearly shows the advantage of excitation by resonance energy transfer as compared with excitation by electron impact in a single component system.

In this treatment of the conditions in a gas discharge, the ratio of electron collision rates $\Gamma_{m1}^e/\Gamma_{1m}^e$ did not appear. Where this ratio has appeared in other treatments of this problem, it has been customary to use the relation $\Gamma_{m1}^e/\Gamma_{1m}^e = \exp{(E_m - E_1)/kT_e}$. This equation follows from the principle of detailed balancing when there is a Maxwellian distribution of electrons at temperature T_e. It should be noted, however, that the validity of assuming a Maxwellian velocity distribution for the electrons in a gas discharge and the use of an effective electron temperature to describe excited state populations has been strongly questioned (13).

Thus far, we have been concerned with the pumping of rare gases by electron-atom collisions in a gas discharge. It should be possible also to produce population inversion among molecular states by electron-molecule collisions. In particular, it has been proposed by Muller et al. (243) to utilize the Franck-Condon principle to produce population inversion among molecular vibration states. In order to have a long lifetime in the excited electronic-vibrational state it is necessary that the excited state be metastable, a condition which is contradictory with the requirement that there be a fast rate of creating excited molecules. This and other considerations led the authors to suggest the system $HD \rightarrow HD^+$, i.e., the electronically excited state is the ground state of the molecular ion and so is stable except for collisions of the type $H_2^+ + H_2 \rightarrow H_3^+ + H$. Although excitation may be brought about by radiation or electron impact, the fact that the electronic excitation lies in the vacuum ultraviolet suggests the use of the discharge.

2. Dissociative Excitation in Gas Discharges

Selective excitation of a given level may be obtained not only by inelastic atom-atom collisions, but also, as demonstrated by Bennett et al. (244), by inelastic atom-molecule collisions in which the molecule is dissociated, leaving one of the atoms in an excited state. In particular, they obtained continuous maser oscillation at 8446Å using the $3\,^3P_2$–$3\,^3S_1$ fine structure transition of atomic oxygen. The excitation scheme with an Ne-O_2 mixture follows the reaction

$$Ne(^3P_1 , \,^3P_0) + O_2 \rightarrow O(3^3P, 3^5P) + O(2^3P) + Ne , \qquad (10.9)$$

where the excited neon $Ne(^3P_1 , \,^3P_0)$ is obtained by electron collisions. With the Ar-O_2 system, the excitation arises almost entirely through the two-step process

$$Ar^* + O_2 \rightarrow O^* + O + Ar$$
$$(energy) + e + O^* \rightarrow O(3\,^3P) + e, \qquad (10.10)$$

where O^* represents a metastable level of atomic oxygen.

Reactions (10.9) and (10.10) may be regarded in an approximate way as a transition induced from the ground state of molecule Y_2 to a high-lying repulsive state, Y_2^*, which is unstable and yields $Y + Y^*$. This way of regarding the reactions is illustrated in Fig. 34, where the ground state and excited state potential curves are shown as a function of the internuclear separation, R, and the excitation path is indicated by the arrows. The region over which the Franck-Condon principle would hold, when it is applicable in the excitation process considered here, is indicated by the vertical lines.

In dissociative collisions, there are usually a moderate number of repulsive states of the molecule within the energy range 1 or 2 ev at typical internuclear separations. Furthermore, these different molecular repulsive states terminate in the same states of the atoms of the dissociated molecule. From this, it follows that, unlike the excitation method based on inelastic atom-atom collisions, a close coincidence with the energy of the initial metastable carrier is not required. In view of this, a greater number of possible systems using dissociative excitation transfer may be expected. Continuous optical maser oscillation has in fact recently been obtained by Patel *et al.* (*244a*) on a number of atomic transitions of carbon, nitrogen, oxygen, sulfur, and bromine by dissociation of various diatomic and polyatomic molecules.

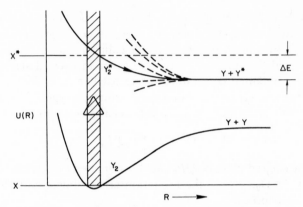

FIG. 34. Molecular potentials for illustrating the dissociative excitation transfer process [Bennett (*13*)]. The energy in the metastable state of molecule X^* is absorbed in a collision by molecule Y_2. The dashed curves represent a large number of excited molecular potentials which can terminate in the same dissociation limit. The region over which the Franck-Condon principle would hold in the excitation process is indicated by the vertical lines.

3. *Molecular Photodissociation*

Many molecular dissociative processes which produce excited atoms are known (*187*). The molecular photodissociation may be represented by

$$AB + h\nu \rightarrow (AB)^* \rightarrow A^* + B. \tag{10.11}$$

It has been suggested (*246, 247*) that this process offers possibilities for maser systems, since the pumping is irreversible, may be relatively broadband, and can continuously generate an almost completely inverted population of excited atoms. The only way in which the mechanics of the molecular dissociation enters is via its influence on the Doppler line shape of the atomic fluorescence. It has been shown by Zare and Herschbach (*248*), in a semiclassical treatment of the photodissociation of a diatomic molecule, that the angular distribution of products will often be peaked parallel or perpendicular to the direction of the incident light beam. They obtained the Doppler line shape of the fluorescence emitted by an excited fragment and applied these results to the photodissociation of NaI for possible use in a maser system.

4. Vibrational Excitation in Chemical Reactions

A proposal for an infrared maser using vibrational excitation resulting from chemical reactions has been put forward by Polanyi (249), who has discussed a number of possibilities. For example, in the reaction $H + O_3 \rightarrow OH^* + O_2$, the rate of OH* formation in the vibrational state v, Γ^v, has been calculated as $\Gamma^9 > \Gamma^8 > \Gamma^7$; $\Gamma^4 > \Gamma^3 > \Gamma^2$ (250). Indications of population inversion under steady state conditions has been reported between vibrational levels $v = 2$ and 3 of HCl* formed from $H + Cl_2$ at low pressure (251). In cases where chemical excitation does not result in an initial population inversion, Polanyi (252) makes several suggestions on how this may be accomplished.

B. SURVEY OF GASEOUS OPTICAL MASERS

As of the present writing, continuous oscillation has been obtained on about two hundred different optical transitions ranging from the ultraviolet (0.33μ) through the infrared (85μ), using many different gas systems and four different excitation mechanisms. There is no reason to believe that the excitation methods and supply of gas systems has been exhausted, and that this wavelength range will not be extended by future gas masers.

The optical masers that have been developed thus far and their characteristics are summarized in Tables I.4 to I.9, and have been discussed by Bennett (13), and Patel (258). Maser action has been achieved by inelastic atom-atom collisions in the He-Ne mixture, by direct electron excitation in the noble gases, N_2, I, and Hg vapor, by optical pumping of Cs vapor, and by dissociative excitation of O_2, CO, CO_2, NO, N_2O, SF_6, and Br_2. Of these systems, it is the He–Ne maser that has been most throughly investigated to date. The gaseous maser design which appears to have become practically standard in current practice consists of a confocal type interferometer with external mirrors, and a quartz tube with windows placed at the Brewster angle. The general arrangement of the apparatus is shown in Fig. 35. The increased flexibility obtained with using external mirrors has been very valuable for investigating new gas systems.

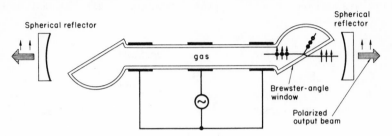

FIG. 35. Schematic diagram of an experimental arrangement for gas masers [Yariv and Gordon (*14*)]. Vertical arrows and dots indicate polarization directions, respectively, in the plane and perpendicular to the plane of the figure.

C. The He-Ne Maser

1. *Design and Operating Characteristics*

Although some evidence for the presence of inverted populations in a Hg-Zn mixture had been reported (*263*), the first successful gas maser was achieved by Javan, Bennett, and Herriott (*237*) using a He-Ne mixture. Population inversions were achieved between several of the 2s to 2p levels of Ne by means of excitation transfer from the metastable He (2^3S) to the 2s levels of Ne (see Fig. 33). The energy gap between the 2^3S level of He and 2p levels of Ne is much too large to permit direct population of the 2p states in the collisions between Ne and metastable He. The 2s levels of Ne may radiate to the ground state, but at a pressure of about 0.1 mm Ne, complete trapping of this radiation takes place. In this circumstance, the lifetimes of the 2s levels are determined primarily by radiative decay to the 2p levels. Atoms in the 2p levels decay radiatively to the metastable 1s levels, and from there to the ground state by collisions with the walls of the container. Among other sources of excitation of the Ne 2p levels, it was found that inelastic collisions of electrons with Ne in the 1s metastable levels are the most important. In view of this, the adjustment of the electron density was found to be very critical. The discharge was excited by means of external electrodes connected to a 27 Mc generator. The power dissipation which controls the electron density and which was critical was between 50 and 80 watts. The conditions for oscillation were satisfied in a simple discharge tube about 1 cm in diameter and 1 meter long containing 1 mm pressure of He and 0.1 mm pressure of Ne. It has been found in gain studies that the gain varied roughly as the reciprocal of the tube diameter (264). This result is in qualitative agreement with the fact that unless the $1s$ level is emptied sufficiently rapidly by collisions of $1s$ metastables with the container wall, photons emitted by decaying $2p$ atoms will be trapped and thereby inhibit the emptying of the $2p$ level, the terminal maser level.

The determination of the radiative lifetimes and collision cross sections of the excited $2s$ and $2p$ states of Ne has been discussed by Bennett (13, 265). The conditions in a gaseous discharge of Ne and He has been discussed by Javan (266) and more fully by Bennett (13). The influence of such condensible impurities as hydrogen, cyanogen, and CH on the operation of the He-Ne maser has been reported (267).

The optical properties and construction details of a He-Ne maser utilizing flat mirrors placed within the gas vessel have been reviewed by Herriott (94). Similar devices have been constructed by others (268, 269). The power output from each end of the maser was about 4 mW for the strongest transition ($2s_2 \rightarrow 2p_4$) at 11,523Å. From measurements of the width of the far field pattern, the angular divergence of the beam was found to be 32 sec. The phase variation over the area of the beam was studied by placing a double or multiple slit in the beam and observing the diffraction pattern. The normal multiple slit patterns obtained indicated that the radiation was coherent over the aperture of the maser, about 1 cm. A later model of the He-Ne maser used concave mirrors external to the gas discharge tube with windows at the Brewster angle with respect to the axis of the beam, which served to minimize reflection losses for radiation polarized in the plane of incidence (270, 271). As expected, the output beams were found to polarized as shown in Fig. 35. As expected, the beamwidth $\sim$3 min, is greater than that obtained with plane mirrors, 32 sec. The power attainable with the confocal system and a conventional 27-Mc rf exciter was approximately 8 mW. By using instead a pulsed voltage which produced an electric field in the gas of several hundred volts/cm, a peak power 50 times larger than the cw power was observed (271a, 272). By pulsing a high pressure mixture of helium (240 mm Hg) and neon (5 mm Hg) with 35 kV at 35 amp, a peak power output of 84W was obtained at a repetition frequency of 250 sec^{-1}. The mean power was 27.3 mW (*272c*).

Freedom to change the mirrors by using mirrors external to the quartz gas chamber has permitted operation with two plane mirrors in the visible (6328Å), the near infrared (1.153μ), and the intermediate infrared (3.39μ)(*95*). It also permitted the selection of optimum mirror transmittance for maximum power output in the dominant mode, 40 mW at 1.15μ, and 28 mW at 3.39μ. The 7 : 1 helium-neon mixture at a pressure of 0.8 mm Hg was excited by currents ranging from 10 to 110 ma, with a voltage drop from 1710 to 1400 volts. At 1.15μ one of the flat dielectric-coated mirrors had a transmittance of 0.3% and the other 5%. The power output, over 40 mW in a beam about 1 cm in diameter, was about 4 times the maximum power observed with the same tube in a semiconcave resonator restricted by an iris to its fundamental mode in a beam about 2 mm in diameter.

With the view toward developing the optical maser as a practical research tool, Bennett and Kindlmann (*272a*) have designed a magnetostrictively tuned He-Ne maser with the possibility of obtaining a long-term frequency stability good to several tens of kilocycles per second at the optical frequency. A He-Ne maser of the plane parallel Fabry-Perot type was constructed in which both the angular adjustments and the plate separation may be controlled through magnetostrictively produced distortion in a rigid Nilvar mounting frame. This design allows the eventual use of negative feedback for frequency stabilization.

2. *Interaction of Oscillating Transitions*

White and Rigden (*253*) have obtained continuous maser oscillations in the visible region at 6328Å from the 3s_2 to 2p_4 levels of Ne (see Fig. 33). The 3s level was populated by energy exchange collisions with He excited by electron collisions to the 2^1S level. Through the use of multiply peaked mirrors, these authors have obtained simultaneous oscillation with a He-Ne maser in the visible region, 6328Å, (3$s_2 \rightarrow$ 2p_4), in the infrared region at 11,523 Å (2$s_2 \rightarrow$ 2p_4) and other infrared transitions (2$s \rightarrow$ 2p) (*255*). By the same technique, they were also able to suppress oscillation on the strong 1.1523μ line originating from the 2s_2 level by virtue of the fact that oscillation on the 3$s_2 \rightarrow$ 2p_4 transition increases the density of atoms in the 2p_4 state and hence reduces the gain on the 2$s_2 \rightarrow$ 2p_4 transition (see Fig. 36). Thus, by suppressing oscillation on the $2s_2 \to 2p_4$ transition sufficient population can be obtained in the $2s_2$ levels to permit weaker transitions to oscillate. This technique has permitted oscillation on other infrared transitions from the $2s_2$ state in close proximity to the dominant $2s_2 \to 2p_4$ transitions, namely the $2s_2 \to 2p_3$ and $2s_2 \to 2p_5$ transitions.

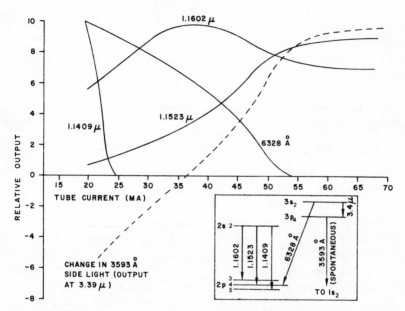

FIG. 36. Relative power output of five simultaneous maser oscillations versus tube current [Rigden and White (255)]. The output at 3.39μ was monitored by measuring the change in the $3p_1 \to 1s_2$ light (3593 Å) from the side of the maser tube. The total change from no oscillation to oscillation in this light can be either negative or positive. The maximum output at each wavelength measured has been arbitrarily set at 10 units.

By introducing a quartz prism as a dispersive element in the resonator, Bloom (253a) suppressed the strong transition ($3s_2 \to 3p_4$) at 3.39μ in order to observe the following weaker transitions: $3s_2 \to 2p_2$ at 6401 Å, $3s_2 \to 2p_5$ at 6293 Å, and $3s_2 \to 2p_6$ at 6118 Å. The prism bends the mode axis by about $42°$ and causes the 3.39μ radiation arising from the $3s_2 \to 3p_4$ transition to miss the mirror (Fig. 37a). Thus oscillation of the very high gain 3.39μ line which originates from the same level as the visible lines is suppressed, and sufficient population can be obtained in the $3s_2$ level to allow the oscillation of the much weaker visible line. However, the dominant visible line at 6328Å resulting from the $3s_2 \rightarrow 2p_4$ transition must also be suppressed to observe the lower gain visible lines originating from the $3s_2$ level. Using the double prism arrangement shown in Fig. 37b, White and Rigden (256a) observed maser oscillation on several $3s_2 \rightarrow 2p$ transitions.

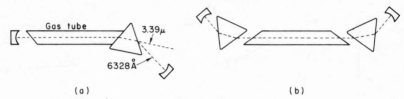

(a)   (b)

Fig. 37. Schematic diagrams of experimental arrangements for suppressing oscillation on a given maser transition by deflecting the unwanted beam with prisms.

3. Zeeman Effects

Zeeman effects in the He-Ne maser arising from the earth's magnetic field parallel to the maser axis has been reported by Statz et al. (273, 274). The $2s_2$ and $2p_4$ states of neon have angular momenta and are split in a magnetic field. As a consequence of this splitting, the maser output contains two circularly polarized radiations of slightly different frequencies. If a polarizer is inserted between the maser and the photodetector, a modulation of the output at about 1050 cycles is observed, a result which indicates that the output of the maser is linearly polarized and that the plane of polarization is rotating at a frequency of 525 cps. In addition to these Zeeman effects, the effect of weak magnetic fields on the modes and polarization of the He-Ne maser has been studied by Culshaw et al. (275).

The broadband magnetic field tuning of optical masers and in particular the 2.026μ line of the He–Xe maser has been discussed by Fork and Patel (277b).

D. GASEOUS OPTICAL MASERS (OTHER THAN He-Ne)

1. Noble Gases

Faust et al. (260) have obtained maser oscillation by the electron excitation of the pure noble gases on a very large number of transitions at wavelengths from about 1 to 35μ (Table I.9). A schematic representation of the first few electron configurations of neon, argon, krypton, and xenon, which are rather similar, are shown in Fig. 38. The ground states in Ne, Ar, Kr, and Xe consist of closed-shell $(np)^6$ configurations in which $n = 2$, 3, 4, and 5, respectively. As indicated by the dashed arrows, the main electronic excitations quite likely occur through strongly allowed transitions of the type

$$e + (np)^6 \rightarrow (np)^5 ms + e,$$
$$e + (np)^6 \rightarrow (np)^5 md + e,$$

where $m = n + 1$, etc. The p levels are not excited because of electric dipole selection rules which allow $p \rightarrow s$, $p \rightarrow d$, but not $p \rightarrow p$. As discussed in Section IX, B, the pressure (few tens of microns) must be adjusted to produce resonance trapping of the s and d states, but low enough to prevent collisional transfer to other electron configurations.

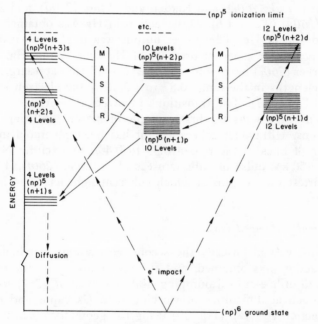

FIG. 38. Schematic indication of the first few electron configurations of neon, $n = 2$; argon, $n = 3$; krypton, $n = 4$, and xenon, $n = 5$. The dominant excitation paths are indicated by arrows [Bennett (13)]. For simplicity excitation of the $(np)^5(n+2)p$ levels and maser transitions to the $(n + 2)s$ levels are not shown. There is a gradual depression of the excited d- and p-shells in respect to the s-shells in going from neon to xenon, and the levels in the s-shells break into widely separated pairs.

The addition of helium to xenon increases the gain of a number of transitions, in particular the 2.026μ line *(276)*. For Xe, as well as Ar and Kr, excitation by collisions with He metastables is not energetically possible. The improvement in gain appears to arise from an increase in electron density *(276a)*.

The unusually high gain of over 50 db / m on the 3.508μ line of Xe has been measured in a He-Xe mixture (277) and in pure Xe (277a). With such high gain, a gas maser can be constructed at 3.058μ with size comparable with solid state masers, but having high spectral purity.

2. *Electron Excitation of Gases Other than the Noble Gases*

Electron excitation of gases is obviously not limited to the noble gases. Optical maser action has recently been reported in Hg* by Paananen *et al.* *(260c)*, and Rigden and White *(260d)*, and in iodine vapor *(260d)* (Table I.6). Maser action in Hg was obtained only on the addition of He. The power output was in the sub-mW range, and it peaked at a partial pressure of He about 2 mm Hg. Mathias and Parker *(260e)* have produced maser oscillation at a large number of wavelengths in the range 0.87 to 1.23μ by the electron excitation of N_2 (Table I.7). The transitions involved are between molecular levels and represents the first example of maser oscillation on such transitions. Ultraviolet coherent light has been generated in a large number of lines in the region 0.33 to 0.40μ by exciting N_2 with a 100 to 150 kV pulse of submicrosecond duration *(260f)*. These are the shortest wavelengths at which coherent light has been produced thus far.

3. *Optically Pumped Gases*

Cesium was historically the second gas system in which optical maser action was obtained, and the first (and so far the only) gas system to utilize optical pumping. Rabinowitz *et al.* *(262)* solved the great practical difficulties in working with Cs vapor and obtained maser action at 7.18μ (Fig. 39) using the geometry illustrated schematically in Fig. 40. The pumping lamp consisted of an electrodeless helium discharge tube placed on one axis of the ellipsoidal reflector. BaF_2 windows were held against each end of the gas cell with approxi-

---

* Maser action has been observed for the first time from ionized atoms, namely Hg^+ in a pulsed Hg-He discharge *(260g)*.

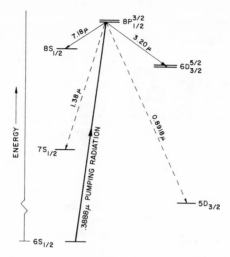

FIG. 39. Energy level diagram of cesium [Rabinowitz and Jacobs (262)]. Oscillation has been obtained at 7.18μ and 3.20μ. The dashed lines indicate transitions which may be made to oscillate.

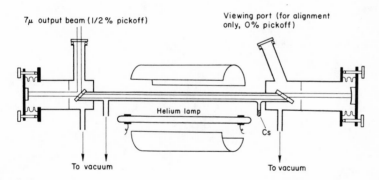

FIG. 40. Experimental arrangement of an optically pumped cw cesium maser [Rabinowitz et al. (261)].

mately optical contact, because no sealant was found sufficiently resistant to cesium attack. The cell was connected to a vacuum system for the continuous removal of foreign gases liberated from hot cesium and glass, which could cause quenching of the excited states of Cs. The outer chambers, containing the reflectors, were also maintained in vacuum to insure a vacuum seal for the cell.

The resonator consisted of a plane and spherical mirror. Detailed measurements of the energy distribution in the dominant mode agreed within several percent with the theoretical values calculated from (6.5a). The power output was about 25 μW per beam. Oscillation has also been obtained at 3.20μ on the $8P_{1/2} \rightarrow 6D_{3/2}$ transition (262). In addition, two other transitions from the $8P_{1/2}$ level at 1.38μ ($8P_{1/2} \rightarrow 7S_{1/2}$) and 0.8919$\mu$ ($8P_{1/2} \rightarrow 5D_{3/2}$) may be made to oscillate; however, these transitions have much higher thresholds.

XI. Semiconductor Masers

A. CONDITION FOR GAIN

Thus far we have considered substances whose energy levels are associated with localized wave functions, in which case the condition for amplification is that there be a population inversion between two atomic energy levels. In semiconductors, where one deals with electronic states represented by Bloch type waves defined over the whole system, the condition for emission, as we shall see, takes a different form.

Electromagnetic absorption in semiconductors is due basically to the following mechanisms (*281b*):

(1) electron transitions from the valence band to the conduction band;

(2) transitions from Landau levels in the valence band to Landau levels in the conduction band, transitions between Landau levels in a given band;

(3) transitions involving impurity levels;

(4) transitions involving exciton states;

(5) intraband transitions by negative mass carriers;

(6) internal band absorption associated with the presence of free carriers; and

(7) absorption by the crystal lattice.

Interband transitions may be of the direct or indirect (phonon assisted) types. Absorption mechanisms (6) and (7) are always dissipative and hinder maser action. Mechanisms (1) to (5) for direct and indirect transitions have been examined theoretically by a number of investigators (*278–281b*) for the possibility of obtaining maser action.

A direct transition, which involves only a photon, may occur when the conduction and valence band extrema are at the same point of the Brillouin zone. However, when this situation does not obtain

155

optical transitions must be accompanied by the emission or absorption of a phonon in order to conserve momentum. Such indirect transitions give rise to a considerably weaker absorption than do direct transitions. However, at low temperatures there will be virtually no phonons present of the type required for the indirect absorption process. It is interesting to note, then, that even the presence of a few excited electrons and holes will constitute a population inversion. However, the transition probability for indirect transitions is much lower than that for direct transitions since the former is a second order process.

Lax (281) has considered the possibility of a cyclotron resonance maser, mechanism (2). Basov et al. (281a) have discussed among other possibilities the idea of using negative mass effects, mechanism (5). Dumke (280) has presented the criteria for emission using mechanisms (1), (3), and (4) in a way which allows the most direct use of optical absorption data. However, Bernard (278) has treated the emission criteria for different possibilities in the following unified way.

If the crystal is not in thermal equilibrium, the occupation of any state of the conduction band is given by

$$f_c = \frac{1}{1 + \exp[E(k_j) - F_c]/kT} , \qquad (11.1)$$

where k is Boltzmann's constant, k_j is the wave number, and F_c is the quasi-Fermi level (282), which replaces F_0, the Fermi level or chemical potential for electrons. In the same way a quasi-Fermi level F_v for the holes of the valence band may be defined. At thermal equilibrium $F_0 = F_v = F_c$. Now a state $E_v(k_i)$ of the valence band is in general connected to a state $E_c(k_j)$ of the conduction band by a direct radiative process. In the presence of a radiation field the number of quanta absorbed per unit time, J_a, is

$$J_a = K\Gamma^i_{vc} f_v(k_i) [1 - f_c(k_j)], \qquad (11.2)$$

and the number emitted per unit time, J_e, is

$$J_e = K\Gamma^i_{cv}[1 - f_v(k_i)] f_c(k_j), \qquad (11.3)$$

where K includes the densities of states of the valence and conduction band. From the condition for amplification, $J_e > J_a$, and

$$E_v(k_i) - E_c(k_j) = h\nu,$$

it follows that the condition for stimulated emission is simply

$$\Delta F > h\nu, \qquad (11.4)$$

where ΔF is the difference of the quasi-Fermi levels of the conduction and valence bands, and ν is the emitted frequency. Equation (11.4) is to be compared with (2.10), which applies for systems obeying Boltzmann statistics. The concept of a quasi-Fermi level for a group of states is valid if the electrons of the group exchange energy with a heat reservoir in a time short compared with the time necessary for the electrons to return to equilibrium by transitions between states of the different groups. Once the energy of the quasi-Fermi level is known, the occupation of any state of the valence or conduction band for some nonequilibrium situation is obtained from the Fermi-Dirac distribution function by using the quasi-Fermi energy instead of the Fermi energy, which is appropriate at equilibrium. Condition (11.4) is shown to hold for indirect transitions and for transitions between the conduction band and a given impurity level for which the quasi-Fermi energy is defined.

B. CURRENT INJECTION IN p-n DIODES

Semiconductors have the interesting feature that it is possible to excite electrons with an external electric field by current injection or by ionization as well as by optical pumping. Basov et al. (281a) have considered the possibility of obtaining nonequilibrium carrier distributions by pulsed electric fields strong enough to ionize the valence band. Lax (281) has proposed optical excitation for a cyclotron resonance maser using nonequally spaced Landau levels. However, comparatively short relaxation times of carriers in these levels make it difficult to create states of negative temperature, and for this reason, the use of an optical maser as a pumping source was suggested.

As it happened, it was with forward biased semiconductor diodes rather than bulk semiconductors that stimulated emission was obtained. The feasibility of a semiconductor injection maser* was made apparent by the discovery that GaAs p-n junctions have a

---

* Evidently the p-n junction injection maser was anticipated by von Neumann (283).

very high efficiency for radiative recombination (*284*, *285*), i.e., that for every electron crossing the junction, nearly one photon is emitted. Furthermore, it was shown theoretically, that in a direct band gap semiconductor such as GaAs, the induced transition probability is sufficient to overcome losses that are due to free carrier absorption (*280*).

Figure 41 illustrates schematically how an emissive condition may be obtained in a forward biased diode which is highly doped to degeneracy (*285a*). The application of the forward bias lowers the bands on the *p*-side relative to those on the *n*-side, and the injected

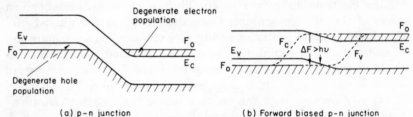

(a) p−n junction   (b) Forward biased p−n junction

FIG. 41. Schematic energy band diagram of a degenerate *p-n* junction at zero bias (*a*), and with forward bias (*b*). E_c and E_v are the energies of the conduction and valence band, respectively. F_0 is the Fermi level. F_c and F_v are, respectively, the quasi-Fermi levels of the conduction and valence band. The junction is emissive in the region where the condition $\Delta F > h\nu$ applies.

electrons and holes overlap in the normally neutral depletion layer of the junction. The condition $\Delta F > h\nu$ for stimulated emission is satisfied by a direct transition from the low-lying levels of the conduction to the uppermost levels valence band. In the specific case of the GaAs diode, evidence has been presented to indicate that the emission is due to recombination involving an acceptor level as the terminal state (*286*, *287a*), but this question does not appear to be definitely settled. Among other probable electron transitions for the recombination radiation are those involving donor (*287b*) and exciton states (*287c*).

Equation (11.4) states the condition for stimulated emission, but not oscillation. To obtain the latter, one must compute the negative absorption, or gain per unit length. Now in the injection semiconductor maser excitation is by the flow of an electric current across a *p-n* junction, which results in the emission of light in a thin layer adjacent to the junction. The total number of quanta spontaneously emitted per unit time per unit volume is $j\eta/ed$, where j is the current density in the device, η is the quantum efficiency (average number of radiation quanta per injected carrier), e is the charge on the electron, and d is the penetration depth of the field (Fig. 42). With this result, the negative absorption is immediately obtained from (2.32). Equating this absorption to the various losses in the system, we obtain the expression for threshold current density in the form given by Yariv (285b) and Lasher (285c),

$$j = \frac{8\pi e d \Delta \nu}{\eta \xi \lambda^2} \left(k + \frac{\ln R^{-1}}{D} \right). \tag{11.5}$$

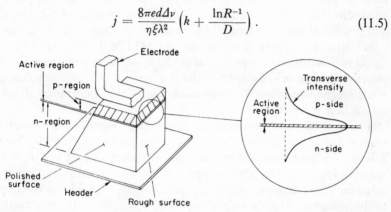

FIG. 42. Schematic drawing of a Fabry-Perot, p-n junction diode [after Fenner and Kingsley (297d)]. Diode dimensions are 300–500μ; the p-region is 25–200μ; the active region is of the order 1μ. The inset schematically shows the transverse intensity distribution of the radiation propagating along the active region.

Here $\Delta \nu$ is an effective line width defined by $\Delta \nu S(\nu_a) = \int S(\nu)\, d\nu = 1$, R is the power reflection coefficient, k is the absorption coefficient due to the bulk losses in the n and p regions, and λ is the wavelength in the medium. The evaluation of the penetration depth d is considered in the following section. The factor $\xi(\sim 1)$ is equal to $(1-N_1/N_2)$ (with $g_1 = g_2$), where N_2 is the total number of carriers which are present prior to recombination at the junction. The number of carriers which had just undergone a recombination transition is taken as N_1. An important parameter in (11.5) is the quantum efficiency, η. This quantity has been measured for GaAs injection masers and found to be 0.7 at liquid N_2 temperature (286b).

A complicated expression for j has been given (286a) in which k does not explicitly appear but the effect of absorptive transitions on the inversion has been evaluated.

C. Confinement of Radiation in p-n Junctions

The electromagnetic structure consists of a narrow region of negative absorption at or right near the junction plane of the diode, surrounded on either side by the p and n regions which contain free holes and electrons, respectively. The estimated width of 1μ for the active region is considerably greater than the width of the depletion layer or junction which is about 0.1μ. The maser action apparently occurs in TE or TM modes confined to the vicinity of the junction and guided along the plane of the junction like the surface waves on a dielectric slab (295c). Since as shown by (11.5) the threshold current density, j, is directly proportional to the distance of penetration of the electromagnetic field away from the junction, d, the dielectric confinement mechanism plays an important role in the occurrence of maser action in p-n junctions.

Theoretical considerations of the propagation of electromagnetic energy near a p-n junction show that the sandwich formed by having a depletion layer bounded by the p and n regions can act as a dielectric waveguide (294, 295, 295a). For a junction thickness of the order 0.1μ, the penetration depth of the electromagnetic field was calculated to be roughly 45μ, which compared favorably with observations which yielded 30μ–50μ for GaAs diodes, and moreover showed that the field extended more or less equally into the n and p regions as indicated in Fig. 42 (295).

It has been proposed that the dielectric discontinuity responsible for the confinement may be due to the dispersion accompanying the resonant recombination transitions in the active layer rather than the polarizability of the free carriers in the p and n regions (293). This assumption leads to an expression for the threshold current density (295d) which is

$$j_r = \frac{2.48e(2\pi/\lambda)^{3/2}\Delta\nu}{\pi\eta}(k + D^{-1}\ln R^{-1})^{1/2},$$

where $\Delta\nu$ is defined as in (11.5). Now the penetration depth for the resonant recombination mechanism, d_r (295b), is approximately $d_r \simeq 2(2\pi/\lambda k)^{-1/2}$, where it was assumed that the emission line shape is Lorentzian. By a slight generalization of the argument leading to this result, we have

$$d_r \simeq 2(2\pi/\lambda)^{-1/2}(k + D^{-1}\ln R^{-1})^{-1/2}.$$

Substituting this in (11.5), we obtain, apart from a numerical constant of the order of unity, the expression for j_r given above.

Typical values of k (presumably at liquid N_2 temperatures) and $D^{-1} \ln R^{-1}$ for GaAs diodes are $\sim 30 \text{ cm}^{-1}$, which lead to $d_r \sim 5\mu$ for $\lambda = 8.4 \times 10^{-5}$ cm and $n = 3.6$. However, direct experimental proof as to the origin of the dielectric discontinuity is still lacking.

D. THE GaAs DIODE INJECTION MASER

1. General Characteristics

Stimulated emission was observed by Hall et al. (287), Nathan et al. (288), and Quist et al. (289) from a gallium arsenide p-n junction excited by current pulses with a duration of 0.1 to 10 μsec.* The diode is schematically illustrated in Fig. 42. The conclusion that the radiation peaked at 8420 Å was stimulated emission was based upon the following evidence: the sharply beamed radiation pattern of the emitted light, the observation of a threshold current beyond which the intensity of the beam abruptly increased, and upon the well-defined narrowing beyond threshold of the spectral distribution of the beam. Stimulated emission at 7100 Å from Ga$(As_{1-x}P_x)$ junctions immersed in liquid nitrogen and subjected to short pulses of current has also been observed (290). The results in this system show that a p-n junction maser can be selected in the wavelength range from about 6400 Å (290d) to 8400 Å by varying the As and P concentrations. The characteristics of the GaAs maser and other p-n junction masers are summarized in Table I.10.

The requirements for maser action and the way in which they are satisfied are as follows:

(1) The electron and hole populations within the junction must be large enough that their quasi-Fermi levels are separated by an energy greater than that of the radiation. This condition is satisfied by the injection of a sufficient number of carriers from the degenerate n- and p-type regions into the transition region.

(2) The region of negative absorption is very thin and the stimulated radiation extends into the surrounding absorbing

---

* Spectral narrowing of the recombination radiation from GaAs p-n junctions at high current densities was evidently first reported by Nasledov et al. (286c).

layer. However, maser action is favored by the large matrix element for interband radiative recombination compared to that for free carrier absorption in GaAs, and by the fact that the wavelength of the emitted radiation is slightly longer than that of the absorption threshold of the degenerate material bounding the junction.

(3) The active material must be contained within a suitable resonator to build up the energy density at the wavelength of the stimulated radiation.

As an example of the initial performance characteristics of the GaAs maser, we quote from the work of Quist et al. (289). At 77°K the radiation was spontaneously emitted in the usual fashion until the current reached a threshold value of about 90 amp, approximately 10^4 amp/cm^2, above which the light radiated from the end increased drastically. At 4.2°K, the threshold was lowered by a factor of 15 to approximately 6 amp or about 700 amp/cm^2. At 77°K the emission line narrowed from about 175 to 30 Å above threshold, whereas at 4.2°K the line narrowed still further from about 100Å to less than 5Å.

Burns et al. (291) found that very clear indications of maser action were obtained from rectangular parallelepipeds whose typical dimensions were 5×10^{-3} by 50×10^{-3} inch. It was not necessary to coat the small face of the specimen with any reflecting surface since the high index of refraction of GaAs will cause 35% reflection of the 8400 Å emission. As the injection current was increased above 8 amp, the emitted radiation parallel to the long axis became highly collimated. Slightly above threshold, the coherent light intensity increased by a factor of more than 12 for a current change of 0.1 amp. In the junction plane the width of the cone of emitted light was 2.5°, whereas perpendicular to the junction plane the width was twice as large. At higher injection currents the radiation pattern became more complicated. The total light output was linear with current, even though there was strong directionality effects and line narrowing. Using the known geometry of the sample, it was possible to obtain some correlation of the directions of intensity peaks with certain simple standing electromagnetic waves in the structure (292).

Stimulated emission has been observed in GaAs junctions at room temperature, 25°C (296). Emission from some of these diodes has been observed to narrow to as little as 1.5 Å. The threshold for stimulated emission in good units was approximately ten times larger at room temperature than at 77°K. The duration of the injection pulse was 60×10^{-9} sec.

It has been found that the threshold current density increases from a plateau of 80 amp/cm² below 20°K to about 10^5 amp/cm² at 300°K (*297a*). The increase in threshold is attributed partly to increased absorption by the free carriers and holes on either side of the active region, and also by the reduced effectiveness of stimulated emission due to the competing process of reabsorption as empty states are created in the initial and terminal levels at higher temperatures.

Continuous stimulated emission was achieved at an injection current density of 70 amp/cm², with the diode immersed in liquid helium II at temperatures between 1.95 and 2.0°K (*297*). When the current was raised to 160 amp/cm², stimulated emission disappeared due to crystal heating. Continuous maser action has also been observed at 77°K (*289a, 297a*).

Continuous operation has produced 1.5 watts at an over-all efficiency of 30 % from electrical input to coherent radiation output (*297h*). Under pulsed conditions, peak power in excess of 100 watts has been reported with an average power of 1 watt (*281b*).

2. *Frequency Shifts Due to Temperature and Pressure*

The frequency shift with temperature of the broad emission line which gives rise to the stimulated emission follows the band gap, and is about 2.5 Å/degree at room temperature and 1 Å/degree at 77°K (*297b*). However the individual stimulated emission lines were observed to shift at a rate 0.4 Å/degree less than the band gap. Thus as one lowers the temperature new modes are observed to appear at shorter wavelengths replacing the ones at longer wavelengths. Some modes, however, persisted as the temperature was changed.

Hydrostatic pressure studies were made on diodes at 77°K whose emission line width at threshold was less than 0.2 Å and even as low as 0.05 Å (*297c*). All of the well resolved modes shifted identically to higher energy with increasing pressure at a rate of 3.5×10^{-6} ev/kg/cm² (-0.0020 Å/kg/cm²). The dominant effect in changing the oscillation frequency was the change in refractive index and hence optical cavity length with pressure. The wavelength of the spontaneous recombination radiation itself decreased with increasing pressure at a rate 12×10^{-6} ev/kg/cm², more than three times greater than the modes. It is therefore evident that the frequencies of individual modes begin to lag behind the spontaneous emission, causing the intensity of the radiation in the modes to decrease to the point where the modes drop below threshold and new modes appear. Such mode shifting and jumping is analogous to the behavior of the stimulated emission with temperature. Detailed studies have been made of the effect of hydrostatic pressure on the frequency of the coherent and incoherent emission of GaAs junction masers operating at 200°K (297k) and room temperature (297i). Frequency tuning by the application of a uniaxial stress and its effect on the threshold current has been investigated (297j, 297l).

3. Characteristics of the Emitted Radiation

The emission characteristics of a GaAs diode at 77°K with front and back surfaces polished flat and parallel and side surfaces tapered and roughened to inhibit modes which involve their reflection have been studied (297e). The diode was roughly a cube with dimensions of the order 0.3 to 0.5 mm on edge and the current was applied in pulses from 1 to 50 μsec long, at repetition rates of one to several thousand per second. As the current was increased from 10 to 34 amp, the width of the emission decreased from 120 to 22 Å (the junction area was 2×10^{-3} cm²). This type of spectral narrowing is often called super-radiance, and, as explained in Section IV, C, 1, can occur when the resonator is lossy and has poor mode discrimination. Although stimulated emission is occurring, the feedback is too low for the system to oscillate. As the current was increased from 34 to 36 amp, the diode broke into oscillation as manifested by an emission peak about 0.5 Å wide. Other narrow but weaker emission peaks, the axial modes of the resonator, appeared on either side of the main emission line at higher values of the current. With diodes optically flat on all four sides the threshold was lower than with only two sides optically flat. In the latter case there was very little spectral narrowing below threshold as shown in Fig. 43 (297b). It may be noticed that the sharp spike tends to appear on the long wavelength side of the broad base. Well above threshold other sharp lines, i.e., axial modes, were observed. Above threshold the spontaneous radiation did not saturate but increased linearly with pumping although at a slower rate than below threshold (Fig. 43). The lack of saturation of the spontaneous radiation above threshold has been observed in other solid state masers.

The separation between adjacent modes, $\Delta\lambda$, when $dn/d\lambda_0$ cannot be neglected is given by

$$\Delta\lambda = \frac{\lambda_0^2}{D} \frac{1}{2[n - \lambda_0(dn/d\lambda_0)]}, \qquad (11.6)$$

where λ_0 is the wavelength in free space. The quantity $(n - \lambda_0 \, dn/d\lambda)$ varies rapidly with λ_0 in GaAs diodes because λ_0 is very close to the direct absorption edge (297g). Approximate agreement with (11.6) has been obtained (297a).

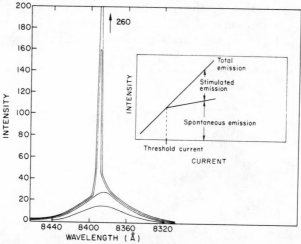

FIG. 43. Emission at 77°K from a GaAs diode at 0.6, 1, 1.2, and 1.4 amp. The diode had all four sides polished and perpendicular to the plane of the junction. The stimulated emission line is less than 0.5 Å [Burns and Nathan (297b)]. The inset shows schematically the intensity of the stimulated and spontaneous emission versus the injection current. [With the Fabry-Perot geometry the total emission increases strikingly as the current is increased beyond the threshold value (286b).]

Equally spaced lines far below threshold for single mode operation, due presumably to the excitation of the axial modes by spontaneous emission, has been observed by Sorokin et al. (297f) and Nathan et al. (297g) with a cw GaAs maser. This unusual behavior is shown in Fig. 44. The diodes that were studied had cleaved ends, and sawed sides to eliminate unwanted modes. The shift of the emission peak to shorter wavelengths was not explained. However, the narrowing of the emission band below threshold, i.e., before the appearance of a single spike, is characteristic of diodes with cleaved ends and sawed sides (277e).

The spatial distribution of radiation from GaAs masers has been studied by Fenner and Kingsley (*297d*). In order that the emission pattern at one mode of oscillation might be studied, the emitted radiation was passed through a monochrometer with a spectral resolution of better than 1 Å. The diodes had Fabry-Perot resonators formed by polishing two sides parallel to each other and perpendicular to the junction. The current pulses used to excite the diode were from 0.1 to 1.0 μsec long at repetition rates of 100 to 1000 pps. When the diode oscillated, there was a dramatic narrowing in the angular distribution of the radiation from the junction. Typical results above threshold of the radiation patterns in the horizontal (plane of the junction) and vertical planes, Figs. 45 and 46, respectively,

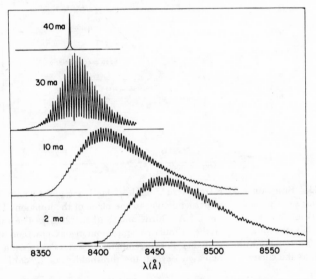

FIG. 44. Spectrum of a continuously running GaAs diode maser at 2°K [Nathan *et al.* (*297g*)]. The gain is reduced between each current. The diode had the Fabry-Perot configuration, namely, cleaved ends and sawed sides.

show that the radiation is emitted in many beams, even at a particular wavelength. For comparison one of the most ideal patterns that were obtained are also shown in Figs. 45 and 46. The highly structured pattern suggests that the radiating surfaces are illuminated with an intensity and phase that varies periodically along the junction. This may be due to the fact that the reflecting faces are not perfectly

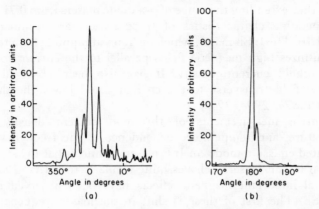

Fig. 45. Radiation patterns of a GaAs diode maser in the horizontal plane: (*a*) a typical pattern; (*b*) one of the most ideal patterns [Fenner and Kingsley (*297d*)].

parallel (*88*). The typical beam width in the vertical plane is about 10° and in the horizontal plane several degrees. These results are correlated with a field distribution extending about 5μ high by 50μ wide. The value 5μ is roughly consistent with estimates of the penetration depth of the field.

E. *p-n* DIODE MASERS (OTHER THAN GaAs)

Maser action has been observed in InAs at 3.1μ by Melngailis (*290a*), InP at 0.91μ by Weiser and Levitt (*290b*), In$_x$Ga$_{1-x}$As at 1.77 and 2.07μ by Melngailis *et al.* (*290c*), and InSb at 5.2μ by Phelan *et al.*

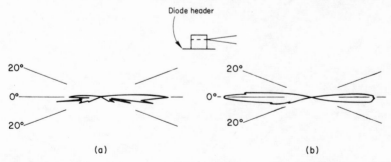

Fig. 46. Radiation patterns of a GaAs diode maser in the vertical plane: (*a*) a typical pattern; (*b*) a nearly ideal pattern [Fenner and Kingsley (*297d*)].

(*290f*), thus extending the range of *p-n* diode masers from 0.71 to 5.2μ. The operating characteristics of these masers are summarized in Table I.10. The InSb maser, which operates at liquid helium temperatures, utilizes high magnetic fields parallel to the current to reduce the threshold current density. It has also been observed that a magnetic field transverse to the current could lower the threshold current (*287b, 290c, 290e*).

Extensive measurements of threshold current density versus temperature, and temperature dependence of the frequency of the stimulated emission modes of InP masers confirm that the stimulated emission in InP masers behaves quite similarly to GaAs (*290g*).

Several important magnetic effects have been observed in InAs and InSb. The first of these is shift in the maser frequency which can be explained by the shift of the energy gap with magnetic field. Thus, as the field is increased the excitation is transferred from one axial mode to the adjacent mode at a shorter wavelength. In addition the frequency of each mode is shifted to shorter wavelengths with increasing magnetic field. This can be explained by the effect of the magnetic field on the dielectric properties of the semiconductor at photon energies close to the energy gap. Another effect which has already been mentioned is the lowering of the threshold current density. The reasons for this are discussed by Lax (*295d*).

XII. Output Radiation Characteristics
of Optical Masers

A. Introduction

It is clear from the previous chapters that an enormous variety of effects are possible in optical masers whose behavior depends on the method of population inversion and details of the pumping arrangements, spectral properties of the active substance, its freedom from imperfections in the case of solids, the resonator design, the amplitude of the pumping power, the operating temperature, and the control of the regeneration process. Many of these questions have been discussed in previous chapters. This chapter deals with studies of the characteristics of the stimulated radiation of gaseous and solid state optical masers. Because of the special features of p-n diode masers, its radiation characteristics are discussed elsewhere (Chap. XI). Sections XIII,B to XIII,D deal with the spectral characteristics of optical masers, and the important subject of coherence. Sections XIII,E to XIII,H are concerned essentially with mode studies, and relaxation oscillations in solid state masers.

B. Methods of Measuring the Characteristics of Maser Radiation

1. *Power and Energy*

The output power of optical masers may be estimated by using neutral density filters as attenuators, and phototubes or other photodetectors whose output is proportional to the incident power (*150*). The phototubes may be calibrated in terms of thermopiles which are calibrated with an NBS standard lamp. The total energy incident upon the phototube is obtained by a time integration of its output. A simple procedure for calibrating the filter at the maser wavelength is described in (*298*). The measurement of power output using the photodetector is especially suited for the small power levels obtained at threshold.

At higher power levels, a wide band and easily calibrated calorimeter has been constructed by Li and Sims (*299*). The device consists essentially of several thermistor beads connected in a bridge and placed in intimate contact with a carbon cone into which the maser beam is directed. The response of the calorimeter is almost linear; the sensitivity is 50 mv per joule. A similar device has been constructed which uses as a blackbody a cone painted black and a platinum bolometer embedded in this cone to measure its temperature rise (*300*). The minimum energy that can be determined is 10^{-2} joules. A method for calibrating the output of a ruby maser has been devised which uses a diffuse reflector and controls the distance of the reflector to the filters and photocell so that the intensity of the maser radiation stays within their linear range (*300a*). A liquid calorimeter for high energy masers (*301*) has been constructed using water dyed with ink to an absorptivity of 80% per cm. Maser energies greater than a few tenths of a joule were easily measured, although operation of this calorimeter up to 50 joules should be possible. A method for measuring optical maser output by light pressure has been experimentally explored (*302*). Although not sufficiently sensitive for low energy pulses and current cw masers, this method is suggested by the authors as offering a good means of handling the extremely high energies that are certain to be produced in the future.

2. *Spectral Distribution*

a. *Heterodyne and Homodyne Detection.*   To investigate the spectral distribution of radiation in the maser beam, an instrument of extremely high resolving power is needed because of the tremendous narrowing of the natural fluorescent line width by the feedback process. A resolution of 0.02 cm^{-1} can be realized with a 40-ft grating spectrograph using a 10-in. Harrison and Stroke grating. Enormously greater resolution, about 4×10^{-5} cm^{-1} at 10^4 cm^{-1}, has been obtained with a Fabry-Perot interferometer designed to scan the output of optical masers (*302a*). However, instead of using the methods of physical optics to investigate spectral distributions, one may use those of electronics. This was first demonstrated by Forrester, Gudmundsen, and Johnson (*303*) who obtained beats in the microwave region between incoherent light sources by mixing Zeeman components of a visible line at a photosurface. The use of the photo-electric effect for nonlinear detection of light was also demonstrated by the experiment of Brown and Twiss (304), in which the existence of correlations between intensity fluctuations in partially coherent beams of light was first established. What was observed in both experiments was fluctuations in the photoelectric current which may be interpreted as beats between frequency components of the electro-magnetic field.

The following distinction between detection and mixing may be made. Detection refers to the heterodyning of the components of a signal with itself, i.e., homodyning, and yields a frequency distribution around zero frequency. Mixing refers to the heterodyning of two different signals and yields a frequency distribution about the difference frequency.

The spectral character of the current obtained by photodetection and mixing has been discussed by Forrester (305); however, some aspects of this paper have been criticized (see Smith and Williams, 306). In the case of homodyne detection, a direct analytical procedure for deriving the spectrum of the optical radiation from the spectrum of the photoelectric current has not yet been developed. However, it is stated that within a factor of 2 the width of the frequency spectrum of the photoelectric current yields the width of the optical spectrum (305). On the other hand, with superheterodyne detection, the output frequency distribution identically mirrors the input frequency distribution.

The output signal to noise ratio, SNR, which is obtainable through photoelectric mixing and detection, has been discussed by Forrester (305) and by Oliver (307). The SNR of the photoelectric detector is, in the limit of very large local oscillator signal compared with the incoming signal (307),

$$\frac{S}{N} = \frac{\eta \langle P_s \rangle}{h\nu B}, \tag{12.1}$$

where η is the quantum efficiency of the photocell, $\langle P_s \rangle$ is the average power input, and B is the bandwidth of the circuit following the mixer. In the limit that $h\nu \gg kT$, the SNR of an ideal amplifier with bandpass B is $\langle P_s \rangle / h\nu B$. Thus if the quantum efficiency were unity, the photoelectric heterodyne converter would have the same SNR as the ideal amplifier. The SNR of the homodyne converter is essentially the same as (12.1); see, however, Haus and Townes (308) and Oliver (*309*). In any case, with input and local oscillator signals from masers, the bandwidth B can be made so small that enormous signal to noise ratios can be realized.

The role of the phase of the incoming wave and the possibility of making phase measurements on the amplified wave has been considered (*308, 309*). Although this matter will not be pursued here, the following comments may be of interest. When amplifier-noise theory is carried to the point of considering signals with only a few quanta, it is usually important to consider the principle of complimentarity (*310*). This states that the phase and energy in an electromagnetic wave can never be determined simultaneously with a precision greater than allowed by the relation

$$\varDelta\phi\varDelta n \geqslant \tfrac{1}{2}, \tag{12.2}$$

where $\varDelta\phi$ is the rms uncertainty in the phase of the wave and $\varDelta n$ is the rms uncertainty in the number of quanta which it contains. If one were willing to sacrifice all information about phase so that $\varDelta\phi$ becomes very large, then $\varDelta n$ may approach zero. This is the case for the perfect photon counter ($\eta = 1$) which, in principle, counts individual photons with no background noise at all.

As an example of heterodyne detection, consider the investigation of the spectral output of the He-Ne maser (*94, 311*). The beams of two masers were intercepted by the photocathode of a 7102 photomultiplier tube whose output was displayed on a conventional radio frequency spectrum analyzer as shown in Fig. 47. The beams must

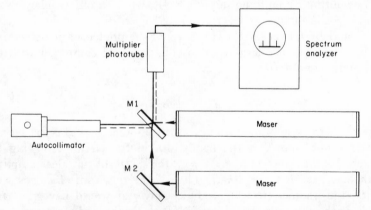

Fig. 47. Experimental arrangement for heterodyning the radiation from two masers [Javan *et al.* (*311*)]: M_1 half-silvered mirror; M_2 full-silvered mirror.

be aligned well enough so that over the area of the photosurface their wavefronts diverge by an amount small compared with the wavelength. In addition, the directions of polarization of the two beams must be parallel. With such an arrangement it has been observed that the variation in beat frequency (due to microphonics) between two He-Ne masers is 10^5cps (*311*). Clearly, the application of radio techniques to optics makes possible a detailed study of maser frequency and line shape that would not be practical or possible with the methods of optical interferometry.

Homodyne as well as heterodyne detection is illustrated in Fig. 48. The signals at 148 and 296 Mc are due to the heterodyning of axial modes, while those separated from these frequencies by 1.3 Mc involve an off-axial mode. The signal at zero frequency is due to the mixing of the frequency components contained within the linewidth of a given oscillating mode.

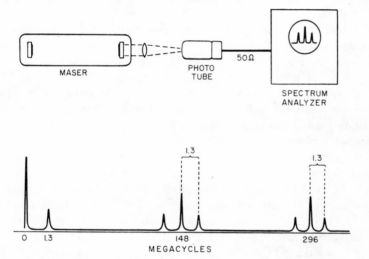

FIG. 48. Heterodyne signals between different oscillating modes of the He-Ne maser [Herriott (*94*)].

b. *Photomixing in the Microwave Region.* To observe microwave signals produced by photomixing, McMurty and Siegman (*312, 313*) used a standard *S*-band traveling-wave tube upon whose oxide cathode the output of a ruby maser was focused. The maser output was found to consist of simultaneous, discrete optical components separated by 600 Mc which corresponded to the interval between axial modes in a 12.5 cm ruby rod. The optical frequencies heterodyne on the cathode, and the resultant signal was amplified by the travelling wave tube. The output of the tube may be detected either with video or super-heterodyne microwave receivers. Some results of photomixing in the S-band region with an experimental image tube has been reported (314).

A high gain microwave tube devised by Gaddy and Holshouser (315) was used by them to detect microwave modulated light (316) by suitably locating a photoemissive surface within the tube. The operation of this tube requires that it be driven by a microwave field. By choosing the driving frequency higher than the microwave modulation frequency, the photomultiplier output current is modulated at the difference frequency, thus providing superheterodyne detection.

Simpler microwave phototubes than those mentioned in the preceding paragraphs have been devised (316a–316c). However, these tubes do not amplify the photocurrent and are consequently limited to studying the output from high power masers.

In the demodulation of a frequency modulated signal, a discriminator is used to change the frequency modulation into an amplitude modulation. Harris and Siegman (317) have proposed a microwave discriminator phototube for demodulating frequency-modulated light by converting such light into space modulated light via an optical dispersing element such as a Fabry-Perot etalon. This space modulated light is then incident on a photocathode where it is the source of transverse electron beam waves.

Microwave photomixing has been observed with PIN-junction photodiodes (318–321) and in bulk semiconductors (322, 322a).* Although compact and simple, these photodiodes do not have the advantage of the internal amplification of the traveling wave photo-tubes. However, by using a photodiode in a parametric amplifier arrangement, amplification of the microwave signals resulting from the photomixing of a ruby maser output has been observed (323). A simple approach has been presented to the problem of the performance of semiconductors as detectors of optical signals (324).

Before leaving the subject of photomixing, let us consider the frequency limitation on the process discussed by Bernard (325). Apart from instrumental difficulties, a fundamental limitation is the time lag τ of the photoelectric process. If beats are to be observed

---

* Microwave photomixing has also been obtained with point contact germanium diodes (322b).

between two frequencies ω_1 and ω_2, then clearly $\tau(\omega_1 - \omega_2) < 1$. On the quantum level, if a quantum $\hbar\omega_1$ or $\hbar\omega_2$ is transferred from a radiation field to matter in the time τ, then the uncertainty principle requires that $\hbar\Delta\omega_1 \geqslant \hbar/\tau$. If $\Delta\omega_1$ (or $\Delta\omega_2$) is greater than $\omega_1 - \omega_2$, then it is not possible to tell which photon is absorbed and modulation should result. A general proof has been given that τ has to be interpreted as the correlation time of the electron-phonon interaction(*325a*). In particular this time would appear to be the electron collision time, which in a metal at room temperature is of the order 2×10^{-14} sec.

In the case of the *PIN* photodiode, for example, it appears that the transit time of the photon excited carriers will limit the response to modulation frequencies up to 50 or perhaps 100 kMc (*319*).

c. *High Speed Photography.* In the microwave region the electromagnetic field must be probed point by point in order to obtain a picture of the field distribution. In the optical region field distributions can be studied by photographic techniques, although no knowledge of phase can be obtained this way. Much use has been made of photography to study beam and mode patterns, and to observe their transient behavior, high speed photography has been employed (*326, 327, 328*). The sequence of phenomena occurring when a ruby maser is flashed was studied on a microsecond time scale (*326*) by means of a high-speed framing camera taking about 5×10^5 frames/sec (*329*). It was found, for example, that each oscillation pulse showed a grainy or flocculated distribution of light across the face of the crystal, and that this distribution changed in fine detail from frame to frame. Another investigation using a high speed camera (*330*) to observe the radiation from a ruby maser reported that in a particular ruby the emission was time coincident over most of the crystal but that there were unexplained periodic intensity variations of about 40 Mc during a spike of the emitted lights (*328*).

C. Spectral Width of an Oscillating Maser Mode

An important characteristic of optical masers is the sharpness of the spectral output. It is well known that masers oscillate in more than one mode and consequently exhibit a number of sharp spectral components. However, we are concerned here with the width of a single component arising from oscillation in a given mode. An ideal maser utilizing a transition which is homogeneously broadened would oscillate in a single mode with a spectral width given by (4.20). For $P = 1$ mW and $\Delta v_c \sim 0.2$ Mc, values appropriate for gas masers in general and the He-Ne maser in particular, this equation yields at 1μ, $\Delta v_{os} \sim 10^{-3}$ cps. Since the oscillation frequency is determined to the first order by the length of the interferometer, it would be necessary to hold the length stable to 3 parts in 10^{17} over a period of 10^3 sec to obtain this degree of spectral purity. It is obvious then that the actual spectral purity obtained in a practical maser is many orders of magnitude worse due to mechanical variations, thermal drift, and variations in mode pulling effects. To minimize the effect of such variations Javan et al. (311) heterodyned the frequency of two modes in the same maser and found the spectral width to be less than 2 cps over a period of a few seconds.

The most recent report of the stability of the He-Ne maser (311a). stated that fluctuations in the beat frequency between two masers has an rms width of 30 cps over a period of a few tens of milliseconds. This corresponds to a frequency fluctuation in one maser of 8×10^{-14}. The frequency resettability was at least as good as 1×10^{-9}. These results were obtained by performing the experiment in a cellar room of an isolated building where noises and ground tremors were very small, and by supporting the masers on a massive shock-mounted table with resonant frequencies of many seconds.

In the ruby maser, it was found from the photomixing of several modes of oscillation that the spectral width of the microwave difference frequency was about 2 Mc (313). This width, however, appeared to be set by the $\frac{1}{2}$ sec duration of the modulation spikes that characterize the output of ruby masers. As will be illustrated by the following examples, this is by far the smallest spectral width for an oscillating mode reported for a solid state maser. In the continuous $CaWO_4 : Nd^{3+}$ maser operated at 85°K, the output showed a single line 0.2 cm^{-1} wide, a reduction of the natural fluorescence line width by a factor of only 30 (158a). In the continuous GaAs maser operated at 77°K, a line width at threshold as low as 0.05 Å has been reported, a reduction in the width of the fluorescent line by a factor of 2000 (297c).

D. COHERENCE

1. The Concept of Coherence

Once the spectral width $\Delta \omega$ of a radiation field is known, one may approximately define a characteristic time called the coherence time by $\Delta\tau \simeq \Delta\omega^{-1}$. This time is the interval in which the change of the relative phase of any two Fourier components is much less than 2π, and the addition of such components represents a disturbance which in this time interval behaves like a monochromatic wave with the mean frequency. The need for caution in using this relation between spectral width and coherence time is obvious when the radiation consists of a number of sharp spectral components each with its own width (331). There is also the concept of a region of coherence around any point in a wave field, or the correlation in phase between two points. The coherence length may be defined by $c\Delta\tau = c/\Delta\omega$, where the same precaution applies as for the relation between coherence time and spectral width.

The coherence properties of light may be defined in a precise way by the correlation function of the complex amplitude of the field at two different points in space, where the field at one point is considered at a time τ later than the other, viz. (330a),

$$C_{12}(\tau) = \lim_{T \to \infty} \frac{1}{2T} \int_{-T}^{+T} E_1(\mathbf{r}, t)\, E_2^*(\mathbf{r} + \Delta\mathbf{r}, t + \tau)\, dt . \tag{12.3}$$

The vector $\mathbf{r}$ specifies the point at which E_1 is taken, and $\Delta\mathbf{r}$ is the vector displacement from E_1 which specifies the point at which E_2 is taken. When $\Delta\mathbf{r} = 0$, (12.3) becomes the self-correlation function $C_{11}(\tau)$, which describes the coherence properties of light at a given point in space, but at different instants of time. The coherence time $\Delta\tau$ may be defined by

$$(\Delta\tau)^2 = \frac{\displaystyle\int_{-\infty}^{\infty} \tau^2 C_{11}(\tau)\, d\tau}{\displaystyle\int_{-\infty}^{\infty} C_{11}(\tau)\, d\tau} , \tag{12.3a}$$

although other definitions may be used (331). An important result of this integral is that $\Delta\tau$ may be shown to be related to the effective spectral width $\Delta\nu$ by

$$\Delta\tau\Delta\nu \geqslant (4\pi)^{-1}, \tag{12.4}$$

which becomes

$$\Delta\tau\Delta\nu = (4\pi)^{-1}, \tag{12.5}$$

if the spectral profile is Gaussian and if $\Delta\nu$ is much less than the peak frequency (332). The meaning of (12.4) and (12.5) is that no interference fringes can be observed when the delay time τ is greater than $\Delta\tau$. It has been emphasized that interference phenomena observed with coherent sources during short observation times can be properly explained by a correlation function provided the integral is taken over the observation time instead of over an infinite length of time (*333*).

The correlation function $C_{12}(\tau)$ may be expressed in terms of observable quantities by the relation (332),

$$V(Q) = \frac{I_{max} - I_{min}}{I_{max} + I_{min}} = 2\frac{[I_1(Q)I_2(Q)]^{1/2}}{I_1(Q) + I_2(Q)} \mid C_{12}(\tau) \mid, \qquad (12.6)$$

where $V(Q)$ is the visibility of the interference fringes at Q, and $I_1(Q)$ and $I_2(Q)$ denote the time averaged intensities which would be obtained at Q if the openings respectively at P_1 and P_2 alone were open. If as is often the case the two beams are of equal intensity, $I_1(Q) = I_2(Q)$, then (12.6) reduces to $V(Q) = C_{12}(\tau)$. On this basis, a completely coherent wave has a visibility and correlation coefficient of unity. The mutual coherence function $C_{12}(\tau)$ may be measured by the interference experiment illustrated in Fig. 49a. If the pattern

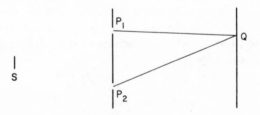

FIG. 49a.   Interference of light from two slits. S represents an extended source.

is observed near the symmetrical position, then information is obtained of the field at P_1 and P_2 at the same time. In this case one speaks of spatial coherence and it is characterized by $C_{12}(0)$. The self-coherence function $C_{11}(\tau)$ may be measured by a Michelson interferometer. However, only in the simplest types of experiments can one sharply distinguish between space and time coherence, since, in general, these two types of coherence are not independent.

2. *Photon Correlation*

The term coherence as we have seen has been used to denote a tendency for two values of the field at distantly separated points and/or at greatly separated times to take on correlated values. The possibility of producing interference fringes with a two slit arrangement or a Michelson interferometer epitomizes this definition of coherence. The photon correlation experiment of Hanbury Brown and Twiss (*304*) is of an altogether new type, and is illustrated schematically in Fig. 49b. The correlator, essentially an integrating device measures

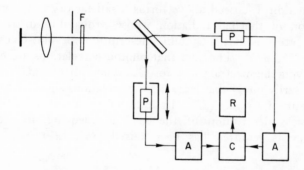

FIG. 49b. Experimental arrangement for measuring photon correlation [Brown and Twiss (*304*)]: A, amplifier; C, correlator; F, filter; P, photocell; R, recorder. Note that the distance between one of the photocells and the mirror can be varied.

the degree of correlation between the photocurrents of the two photomultipliers, and consequently the correlation in the fluctuations in the intensity of the field.

In general the correlation function (12.3) is representative of second order statistics and does not give a complete statistical description of a process for which higher order correlation functions are required. However, an important exception is the Gaussian process which yields statistics to all orders in terms of second order only. Thus the coherence of the field measured by photon correlation is not in general the same thing as the coherence measured by an interference experiment.

A concept closely related to coherence is that of photon degeneracy, which has been discussed with respect to light from optical masers and other sources (*334*). The degeneracy, δ, is defined as the average number of photons in the light beam which are to be found in the same quantum state or the same cell in phase space. The correlation between the fluctuation of the counts recorded by photomultipliers illuminated by partially coherent light is proportional to the degeneracy. For incoherent light $\delta \ll 1$, whereas even for the first He-Ne maser, $\delta \sim 10^{12}$. In view of this result, it may be said that for the first time we now have light beams that behave as waves rather than particles in their fluctuation properties (*334*).

The question of the proper way to describe the electromagnetic field to account, in particular, for the results of experiments on photon correlation is currently under discussion. Whereas the coherence function discussed above forms a satisfactory criterion for the description of thermal radiation whose probability distribution is Gaussian, this is not a suitable description for non-Gaussian radiation (*335, 336*). The fact that photon correlations are enhanced by narrowing the spectral width for Gaussian radiation (*337, 338*) does not necessarily imply that large scale correlations should be observed in the beam of a maser (*335*). In addition, the question of whether a semiclassical description of the field is adequate or a quantum description is required has been raised (*335, 339*).

3. Interference Experiments with Masers

The optical maser appears to be most different from other light sources in that there exists a surface coherence across the radiating face of the maser. That this coherence should exist follows from the fact that the field in a maser consists of the standing waves of one or more modes which have a fixed phase difference between any two points. Nelson and Collins (*342*) demonstrated the coherence of the ruby maser by placing two slits in contact with the ruby rod. In observing interference fringes produced by the light emerging from the slits, they repeated the classic experiment of Young, but with a coherent light source. The slits were separated by 0.00541 cm, or the order of 100 wavelengths. This experiment performed with a crystal of better uniformity produced interference fringes for a slit separation of 0.32 cm (*343*). A similar experiment was performed with the He-Ne maser with multiple slits inserted in the maser beam and covering its full aperture, 1.1 cm (*237*). The minima were very low indicating small variation in phase over the area of the beam.

It is interesting to compare these results with incoherent light sources for which the area of coherence A, is given (*332*) by

$$A = \beta \frac{R^2\lambda^2}{S}. \qquad (12.7)$$

The constant β depends on the degree of coherence that is demanded, and for a circular source is equal to 0.06 when the departure from coherence is to be less than 12%. S is the area of the source, and R is the perpendicular distance from the source. Then for $R = 10^2$ cm and $S = 1$, $A \simeq 6 \times 10^{-6}$ cm², which is many orders of magnitude smaller than what is obtained with maser sources.

Coherence studies of emission from a pulsed ruby maser were made by studying the visibility of the interference fringes from two slits that were separately illuminated by different parts of the beam cross-section, and with variable delay τ between the illumination of one slit and the subsequent illumination of the other slit by a portion of the same wavefront (*344*). By varying the delay length ΔD and consequently the delay time $\tau = \Delta D/c$, the fringes were found to disappear at $\Delta D = 3000$ cm or $\tau = 0.1$ μsec. Since the average duration of a spike of radiation was 0.56 μsec, the value $\tau = 0.1$ μsec represents a premature loss in fringe visibility, the origin of which was not determined.

Interference between beams from the opposite ends of a pulsed ruby maser were observed (*345*) and interpreted to signify that the relative spatial distribution of the light over the ruby faces was essentially constant even though the light was emitted in short bursts. However an objection against this interpretation has been raised (*346*). Interference between the beams from opposite ends of a GaAs maser has been observed (*347*). The light from two independent ruby masers has produced interference fringes (*349, 349a*).

Interference fringes from the light of a He-Ne maser has been observed at optical path differences up to 9 meters. However, an examination of the visibility of the interference fringes indicated that the coherence limit was of course far greater than 9 meters (*348*).

4. *Statistical Nature of Maser Radiation*

In the theory of the optical maser presented in Chapter IV, it was shown how the regenerative process narrows the spontaneous emission noise driving the resonator modes into an extremely small bandwidth.

In this description the spectral output of the maser, however narrow, contains no truly monochromatic wave and is similar in its statistical properties to thermal radiation. However, this theory assumes that the noise fields are not so large that the off-diagonal elements of the density matrix must be included, and ignores the effect of the maser atoms in suppressing the magnitude of electric field fluctuations. Thus, the statistical nature of maser beams is not likely to be Gaussian. Preliminary noise measurements on a He-Ne maser indicated in fact that the radiation does not have a Gaussian amplitude distribution but possesses a steady state amplitude with a small superimposed noise modulation (340). An interesting experiment has been suggested to distinguish a coherent signal plus noise from a narrow bandwidth noise signal in masers as well as regenerative electrical oscillators (341).

E. MODE STUDIES IN GASEOUS MASERS

1. *Introduction*

Since the radiation of optical masers may be characterized in terms of the oscillating modes, the importance of the identification and study of these modes is apparent, and it is, therefore, not surprising that a considerable amount of effort has been expended in this direction.

The studies discussed in this section are concerned with identifying maser modes, their frequency separation, the width of the maser beam, and the way in which these characteristics vary with pumping power. It is with the gas systems where the observations are not complicated by scattering from material imperfections or dielectric boundaries that the mode patterns have been most clearly observed and identified.

2. *Mode Patterns and Frequency Separations*

Unless care is taken to limit the number of modes that can be excited by properly adjusting the resonator, and/or selecting modes through the use of apertures and opaque wires in the resonator, very complicated light patterns may be obtained. An array of dots, often random, are seen in such patterns and are reminiscent of what has been observed in solid state masers. In all cases of complex radiation patterns, the light was found to be a mixture of wavelengths as determined by optical mixing (Fig. 48). (*91a, 94*). However, unlike the solid state masers, it is possible to obtain isolated and identifiable mode patterns in the gas maser, such as those shown in Figs. 9 and 10.

In the He-Ne maser with external concave mirrors and with a diaphragm located 3 cm in front of one of the mirrors to limit the aperture at that plane to 2 mm, the angular beam width was found to be 3 min and the spot size on the mirror 1.4 mm (*271*). These results are in reasonably good agreement with (6.21) and (6.5) for the TEM_{00q} mode in a resonator consisting of two spherical mirrors, with radii of curvature nearly equal to their spacing, 130 cm, and where $\lambda = 11,530$Å. In the case of the He-Ne maser using plane Fabry-Perot mirrors (*94*), the beam divergence was only 32 sec or slightly more than the diffraction limit for 1 cm aperture at 11,530Å.

In the confocal system with $D = R' = 130$ cm, (6.7) yields the frequencies 115.2 Mc and 57.6 Mc for the mode separations $\Delta q = 1$, $\Delta(m + n) = 0$ and $\Delta q = 0$, $\Delta(m + n) = 1$, respectively. With $D = 130$ cm and $R' = 100$ cm, the frequencies from (6.7) are 115.2 Mc and 141.6 Mc for the mode separations $\Delta q = 1$, $\Delta(m + n) = 0$ and $\Delta q = 0$, $\Delta(m + n) = 2$, respectively. The heterodyne frequencies obtained by allowing the output of the maser to fall on a phototube were found to agree with the above values within experimental error (*271*).

The output intensity distribution of the Cs vapor maser which used a flat and spherical reflector were found to be in excellent agreement with (6.4) for the TE_{00q} mode, a result which indicated that only the lowest order mode was oscillating (*262*).

3. *Power Dependent Mode Pulling*

Because of the sharpness of the spectral output of gas masers, it is possible to make detailed studies of the frequency pulling effects, which are generally quite small. In particular, a comprehensive study of pulling effects on the TEM_{00q} modes in a He-Ne maser using a plane parallel Fabry-Perot resonator has been made by Bennett (*43*). In this system where the line is primarily broadened by the Doppler effect, increasing the single-pass gain at one frequency does not imply a proportionate increase in gain at other frequencies. Thus the threshold condition is satisfied by burning a hole in the line whereas the gain over the rest of the line continues to increase with pumping power. At low pumping powers where the gain is sufficient for the two modes near the line center to break into oscillation, there is only one heterodyne component at $c/2D$. At higher pumping power a beat note appears at $2(c/2D)$ indicating that the gain is adequate for three modes to oscillate. The frequency of the $c/2D$ beat was found to increase with power until a power dependent splitting of the $c/2D$ and $2(c/2D)$ beats appeared. This sequence of events is shown in Fig. 50.

At low power levels where only one beat component appeared, the beat frequency was less than the theoretical separation of adjacent modes, i.e., $c/2D$. This result is in agreement with the power independent pulling described by (4.30) or (4.31) which show that the oscillating frequency is pulled toward the center of the atomic line.

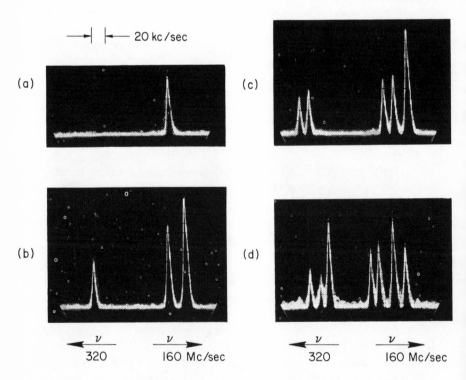

FIG. 50. Power dependent splitting of the $c/2D$ signals resulting from the heterodyning of the axial modes of a He-Ne maser [Bennett (43)]. Power increases from (a) to (d). The scale is 20 kc/sec.

The increase of the $c/2D$ beat with power at higher powers means that the two modes are being repelled. The splitting of the beats in the vicinity of $c/2D$ and $2(c/2D)$ represent the various ways these beats can be formed by three oscillating modes when the frequency separations between adjacent modes are not identical. These nonlinear mode interactions have been qualitatively explained by Bennett as the interaction of holes burned in an inhomogeneously broadened line by the oscillating modes. Such power dependent frequency pulling effects as well as the appearance of a dip in single mode operation as the cavity is tuned through resonance has been explained by the theories of Lamb ($46e$) and Haken and Sauermann ($46f$).

F. Mode Studies in Solid State Masers

Mode studies on solid state masers have been made thus far largely on the pulsed ruby maser, which exhibits relaxation oscillations, and consequently is not even in a quasi-continuous state for the duration of the pumping light pulse. In most of the experiments the method of observation integrated the maser output during one or many relaxation pulsations; however, a number of time resolved studies have been made.

1. *Time Averaged Observations*

Many experiments have identified the sharp frequency components in the maser beam as those generated by oscillation in the longitudinal (also called axial) modes of the resonator, whose resonance wavenumber is $q/2Dn$ and spacing is $(2Dn)^{-1}$. A number of photomixing experiments with ruby have clearly demonstrated the presence of a number of oscillating axial modes. In one investigation, all multiples of the basic adjacent mode separation of 1.65 Gc up to the 21st, 34.65 Gc, have been detected ($316a$).

The ruby maser beam has been examined with a Fabry-Perot etalon and found to contain the wavelengths of three longitudinal modes even very close to threshold when there was only one oscillation spike in the output (350). For a 2.54-cm long ruby, the separation between adjacent longitudinal modes, in agreement with experiment, was approximately 0.11 cm^{-1}. On the other hand the separation between two adjacent transverse modes were of the order of 10^{-3} cm^{-1}, and would not be resolved in this experiment. The simultaneous oscillation of transverse modes of a ruby maser have evidently been detected by observation of their beat frequencies (*350a*).

When many axial modes are excited it is preferable to examine the maser beam with a high resolution grating spectrometer to avoid the confusion of overlapping orders with an interferometer. Such observations made on a ruby (*351*) and $CaF_2 : U^{3+}$ maser (*352*) have given good agreement with the theoretical mode spacing.

Transverse oscillation modes in ruby masers have been observed as intensity variation patterns at the face of the ruby rod by a number of investigators (*350, 353–355*). Among the many observations of such mode patterns is that of Evtuhov and Neeland (*350*), who by working with a ruby crystal of high quality and operating very close to threshold, $\lesssim 1\%$ above threshold, obtained reproducible patterns that were suggestive of the transverse modes observed in the He–Ne maser. In many cases the output consisted of only a single spike, although there was no simple correlation between the mode and spiking patterns. In general, however, an increase in pump power resulted in a blurring of the simple patterns. The beam angles observed for various resonator lengths were 11×10^{-3} rad for 1 cm, 4.4×10^{-3} rad for 2.54 cm, and 2.2×10^{-3} rad for 11.7 cm. Since the pattern sizes ranged between 170 and 850μ, the beam divergences were not inconsistent with the diffraction limit. The spot size on the flat mirror was found to be independent of rod diameter but depended on the square root of the rod length. This result is in qualitative agreement with (6.5) for the case of a confocal resonator, although a nominally plane parallel resonator was used.

Near field patterns of a pulsed $CaWO_4 : Nd^{3+}$ operated at room temperature and $77°K$ showed intensity distributions which were very nonuniform (*158a*). Often the active area for the PPF-P geometry was distributed near the rim of the end face. A number of observations on the $CaWO_4 : Nd^{3+}$ maser in continuous operation at $\sim 85°K$ has exhibited sometimes simple and othertimes complex mode patterns for both the PPF-P and confocal resonator geometries, although it was thought that the patterns suggested that a smaller number of resonator modes were excited at all power levels above threshold with crystals with plane parallel rather than spherical ends. The beam divergence of the Fabry-Perot crystals was typically 0.2–0.3 deg— far greater than the diffraction limit. As expected the beam divergence of the confocal geometry rods was much greater and depended on the radius of curvature of the end faces relative to the crystal length.

Excellent patterns of the TEM_{00} to TEM_{04} modes giving beam angles of the maxima and minima that were found to be in close agreement with theory were obtained by Boersch et al. (356a) using a pulsed ruby maser. Their arrangement consisted of an elliptical focuser, detached spherical mirrors, and a screen, with an aperture to restrict the diameter of the resonator field, located between a mirror and the rod. This arrangement not only used mode selection, but made the ruby a small fraction of the resonator volume thus reducing the perturbing effect of crystalline imperfections on distorting the mode patterns.

D'Haenens and Asawa (204) in their study of oscillation frequencies in ruby noted that in addition to the discrete spectra due to oscillation in the axial modes, there was a broad background of radiation present indicating a more or less continuous frequency distribution which they interpreted as arising from stimulated emission in many transverse modes. They discussed the competition among the various modes for oscillation according to the theory of an ideal maser (42) which shows that the winner will be that mode for which

$$1 - K_m Q_m + \left(\frac{\nu_m - \nu_a}{\Delta \nu_a}\right)^2$$

is a minimum [see Eq. (4.44)]. At low temperatures, the last term becomes significant because of the very small value of $\Delta\nu_a$. Although the theory is strictly applicable to a homogeneously broadened line, whereas the ruby fluorescent line becomes inhomogeneously broadened at low temperatures, they showed how the above expression, the reciprocal of which is essentially the gain of a given mode, may be used to interpret their experimental results.

2. Time Resolved Observations of Mode Patterns

Time resolved observations with a high speed camera of the intensity distribution from ruby masers have shown in general complex patterns which are rapidly changing (353–355). The first few spikes emitted by a ruby maser operated very near threshold gave mode patterns (355) similar to those observed from gas discharge masers. However, different mode patterns have been observed from different regions of the crystal face. At times, the patterns seldom lasted for $0.5\,\mu$ sec and gave evidence that simultaneous transverse modes can occur and change within a spike (354). Different regions of the crystal appear to emit independently of each other (*62, 144*). The tendency of a crystal to become active in filaments has been shown theoretically to be caused by minute randomly distributed variations of refractive index (*356*).

It is clear from this account of the mode studies in solid state masers that complicated results are often obtained which are difficult to interpret, and which depend on the particular material or resonator geometry. To be sure, the sharp frequency components in the maser spectra have been clearly identified as those generated by oscillation in the longitudinal (also called axial) modes of the resonator. However, the number of axial and transverse modes which were excited were found to increase with pumping power, a result which may be expected when the atomic line is inhomogeneously broadened, although the broadening in particular cases was thought to be of the homogeneous type. Such power dependent mode excitation is nevertheless possible because of the spatial modulation of excited atoms in solids (*53*).

G. Oscillation in Imperfect Crystals

This section discusses the nature of some crystal imperfections and their influence on the behavior of solid state masers. The imperfections in question are local refractive index variations which have been shown to be correlated with the filamentary nature of maser oscillations, and minute scattering centers which apparently contribute to the increased thresholds, and which are thought to be the origin of the ring structure in the output of the ruby maser.

1. Interference Measurements

To assess the optical quality of a ruby crystal, Hercher (*343*) made direct measurements of the variations in optical path between the two end surfaces by means of a Twyman-Green interferometer. He found that near threshold, the rubies emitted in those regions where the interferogram showed a definite extremum in optical path. In the ruby with very small refractive index variations (less than $1\frac{1}{2}$ wavelengths variation in phase) the intensity across the face spread out more or less uniformly as the input energy was increased. Such a variation in intensity has been shown to be associated with the concentration of the pumping light by the dielectric rod (*147*).

At 10% above threshold, the phase coherence extended for a separation of 0.32 cm across the end face giving an area of coherence nearly 2000 times greater than that reported previously (*342*) in a crystal evidently of much poorer quality. In a crystal whose interferogram showed it to be of poor quality, the near field patterns had a number of small bright areas, i.e., the so-called filaments, which increased in size as the pump energy was increased until they merged. The time dependent behavior of such filaments has been investigated and their intensity has been found to vary in an irregular manner (*353*).

2. Threshold

The oscillation threshold of solid-state optical masers has often been found to be much greater than the theoretical value and has shown considerable variability from crystal to crystal. In a $CaF_2 : Sm^{2+}$ maser, the observed threshold was found to be approximately 5 times greater than the calculated value (*49*), but no reason was advanced for this discrepancy. In the ruby maser where considerably more data has been obtained, it has been found that as the quality of the crystals has improved, the threshold energy has decreased (*357*). A detailed study of the temperature variation of the threshold energy of a ruby maser indicated a rather large loss of 30% per pass (*358*), which was much larger than the reflection losses at the end plates. Various crystal imperfections and local variations in index of refraction are quite likely a major cause for the observed internal losses and the high threshold.

Extinction losses resulting from optical scattering by small foreign particles within the crystal was experimentally determined, and also estimated from the number and size of the scattering centers by Kaiser and Keck (*359*). Transmission measurements on high purity CaF_2 crystals gave transmission values of 94%, whereas CaF_2 crystals doped with 0.05% U^{3+} gave an additional extinction loss of 24%. These measurements were made with an acceptance angle of 1°. The size of the impurities relative to the optical wavelengths were such that scattering was contained in a narrow cone in the forward direction. In measurements on the scattering loss in ruby, values were obtained which were consistent with the loss of 30% estimated from threshold measurements (*358*).

A comparison has been made of the output intensity distribution of the same rod of $CaWO_4 : Nd^{3+}$ in the PPF-P and confocal resonators (*158a*). The intensity distribution was considered to be more uniform for the confocal resonator, a result which may be understood on the following basis. Because of crystal imperfections, the flat ends of the PPF-P resonator, although parallel to within a few seconds of arc, do not appear parallel to the propagating wavefront. It may be that only around the circumference where there is some rounding of the edge due to polishing that the wavefront finds areas of normal incidence. The confocal geometry is thus less sensitive to distortions of the wavefront in the crystal. A consequence of crystal strain is that thresholds for stimulated emission are generally considerably higher for the PPF-P geometry than for the confocal geometry (*158a*).

3. Ring Patterns

There have been a number of experimental demonstrations of a ring structure in the coherent light emitted by ruby masers (*150, 204,354,360–362a*). Although the rings appear at high pumping powers in ruby of relatively good quality, we believe that scattering of radiation into off axis modes by crystal imperfections is the origin of the rings. The rings may be observed by passing the beam through a lens and onto a photographic plate in the focal plane, i.e., the far field pattern. The observed patterns have been found to correspond within the accuracy of measurement with that of a Fabry-Perot interferometer,

$$R_n^2 - R_{n-1}^2 = f^2 \lambda_0 \sqrt{\epsilon}/D, \tag{12.8}$$

where f is the focal length of the lens, and R_n is the radius of the nth ring on the film. Interference patterns characteristic of coherent sources have been obtained by allowing the light from different rings or different portions of the same ring to interfere (*361*). This means that the off axis modes which add to form the ring are of precisely the same frequency and coherent in phase. In view of this result and the coupling which must exist between the modes, the set of angular modes could be regarded as a single modified mode in which the maser was oscillating.

The power output characteristics of imperfect crystals may be described, at least in a qualitative way, within the framework of (4.60). The first term in the brackets represents the coherent power in the most favored mode. If more than one mode is oscillating, additional terms of this type must be added. The third term, which gives a ring structure in the maser beam, represents the radiation scattered into the transverse or off-axis modes which are coupled to and driven by the oscillating modes. Of course, off-axis modes may be excited without the generation of a well-defined ring pattern. The second term represents the spontaneous radiation in all other modes, some of which may be high gain modes and, consequently, capable of draining off a significant amount of power. It is worth emphasizing that any mechanism which increases the power in the nonoscillating modes will cause the oscillation threshold to increase.

H. RELAXATION OSCILLATION

The spiked or pulsation character of the output of solid-state optical masers (see Table II.1) has received considerable attention since it was first discovered that the output of the ruby maser consists of a continuous train of sharp spikes of irregular spacing and amplitude (151). The theoretical basis for such behavior has been discussed in Section V,A in terms of a pair of coupled rate equations for the population excess and the photon density in the resonator. It will be seen that these equations, originally proposed for single mode operation by Statz and DeMars (56), account for a number of the observations in a reasonably satisfactory way. On the other hand, a number of other observations remain unexplained. Characteristic photographs of the ubiquitous spikes that are observed several percent above threshold are shown in Fig. 51.

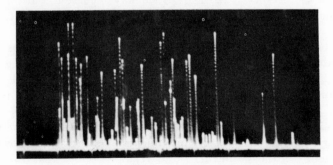

FIG. 51. Random spiking of a ruby maser operated several percent or more above threshold.

The relaxation oscillations of the pulsed $CaF_2 : U^{3+}$ infrared maser were studied qualitatively by Sorokin and Stevenson (144). The oscillations appeared as a train of perfectly regular damped spikes or as a damped sinusoid with a period (in the microsecond range) and decay rate that depended on the exciting power. Although quantitative comparison of these results with theory could not be made because precise pumping power measurements were lacking, they reported good qualitative agreement with the picture presented by the coupled equations. A quantitative study of the pulsations characteristics in both the $CaF_2 : U^{3+}$ and $BaF_2 : U^{3+}$ masers by Bostick and O'Connor (363) showed them to be in reasonable agreement with (5.11) and (5.12). In the continuous $CaF_2 : U^{3+}$ maser, the relaxation oscillations were observed to die out in a few milliseconds after the onset of maser action (170). Such behavior also has been observed to be the case in the continuous Nd^{3+} maser (161). It has been found, however, that the presence or absence of spikes was entirely dependent on resonator geometry. In the experiments just cited on the continuously operating U^{3+} and Nd^{3+} masers, a confocal resonator was used. With a Fabry-Perot resonator, severe spikes at all levels of power input were always present in the continuous Nd^{3+} maser (158a). With a confocal geometry, spikes to a limited extent ($\sim$5% of the total output) at power levels slightly above threshold were present, but essentially no spikes were observed at power levels well above threshold. Now in the same investigation it was found that crystals with the Fabry-Perot geometry displayed mode patterns which could be taken to indicate a smaller number of oscillating modes at all power levels above threshold than with the confocal geometry. It was provisionally suggested that this result and the results on spiking would seem to imply that an interaction between many excited modes suppressed spiking.

In contrast to the absence of pulsations in $CaF_2 : Sm^{2+}$ masers (49, 144), the output of the $SrF_2 : Sm^{2+}$ maser is characterized by strong relaxation oscillation (167). This result may be explained by the large difference in lifetime between the two systems: 1.5×10^{-6} sec in $CaF_2 : Sm^{2+}$ and 1.5×10^{-2} sec in $SrF_2 : Sm^{2+}$. For $CaF_2 : Sm^{2+}$, (5.11) and (5.12) give values of μ and λ which are beyond the frequency response of the measuring instruments. On the other hand, in agreement with experiment, these relations show that the spikes should be only slightly damped for the whole duration of the maser pulse for $SrF_2 : Sm^{2+}$.

An interesting observation was made with an ytterbium activated silicate glass maser. It was found that spiking in the stimulated emission pattern was induced by roughening the sides of the glass rod, which was considered to be of poor optical quality (*364*). Since roughening the sides of the rod should reduce the number of high gain modes, this result may perhaps indicate, as in the spiking experiments with Nd^{3+}, that the existance of many high gain modes suppresses spiking.

For the case of the gas masers, (5.11) shows that the spikes should damp out very quickly, and, in agreement with experiment, not be observable. However, when a magnetic field was applied to the He-Ne maser, relaxation oscillations similar to those which occur in the ruby maser appeared (*275*).

Let us next review the situation in ruby. The pulsations have in general an irregular period and fluctuate in amplitude. The period is typically in the μsec region, although structure has been seen in the pulses which indicate modulation frequencies of the order of 100 Mc (*365*). Under some circumstances the pulsations appear to be regular, an instance of which was reported for a 90° oriented ruby with spherical ends and placed in a spiral flash lamp (*366*). At liquid N_2 temperature, and with a highly reflecting multilayer dielectric, it has been observed that the pulsations essentially disappeared and were replaced by a large dc component (*367*). The absence of pulsations was observed for an optically efficient arrangement of four flash lamps in close proximity to the ruby (*133*). In the case of the ruby ring resonator, see Fig. 15b, the pulsations were always absent in one experiment (*113*), but damped pulsations made its appearance in another (*113a*). However, when ruby was made to operate continuously, the surprising result was obtained that the pulsations persisted and did not damp out (*142*). It should be emphasized that the existence of undamped pulsations cannot be accounted for by the Statz-DeMars equations since these equations admit only of damped solutions (*57, 58*). The modification to these equations that is needed to obtain undamped spiking has been discussed (*57, 58, 365a*).

Very good agreement has been obtained (*366a*) between the results of an experiment with ruby operated only 1 % above threshold and the linearized solutions to the coupled equations (5.11) and (5.12) specialized for the three level case. The damped, regularly spaced pulses, which are similar in appearance to the pulsations observed

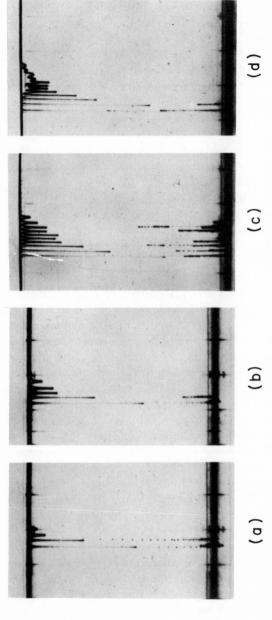

FIG. 52. Spiking of a ruby maser operated near threshold. Upper trace, output of ruby maser; lower trace, heterodyne frequency output at 2.2 Gc. Writing speed: 50 μsec/div, both traces. Note in (c) the slight cw component in the upper trace, and in (d) the well developed cw component in the light output [Birnbaum and Stocker (366b)].

(a)　(b)　(c)　(d)

in $CaF_2 : U^{3+}$ masers, are shown in the upper traces of Fig. 52. Birnbaum and Stocker (*366b*) found that many axial modes were present in the pulsed ruby maser even when a train of regularly spaced, damped spikes, which are described by the single mode Statz-deMars equation, appeared in the output. The pulses in the lower traces of Fig. 51 are the heterodyne frequency output due to the heterodyning of axial modes in a given power spike.

I. Mode Selection and Control

It was clearly recognized by Schawlow and Townes (*1*) that in optical masers, whose resonators are capable of supporting a huge number of modes, it is important to be able to select and isolate modes for amplification. From consideration of the Fraunhofer diffraction pattern resulting from the field excitation on the end walls of an enclosed rectangular box, they suggested that mode selection could be accomplished by focusing the output radiation onto a hole of proper diameter in an otherwise black screen. A method of this sort has in fact been used to selectively excite one or a combination of modes in fiber dielectric waveguides (*101*).

Mode selection by the use of a limiting aperture has been used in solid and gaseous masers. Its application to the solid state (ruby) maser has taken the form shown in Fig. 53 (*368*). By converting the angular divergence of the beam into a linear displacement by means of the lens, the unwanted off-axial modes of oscillation can be

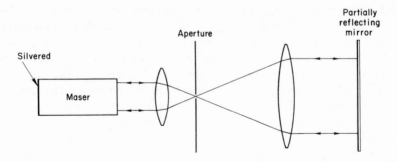

FIG. 53. Mode control by an aperture. The lenses have different focal lengths to illustrate how the output radiation may be collimated by an inverse telescope arrangement.

eliminated on each pass by means of a suitable aperture. It has been reported that by using such a mode selection method, a ruby maser beam has been produced whose divergence is less than twice the diffraction limit even for pumping energies that are well above threshold (369). However, the beam burns the small iris limiting the beam diameter. To avoid this difficulty, the iris, second lens, and reflector were eliminated and a spherical convex mirror located near the focal point of the first lens was used. Good collimation and maser action over all of the maser rod surface was obtained (369b).

Effective discrimination against the axial modes has been achieved by inserting Fabry-Perot plates within the resonator, and tipped with respect to the maser axis (369a). The insertion of the plates was found to limit the frequency spectrum and reduce the beam width to the diffraction limit 1.5×10^{-4} rad. By eliminating the unwanted modes of oscillation within the resonator rather than externally, more energy should be available for the desired oscillating mode. A composite type Fabry-Perot resonator in a ruby maser was devised by simply butting together two or more ruby rods (370a). The interface between the rubies acts as a partially transparent reflector. At an input energy about $2\frac{1}{2}$ times threshold, a three inch rod was observed to oscillate in only three axial modes at room temperature.

An interesting method of mode control was devised by Lipsett and Strandberg (360) who deformed the crystal by means of transverse loading, thus permitting the exercise of a large degree of control over the effective modes that give rise to the output radiation. By deforming the crystal, the internal properties of the active medium were modified so that the greatest volume could work into the lowest order modes that the inhomogeneities of the medium could sustain. They were, in fact, able to simplify the mode pattern, reduce the threshold, and at the same time reduce the divergence of the emergent beam. Other factors which have influence on the modes that appear may be mentioned. These include the optical pumping arrangement or the surface condition of the sidewalls of the maser material (49, 50, 104).

As shown in Fig. 12, the diffraction losses of confocal resonator modes depend on the mirror diameter and consequently may be controlled by a circular aperture located within the resonator on the optic axis. Isolation of the individual modes with rectangular symmetry has been achieved this way in the He-Ne maser (*90*). The modes with azimuthal periodicity have been isolated by means of two straight wires crossing the optic axis at appropriate angles, and by suitable adjustment of the diameter of the aperture (*91, 91a*).* To discriminate against unwanted axial modes, a composite Fabry-Perot resonator, as shown in Fig. 13a, may be used. Kogelnik and Patel (*370*) used, however, the simpler arrangement of replacing just one of the mirrors by a pair of mirrors in the He-Ne maser and obtained essentially a single mode output close to the center of the Doppler-broadened gain curve. The other modes falling within the gain curve could no longer oscillate because of increased loss at these frequencies due to the Fabry-Perot mirror.

---

* Theory predicts that spherical mirrors with circular symmetry will produce radiation patterns with azimuthal symmetry (*83, 84*). However, rectangular symmetry is more commonly observed because it is usually quite difficult to achieve perfect degeneracy between the x and y axis in a circular mirror system, not only in the optical components, but also in the gain distribution of the active medium.

XIII. Multiple Photon Processes

A. INTRODUCTION

This chapter deals with the interaction of radiation and matter via multiple quantum transitions, which become important when substances are illuminated with the intense, monochromatic light obtainable from optical masers.

In principle, there is no such thing as a transparent substance if one considers higher-order radiation processes. A high intensity light beam may be attenuated, for example, by double photon absorption if the photon frequency is one-half that of the separation of two energy levels with the same parity. On the other hand, Raman scattering may occur in which a photon is absorbed with the simultaneous emission of a photon of different energy. As is well known, this process does not require that the pumping light be in resonance with the pump transition. Higher order Raman processes are possible in which two pump photons are absorbed and a signal photon is simultaneously emitted. In the radiation processes enumerated thus far, the final state of the atomic system is different from that of its initial state. However, transparent substances acting as non-

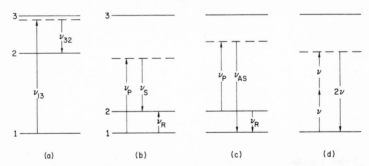

FIG. 54. Schematic energy level diagrams illustrating: (a) Raman emission a number of linewidths removed from resonance; (b) Stokes emission; (c) anti-Stokes emission; and (d) second harmonic generation. The arrows indicate photon emission or absorption except those marked ν_R , which designate the atomic transition.

linear dielectrics may generate light harmonics by absorbing two photons and simultaneously emitting the sum photon. In this case, the atomic system is left in its initial state, the ground state, a type of process which is characteristic of parametric interactions. A number of the nonlinear processes are schematically illustrated in Fig. 54. A general theory of such processes and their interference as the resonances of the material are approached has been developed by Bloembergen and Shen (370b).

B. Two Photon Absorption

Excitation by multiple quanta is a subject that has been studied theoretically for many years (371-374), and has been found experimentally in atomic beam experiments (375), as well as optical-radio frequency double resonance experiments (376). Two photon excitation has been observed in the optical region by Kaiser and Garrett (377) using the red light, 6943Å, of a ruby optical maser to illuminate $CaF_2 : Eu^{2+}$. The observed fluorescence around 4250Å was the indication that the ion was indeed pumped into an excited state by the absorption of two photons from which state it decayed to the fluorescing level. Subsequently, Abella (378) also using the red light from a ruby maser, observed the double photon excitation of the $6S_{1/2} - 9D_{3/2}$ transition in cesium vapor. Double photon excitation in a number of polycyclic aromatic molecules has also been detected (379, 379a). Excitation by two photons is to be distinguished from the lower order process of the absorption of two consecutive photons, which has been observed in $La\,Cl_3 : Pr$ in the infrared (380).

Since a change in parity is required for an electric dipole transition, double quantum transitions via the electric dipole must occur with no change of parity. Thus, a direct double quantum transition to a level accessible by a single quantum transition is forbidden by the parity selection rule for dipole transitions. However, there are atoms in which these selection rules will not be strict and both single and double quantum transitions are possible to the same level by a different component of the dipole operator. The probability that an atom absorbs two photons each of energy $h\nu_b$ has been calculated recently by Kleinman (381) whose expression for the relevant cross section is

$$\sigma = \left(\frac{e^2}{mc^2}\right)^2 \frac{c^2}{n_a^2 \nu_b^2} FS(2\nu_b - \nu_a). \qquad (13.1)$$

Here, ν_a is the frequency of an absorption band at $\sim 2\nu_b$, $S(2\nu_b - \nu_a)$ is the normalized shape factor of this band, F is the incident flux in photons/cm^2 sec, and n_a is the refractive index at ν_a. This expression is based on the assumptions that the charge transfer bands act as intermediate atomic states which are coupled through an electric moment to both the initial and final states of the transition ν_a, and that these bands exist with large oscillator strength $f \sim 1$ at considerably higher frequencies than ν_a or ν_b. The theory of multiple photon excitation has also been developed for the transition of an electron from the valence band to the conduction band (382).

The observed absorption cross section for two photon absorption in CaF$_2$: Eu^{2+} was found to be in semiquantitative agreement with (13.1) (377). No quantitative comparison of measured and theoretical cross sections was reported for the cesium vapor experiment. Although atomic double-quantum transition in gases allows in principle a more straightforward application of the theory than in the case of solids, the quenching of the excited state by collisions, which reduces the number of fluorescent photons emitted as a result of double photon excitation, makes comparison of theory with experiment uncertain.

On a practical level, it is conceivable that multiple photon excitation could be used in obtaining optical maser action at a frequency higher than that of the pump frequency.

C. INDUCED RAMAN EMISSION

1. Nearly Resonant Pumping

It is clear from (3.8) that saturation, or the tendency to equalize the populations of a pair of energy levels, sets in when the pumping rate becomes comparable to the relaxation rate, T_1^{-1}, of the excited level. However, if $T_1^{-1} = T_2^{-1}$, or if the pumping rate becomes comparable with T_2^{-1} if $T_1 \gg T_2$, the states will be so mixed by the radiation field that it becomes inappropriate to distinguish between them and to speak only in terms of population. In this case a variety of quantum mechanical effects appear such as the double quantum transition or Raman emission, and the splitting of the emission line because of the modulation of the wave functions. Actually, both effects are closely related and when one is large the other is likely to be large. As already indicated, the general condition for the marked appearance of these double quantum effects is that the pump transition must occur within the phase coherence time, i.e., the transverse relaxation time of the atomic system, viz.

$$\frac{\mu E}{\hbar} \geqslant \frac{1}{T_2} = \varDelta\omega, \tag{13.2}$$

where E designates the electric or magnetic field strength. For optical transitions the condition $T_1 \gg T_2$ generally applies, and consequently, the quantum effects appear at pumping power levels far beyond the value necessary for saturation, namely,

$$\left(\frac{\mu E}{\hbar}\right)^2 \sim (T_1 T_2)^{-1}. \tag{13.3}$$

Numerous authors have considered multiple quantum transitions in three level systems (27, 383–389), many of them with the microwave region in mind. In the microwave region, the spontaneous emission rate is essentially negligible. Consequently, if the microwave Raman effect is to be seen at all, it is necessary to apply a field at the emission frequency to induce the process. Specialization of the theory to the microwave region is made by taking $h\nu \ll kT$ and linearizing the Boltzmann factors, although the theory is of course general and applicable to the optical region if this approximation is not made. Javan (383) calculated the time dependence of the state amplitudes under the combined influence of the radiation fields and a collision type relaxation process. His method gives a better physical insight than the more compact but essentially equivalent density matrix formulation. On the other hand, his model for the relaxation processes is not sufficiently refined to treat a multilevel system involving several relaxations. This situation can be handled by the density matrix method and has been treated this way by several authors (384–387). The off-resonant behavior, i.e., when the pumping frequency is not resonant with the pumping transition, has been emphasized by Yatsiv (386) and Yajima (27). The relative importance of the single and double quantum processes has been discussed by Yatsiv (386) and Javan (383). Yajima (27) has considered in detail the way in which the Raman emission line splits and shifts at various pumping levels in the resonant and off-resonant case, and extends the theory for the case of Doppler broadened lines.

Consider a three level system (Fig. 54a) where the radiative transitions at ν_{13} and ν_{32} are allowed. The frequency of the pumping field, ν_{13}, is nearly resonant with the 1-3 transition. At low levels of pumping power, only the allowed single-quantum transitions are important. As the pumping power is increased, levels 1 and 3 tend toward saturation and, if the relaxation rates are appropriate, inversion of the populations between levels 3 and 2 or 2 and 1 may set in. When the pumping rate begins to become comparable with $\Delta\omega_{13}$, there is considerable mixing of the wave functions and double quantum transitions become significant. In the double quantum transitions, the atom initially in state 1 makes a transition to state 2 with the simultaneous absorption of one photon of energy $h\nu_{13}$ and emission of another photon of energy $h\nu_{32}$, and the atom initially in state 2 makes a transition to state 1 by the reverse process. Since $n_1 > n_2$, the double quantum transition is emissive even though there is no population inversion. With further increase in pumping power, the emission line may split into a doublet with a separation of the order $|\mu_{13}| E_{13}/2\hbar$. When the pumping frequency is far off-resonance, emission occurs when the signal frequency is off-resonance by the same amount as the pump frequency. This off-resonance emission will be recognized as the induced Raman signal. The more usual situation where the pump and signal frequencies are very far removed from any atomic resonance, as illustrated in Figs. 54b and 54c, will be considered in the next section.

The case of one and two photon stimulated emission in a three-level optical solid-state system with a sharp pump transition has been discussed by Williams (*388*). In addition to the pumping and signal fields at ν_{13} and ν_{21}, respectively, another field resonant with levels 3 and 2 is introduced with an intensity sufficient to induce a transition rate equal to the fast thermal relaxation rate. For this rather specialized system is was found that the one photon transition at ν_{21} which is emissive is split into two lines by the pump field just above threshold.

It is clear from this discussion that three-level systems may be used for frequency mixing, where radiation fields applied at two frequencies produce an oscillating polarization at the third, the phase of which depends on the phase of the applied fields. This problem has been considered by Wells (*389*) who treated the case where fixed power is applied at one of the frequencies from a local oscillator or pump, and the signals at the other two frequencies are treated in a small signal approximation.

We have thus far been concerned with multiple quantum or Raman type effects in three-level systems. However, as discussed by Javan (390), any quantum mechanical system which permits a radiative transition between two energy levels will allow a Raman type transition if at least one of the energy levels has a finite average of the electric or magnetic dipole moment. Winter (391) has observed induced Raman absorption and emission between two energy levels of a paramagnetic substance.

The induced Raman effect in a four-level system has been considered (383, 393) where two strong pumping fields and a weak signal field are applied. Induced emission at the signal frequency appears as the result of a triple quantum transition in which two pump photons are simultaneously absorbed at the same instant that a signal photon is emitted.

In substances with energy level separations in the microwave region, it is common to find $T_1 \sim T_2$, where T_1 is relatively long. Taking advantage of the very narrow line widths that can be obtained in gases at low pressures in the microwave region, Autler and Townes (392) observed multiple quantum effects in the resonant Stark modulation of the molecule OCS, and Yajima (393) observed induced Raman emission in the molecule HCOOH. Induced Raman emission for nearly resonant pumping has not yet been observed in the optical region.

2. Very Far Off-Resonant Pumping

In the optical region the spontaneous Raman emission rate is considerably greater than the induced emission rate, even for the fields which can be supplied by the usual solid state masers. However, the field supplied by the Q-spoil ruby maser is evidently intense enough not only to produce a sizeable induced Raman effect, but also to produce induced Raman maser action. In an investigation of the spectral characteristics of a Q-spoil ruby maser, induced Raman emission in the nitrobenzene of the Kerr cell, used as the Q-spoil switch, was discovered by Woodbury and Ng (394). The effect was verified and explored in a number of organic liquids by Eckhardt et al. (395).

In the experiment of Eckhardt et al. (395), the Raman liquid was placed in a cell inside the cavity of the ruby Q-spoil maser. To avoid the complications of stimulated Raman emission from the nitrobenzene of the Kerr cell, solid potassium dihydrogen phosphate was used instead. Depending on a number of factors, the output pulse of the Q-spoil maser was typically between 0.2 and 2 MW peak power, with a duration of 20–70 nsec. The liquids, aromatic (*395*) and nonaromatic (*395a*), which exhibited Raman maser action and the Raman frequency shifts, are listed in Table II.1. The following observations indicated that maser action was occurring: (i) the beam collimation at the listed frequencies appeared to be within a factor of 2 the same as that of the ruby maser light ($\sim$1 mrad); (ii) the induced Raman line narrowed as the liquid was pumped harder, in some instances to 0.3 Å; and (iii) a marked threshold existed, both in pump intensity and the length of the liquid column. The field at the Raman frequency may become so great that it can act as a pump to produce Raman maser action at $\nu_P - 2\nu_R$, and so on (see Table II.1).

By using highly reflective mirrors, Raman maser action in a normal ruby maser was observed by inserting either benzene or nitrobenzene in the feedback path. The ruby threshold occurred at 270 joules, whereas the Raman threshold occurred at 410 joules. The conversion efficiency in the normal maser was very small, less than 10^{-3}. With the Q-spoil maser, it has been as high as 30% (*395b*).

The gain per unit length, $\alpha = g/D$, due to induced Raman emission may be obtained from (2.31) in the form

$$g/D = \frac{4\pi k_s}{h \Delta \nu_s} (n_1 - n_2) \alpha_{12}^2 E_p^2 , \tag{13.4}$$

where $k = 2\pi/\lambda_s$, $\Delta\nu_s$ is the width of the Raman line, and $\alpha_{12}^2 E_p^2 = \mu_{12}^2/3$; α_{12} is the polarizability matrix element for the transition. For simplicity the pump and Raman fields are assumed polarized in the same direction and the tensor character of α_{12} is neglected. Since $n_1 > n_2$ (for most materials, $n_2 \sim 0$ at room temperature) induced Raman maser action does not require population inversion, as was first emphasized by Javan (*383*). If one absorption line or band at ω_0 with an oscillator strength of approximately unity is much stronger than all the others, the polarizability is given approximately by

$$\alpha \sim \frac{e^2}{m\omega_0^2} , \tag{13.5}$$

the classical result. More detailed accounts of the theory have appeared in the literature (*395c, 395d*).

Terhune obtained stimulated Raman emission outside the resonator by focusing the beam of a Q-spoil ruby maser in a cell filled with nitrobenzene ($395e$). His striking observation of Stokes and anti-Stokes rings is illustrated in Fig. 55. The angular distribution of this radiation has been investigated by Zeiger *et al.* ($395g$). Induced Stokes and anti-Stokes emission has been observed in gases by Minck *et al.* ($395h$) and solids by Eckhardt *et al.* ($395i$) (Table II.2).

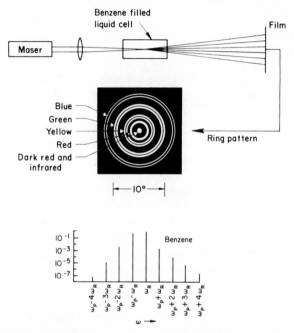

FIG. 55. Schematic of an experimental arrangement where stimulated emission in Stokes and anti-Stokes lines of a number of orders were observed to occur in the form of brightly colored rings at the focus of a Q-spoil ruby maser. [Terhune ($395e$)].

The theory of Raman maser action embodied in (13.4) is based on individual molecular processes of Raman scattering. However, as discussed by Garmire *et al.* ($395f$) higher order Raman effects may be produced by the excitation of intense coherent molecular oscillations at infrared frequencies. These modulate the original light and its Raman scattered radiation producing Stokes and anti-Stokes radiation of many orders, i.e., ($\nu_P \pm n\nu_R$). Lowest order anti-Stokes radiation for example (see Fig. 54c,) may be amplified when the following wave vector relation is satisfied: $2\mathbf{k}_P - \mathbf{k}_S = \mathbf{k}_{AS}$ (*395f*). Because of dispersion in the medium this relation cannot be satisfied by parallel wave vectors, and the anti-Stokes radiation will be emitted in a cone in the forward direction.*

D. Optical Harmonic Generation

1. *Introduction*

The development of optical masers with its intense output of mono-chromatic radiation, which when focused exhibit fields of the order of 10^6 volts/cm and higher, has made it experimentally possible to observe multiple photon processes, in particular, frequency doubling. The first to observe this was Franken *et al.* (*396*) who produced light at 3472Å by focusing the ruby maser beam of 6943Å light in crystalline quartz. The sum frequency of two ruby masers, operated at different temperatures to obtain somewhat different frequencies, was obtained by arranging the beams to be colinear and focusing them on a crystal of triglycine sulfate (*397*). In addition, coherent (ruby maser) light and incoherent (spectral lines of a mercury lamp) light have been mixed (*398*). In crystals where second harmonic production is forbidden or especially weak, third harmonic production, a four photon process, is the next allowed transition, and has been observed by Terhune *et al.* (*399*).

For a given crystal and for given frequencies of input photons, the quantum process which involves the minimum number of photons is likely to dominate the attenuation of the radiation, and a process involving several photons will be experimentally detectable only when there is no competing process in which a smaller number of photons may participate. The theoretical probability for a higher order photon process will be smaller than the next lower order process by a factor of order $(E_1/E_0)^2$ where E_1 is the electric field in the input beam and E_0 is an average atomic electric field characteristic of the crystal. Taking $E_0 \sim 3 \times 10^8$ volts/cm, and $E_1 \sim 3 \times 10^4$ volts/cm corresponding to a light intensity of 2.5×10^6 watts/cm^2, $(E_1/E_0)^2 \sim 10^{-8}$. Thus, even with the intense coherent light sources now available, the probability of a transition involving higher orders falls off very rapidly.

* The detailed explanation of the experimental observations of induced Stokes and anti-Stokes radiation has not yet been completely settled (*395f–395j*).

The theory of second harmonic production has been formulated by several people. A semiclassical theory has been given by Lax *et al.* (*400*). A theory analogous to the classical theory of crystal optics has been developed by Kleinman (*401*), who has also extended the theory for focused beams. A quantum perturbation calculation of the nonlinear source terms arising from the induced nonlinear electric dipole and higher moments in an atomic system irradiated simultaneously by two or three light waves has been given by Armstrong *et al.* (*402*) and Loudon (*403*). Reviews of optical harmonic generation and propagation of electromagnetic waves in nonlinear media have been written by Franken (*396a*), Bloembergen (*404*), and Terhune (*395e*).

2. *The Nonlinear Susceptibility Tensors*

From a classical view point, harmonic production is possible because all dielectrics are nonlinear in high enough fields. In particular, the induced electric polarization P_i may be assumed to have the form (*396a, 399*)

$$P_i = \chi_{ij}^{\omega} E_j^{\omega} + \chi_{ijk}^{0} E_j^{\omega} E_k^{\omega} + \chi_{ijk}^{2\omega} E_j^{\omega} E_k^{\omega} + \chi_{ijkl}^{'2\omega} E_j^{\omega} \nabla_k E_l^{\omega}$$
$$+ \chi_{ijkl}^{''2\omega} E_j^{0} E_k^{\omega} E_l^{\omega} + \chi_{ijkl}^{3\omega} E_j^{\omega} E_k^{\omega} E_l^{\omega} . \tag{13.6}$$

Here and elsewhere the convention of summation over repeated indices is adopted. The quadratic polarization due to induced magnetic dipoles and electric quadrupoles has the form

$$Q_{ij}^{2\omega} = \eta_{ijkl}^{2\omega} E_k^{\omega} E_l^{\omega} . \tag{13.7}$$

χ and η are tensors which characterize the process; superscripts indicate the relevant frequencies, the subscripts denote Cartesian components, and their number denotes the rank of the tensor. The meaning of the various terms are as follows:

$\chi_{ij}^{\omega} E_j^{\omega}$ is the usual linear term for the induced polarization.

$\chi_{ijk}^{2\omega} E_j^{\omega} E_k^{\omega}$. This and the following term are present only if the crystal has no inversion symmetry. This term is associated with doubling due to electric dipole transitions.

$\chi_{ijk}^{0} E_j^{\omega} E_k^{\omega}$. When two signals are mixed the sum and difference frequencies are produced. The preceding term gives the polarization at the sum frequency. This term gives the polarization at the difference frequency which is zero.

$\chi'^{2\omega}_{ijkl}E^{\omega}_j\nabla_k E^{\omega}_l$. This and the following terms are present if the crystal has inversion symmetry. This term arises from an electric quadrupole or a magnetic dipole field, $\nabla_k E^{\omega}_l$, which in conjunction with an electric dipole field induces doubling.

$\eta^{2\omega}_{ijkl}E^{\omega}_k E^{\omega}_l$. This represents the induced electric quadrupole or magnetic dipole polarization. This and the preceding term have the same phase which is 90° out of phase with the radiation produced by the dipole polarization. The amplitudes of the $\eta^{2\omega}_{ijkl}$ and $\chi'^{2\omega}_{ijkl}$ terms are of the same order of magnitude and smaller than the dipole terms by a factor $\sim(r_0 k)^2$, where r_0 is an atomic length and $k = 2\pi/\lambda$.

$\chi^{3\omega}_{ijkl}E^{\omega}_j E^{\omega}_k E^{\omega}_l$ gives the polarization at the third harmonic.

$\chi''^{2\omega}_{ijkl}E^0_j E^{\omega}_k E^{\omega}_l$, which is similar to the preceding term, gives the second harmonic polarization induced by the presence of a dc electric field.

The order of writing the three fields in the $\chi^{3\omega}$ term, and the two E^{ω} fields in all the other terms, is not physically significant. The tensor susceptibilities are symmetric in these indices which refer to physically indistinguishable fields.

Rough magnitudes of the tensor susceptibilities when E is given in stat volts/cm are: $\chi^{\omega} \sim 10^{-1}$, $\chi^{2\omega} \sim 10^{-9}$, $\chi'^{2\omega} \sim 10^{-16}$, $\chi^{3\omega} \sim 10^{-16}$, and $\chi''^{2\omega} \sim 10^{-13}$ (395e). Other terms not included in (13.6) account for such well known nonlinear optical phenomena as electric double refraction, the Kerr, Faraday, Voigt, and Cotton-Mouton effects. Many of the nonlinear phenomena are due exclusively to the electronic motions, although ionic vibrations in an anharmonic potential will make a contribution to second and third harmonic generation.

The nonlinear process of harmonic doubling proceeds via three virtual interband transitions: photons of energy $h\nu_1$ and $h\nu_2$ are absorbed at two of the transitions, whereas a photon $h(\nu_1 + \nu_2)$ is emitted at the third. The atomic system is in the same state before and after the process so that energy is conserved separately in both the radiative and electronic parts of the system. Inasmuch as three photons are involved in second harmonic production (via electric dipole transitions) and the atomic state before and after the process is the same, there is a change in parity in the system as a whole. For this transition to be allowed, parity must not be a good quantum number, which requires that the crystal not have a center of inversion. The restrictions of inversion symmetry on the other terms in (13.6) may be deduced in a similar way.

The elements of the susceptibility tensors are subject to restrictions due to the point symmetry of the crystal. In particular, the elements of the tensor $\chi_{ijk}^{2\omega}$ are identical with those governing the piezoelectric coefficients. This relation which governs the dependence of harmonic generation on direction of propagation and polarization has been predicted and partially verified by Franken et al. (396).

Important permutation symmetry relations have been derived by Armstrong et al. (402), which for the third order tensor χ_{ijk}, for example, is given by

$$\chi_{ijk}(\omega_1 = \omega_3 - \omega_2) = \chi_{kji}(\omega_2 = \omega_3 - \omega_1) = \chi_{jik}(\omega_3 = \omega_1 + \omega_2) . \quad (13.7a)$$

The indices on the tensor elements are interchangeable if the frequencies are interchanged correspondingly. If the medium has no dispersion in the interval that contains the frequencies the tensor is symmetric in all its indices (405). Equation (13.7a) shows that the same constant which describes microwave modulation of light also describes the generation of the microwaves as a beat between two light waves,

$$\chi_{zyx}(\omega_m = \omega_3 - \omega_2) = \chi_{yxz}(\omega_3 = \omega_2 + \omega_m) , \quad (13.8)$$

where ω_m is the microwave frequency. Note that the fields are polarized in the same directions in each case. General symmetry relations have been derived by Pershan (402a) for magnetic dipole and electric quadrupole nonlinearities.

If in (13.8) we let $\omega_m = 0$, then $\chi_{zyx}(0 = \omega - \omega)$ describes the dc polarization produced by the nonlinear interaction of light, and χ_{yxz} ($\omega = \omega + 0$) describes the linear electro-optic or Pockels effect in which the ordinary optical polarizability of a medium is modified by the presence of a strong static electric field. This identity of the dc and electro-optic terms enables one to predict the magnitude of the dc polarization and the production of a beat frequency (up to the far infrared for many substances) by heterodyning two masers of nearly the same frequency.

3. Phase Matching for Second Harmonic Generation

The conditions for second harmonic production, as has been already emphasized, are that the crystal should lack a center of inversion, and that it be transparent to the fundamental and second harmonic frequencies. However, as may be seen by examining the quantum expression for nonlinear susceptibility (402), for maximum efficiency it is necessary to choose a crystal whose forbidden energy gap, E_G, is as little as possible larger than the output photon energy. In addition, it is necessary that the electromagnetic momentum be conserved or nearly conserved for the realization of large coherence volumes as has been discussed and demonstrated by Giordmaine (406), and Maker et al. (407). For the case of a plane wave incident on a crystal of thickness D, the intensity of second harmonic light radiated in the forward direction (407) (see Appendix IV) is

$$S \propto cP^2(k_2/\Delta k)^2 \sin^2(\Delta k\, D/2), \qquad \Delta k = |\, \mathbf{k}_2 - 2\mathbf{k}_1\,|, \qquad (13.9)$$

where P is the magnitude of the induced polarization. The $\sin^2(\Delta kD/2)$ term arises because of the dephasing between the fundamental and second harmonic radiation due to dispersion in the crystal. Since $\Delta k = (4\pi/\lambda)\,(n_2 - n_1)$, we see that the maximum possible intensity is that which can be obtained with a crystal of characteristic thickness D', or odd multiples thereof, namely,

$$D' = \frac{\lambda}{4(n_1 - n_2)}, \qquad (13.10)$$

where λ is the free space wavelength at the fundamental frequency. The thickness D' is often referred to as a coherence length and is only of the order of 20λ or so for typical crystals investigated with the red light of the ruby maser. The periodic variation of intensity of the second harmonic with respect to thickness expressed by (13.9) was verified by Maker et al. (407) by passing a ruby maser beam through crystalline quartz whose effective thickness was varied by rotating the sample. Their experimental arrangement and results are shown respectively in Figs. 56 and 57.

From a classical viewpoint one can think of a plane wave of maser light described by $\exp[i(\omega_1 t - \mathbf{k}_1 \cdot \mathbf{r})]$ as generating a spatial arrangement of dipoles which in turn launches a polarization wave of the form $\exp[i(2\omega_1 t - 2\mathbf{k}_1 \cdot \mathbf{r})]$ because of the nonlinear response of the system to the fundamental. It is important to note that the second-

harmonic polarization is fixed to the spatial dependence of the fundamental wave, i.e., that the space part of the second harmonic polariza-
tion varies as $\exp(-2\mathbf{k}_1 \cdot \mathbf{r})$ rather than $\exp(-\mathbf{k}_2 \cdot \mathbf{r})$. This polarization wave can radiate a wave with wave vector $\mathbf{k}_2$ at frequency

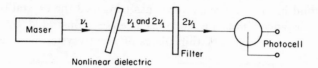

FIG. 56. Experimental arrangement for observing second harmonic generation
as a function of the angle of rotation of the nonlinear dielectric.

$\omega_2 = 2\omega_1$ with maximum efficiency if $\mathbf{k}_2 = 2\mathbf{k}_1$, i.e., if the second
harmonic wave remains in phase with the polarization wave producing
it. This condition implies that $v_1 = v_2$, or equivalently, $n_1 = n_2$.
Since almost all materials have dispersion in the optical region, the
second harmonic radiation will generally lag the polarization wave
except for certain directions in an anisotropic crystal. This can be
done in uniaxial crystals for which the birefringence, i.e., double
refraction, is greater than the dispersion.

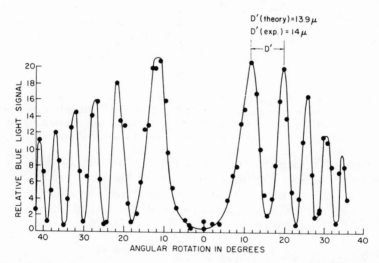

FIG. 57. Second harmonic generation versus inclination of 0.0308-in. thick
quartz platelet to maser beam. Rotation axis normal to beam, and parallel to crystal
z axis. Maser beam unfocused and polarized parallel to the z axis [Maker *et al.* (407)].

In a negative uniaxial crystal it is possible to choose a direction of propagation such that the ordinary refractive index at one frequency is equal to the extraordinary refractive index at the other. The way in which this has been accomplished is illustrated in Fig. 58.

Another approach to the index matching problem is to phase correct the second harmonic wave after it has traversed the crystal through a certain distance. This method has been demonstrated by Franken *et al.* (*408*) in which very thin plates of *x*-cut crystalline quartz were

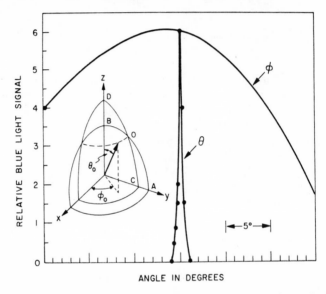

FIG. 58. Second harmonic intensity (blue light) as a function of crystal orientation for KDP. Maximum output occurs at $\theta_0 = 52° \pm 2°, \phi_0 = 45°$. Maser beam collimated to $\pm \frac{1}{4}°$. *AOB* is an arc on the index of refraction surface for ordinary rays at the maser wavelength; *COD*, for blue extraordinary rays [Maker *et al.* (*407*)].

stacked with their *z* axes alternating in direction by 180°. This effectively reverses the direction of second harmonic polarization in alternate plates. Other methods to provide phase correction to match the phase velocities of the fundamental and second harmonic are given in Armstrong (*402*; see in particular Fig. 10).

4. *Second Harmonic Generation*

The susceptibility tensor $\chi^{2\omega}$ governs the dependence of second harmonic generation on the direction of propagation and polarization.

The components of $\chi^{2\omega}$ are given in Table II for a case of practical interest, quartz. The notation conforms with that used for the piezo-electric tensor which is symmetric in the two indices, jk. These are replaced by a single index m according to the convention $xx = 1$, $yy = 2$, $zz = 3$, $yz = zy = 4$, $zx = xz = 5$, and $xy = yx = 6$. From Table II, we find that

$$P_x^{2\omega} = d_{11}(E_x^2 - E_y^2) + d_{14}E_yE_z ,$$

$$P_y^{2\omega} = -d_{14}E_xE_z - 2d_{11}E_xE_y ,$$

$$P_z^{2\omega} = 0 .$$

TABLE II.   THE CONTRACTED FORM $\chi_{im}^{2\omega}$ FOR QUARTZ.
THE NOTATION CONFORMS WITH THAT USED FOR THE PIEZOELECTRIC TENSOR

i \ m	1	2	3	4	5	6
x	d_{11}	$-d_{11}$	0	d_{14}	0	0
y	0	0	0	0	$-d_{14}$	$-2d_{11}$
z	0	0	0	0	0	0

Although the nonvanishing elements of $\chi^{2\omega}$ may be read directly from a tabulation of the piezoelectric coefficients (399a), magnitudes of the piezoelectric and second harmonic tensors are not related. The components of $\chi^{3\omega}$ for third harmonic generation has been tabulated (399b).

To give some idea of the intensity of second harmonic light, we quote the following results (407) where the second harmonic intensity is expressed as the number of red photons (ruby maser) required to produce one blue photon: for quartz, collimated beam, 5×10^{12}, which has been shown to be within an order of magnitude of a theoretical estimate (403); focussed beam (1 in. focal length lens), 6×10^{10}; for 1.5 mm thick KDP, collimated beam incident at optimum angle for velocity matching, 3×10^9; focussed beam (1 in. focal length lens and incident at optimum angle), 10^6. Note that in KDP a sizable intensity of second harmonic radiation has been obtained without the use of focussed beams but by velocity matching. By using a giant pulse ruby maser, Terhune *et al.* (*409*) observed a large increase in optical harmonic generation over their previous results which were obtained with a conventional ruby maser (*399, 407*). The giant-pulse maser had a total output energy of 30 mJ and a pulse duration of 30 nsec. The beam was focused on a KDP crystal oriented for index matching. A pulsed beam of 3470 Å light with a total energy of 6 millijoules and a peak power of 200 kW was obtained. Saturation of the conversion efficiency for second harmonic generation was observed at around 20% efficiency. In view of these results, it appears that second harmonic generation is a very good technique for obtaining coherent radiation at shorter wavelengths, particularly in the ultraviolet region. Continuous second harmonic generation has been observed using the 1.1526μ transition of the He-Ne maser with a focused (*414c*) and unfocused beam (*414d*).

Measurements have been made by Miller and Savage (*411*) on the ability of a number of piezoelectric crystals to generate the second harmonic of the ruby maser light. Some of their results for the relative second harmonic output are: KDP, 1000; ADP, 720; Quartz 34; Tourmaline, 8; and Rochelle salt, 12.

The ratio of 2nd harmonic to fundamental frequency has been determined with considerable accuracy by Boyne and Martin (*412*) and Abella (*413*) and found to be exactly in the expected ratio 2 : 1. These experiments were motivated in part by the possibility that phonon processes in the second harmonic production might be significant. These processes could in principle provide shifts as well as broadening in the observed second harmonic radiation. No evidence for such effects was found.

Harmonic generation of light not only occurs in dielectrics but also, as demonstrated by Lax *et al.* (*400*), occurs in the electron plasma of a metal. They found that the power radiated can be tremendously enhanced and much greater than from an insulator if the metal is selected such that the plasma frequency and maser frequency are related by $\omega = \omega_p$ or $\omega = \omega_p/2$. The harmonics produced in the scattering of light by free electrons has been investigated theoretically (*414*).

An interesting development is the generation of second harmonic radiation from a maser itself, which was observed for the first time by Armstrong *et al.* (*414a*) using a GaAs diode oscillating at 8350 Å. All possible sum frequencies of the various axial modes has also been seen in the GaAs diode maser (*414b*).

Closely related to second harmonic production are the sum frequency experiments. For example in an experiment by Miller and Savage (410) intensity before combination of a ruby maser and a $CaWO_4 : Nd^{3+}$ maser were respectively 115 watts and 30 watts. Of the order of 10^6 to 10^7 photons at the sum frequency were produced by focussing these beams in KDP or ADP oriented for optimum velocity matching. In an experiment with a $CaWO_4 : Nd^{3+}$ maser which contained the 1.0582μ and 1.0652μ lines, they observed not only the second harmonic of each line but also the sum frequency, 5308Å, by focusing the maser beam on an ADP crystal. The ability to produce second harmonic generation with the $CaWO_3 : Nd^{3+}$ maser operating at 1μ extends the possibility of investigating second harmonic generation in a number of crystals which are opaque in the near ultraviolet region.

5. Induced dc Polarization

It is clear from (13.6) that second harmonic production should be accompanied by a dc component of the polarization, analogous with the dc current in ordinary electronic rectifiers. Such optical rectification has been observed by Bass et al. (415) in KDP. According to the theory of Armstrong et al. (402), there is a quantitative relationship between the coefficients of the electro-optic effect, χ_{ijk}^{ω}, and the rectification, χ_{ijk}^{0}, namely, $\chi_{ijk}^{0} = \chi_{jik}^{\omega}$. Using the known optical coefficients for KDP and this relation, Bass et al. (415) found good agreement between theoretical and measured values of the rectified polarization. This nonlinear optical effect is interesting because it is the first which can be predicted quantitatively from the known optical properties of the crystal.

If the frequency of two maser beams differ slightly, the difference frequency may fall in the microwave or far infrared regions. Such a difference frequency is considered low and described by χ_{ijk}^{0} when it is small compared with any ionic or electronic absorption bands in the crystal. According to Franken and Ward (396a), a number of investigators have without success searched for difference frequencies in the microwave and far infrared regions. However, an apparently successful observation of a microwave difference frequency in quartz has recently been reported by Niebuhr (415a). He mixed the axial modes of a ruby maser in quartz contained in a microwave cavity, and detected the beat frequency at 2,964 Mc.

6. Higher Order Effects

Evidence for several higher order effects has come from an interesting set of experiments by Terhune *et al.* (*399*). Although the crystal calcite possesses a center of inversion, they were able to produce second harmonic generation in this crystal by applying a dc electric field. The magnitude of the relevant elements of $\chi''^{2\omega}_{ijkl}$ were estimated to be $\sim 10^{-15}$. In the absence of the applied field very weak second harmonic radiation, in phase quadrature with the dc induced radiation, was also detected. This result is consistent with the processes $\chi'^{2\omega}_{ijkl} E^{\omega}_j \nabla_k E^{\omega}_l$ and $\eta^{2\omega}_{ijkl} E^{\omega}_k E^{\omega}_l$. The magnitude of the relevant elements of $\chi'^{2\omega}_{ijkl}$ or $\eta^{2\omega}_{ijkl}$ were estimated to be 10^{-18} esu. They also observed the third harmonic by orienting the maser beam with respect to the optic axis to obtain an index matching condition such that two ordinary red photons and one extraordinary red photon combine to produce an extraordinary third harmonic ultraviolet photon. About 10^4 third harmonic photons were produced per maser pulse, from which result the magnitude of the relevant elements of $\chi^{3\omega}_{ijkl}$ were estimated to be $\sim 10^{-15}$ esu.

7. The Effect of Boundaries

Thus far the discussion has dealt with the progagation of light and its harmonics in a nonlinear dielectric medium of infinite extent. However, Bloembergen and Pershan (*416*) have obtained solutions to Maxwell's equations in nonlinear dielectrics which satisfy the boundary conditions at a plane interface between a linear and non-linear medium, and in so doing have generalized the well-known laws of reflection and refraction. They have developed expressions for the directions and polarizations of harmonic waves generated at the boundary, and have presented the various conditions for total reflection and transmission of boundary harmonics. Since harmonic waves are generated on reflection from the boundary of a nonlinear dielectric, harmonic power generation may be enhanced by multiple total reflections from a pair of plates. The distance between the plates and the dispersion in the linear medium between the plates should be chosen, however, such that on each reflection second harmonic radiation is generated with the correct phase to add to the harmonic power (*416*).

Ducuing and Bloembergen have observed the second harmonic in the light from a Q-switched ruby maser reflected from GaAs (*416a*).

XIV. Applications of Optical Masers

A. INTRODUCTION

The unique features of the radiation from optical masers are its monochromaticity and coherence, very high power levels, and highly collimated beams. Since the physical properties of coherent light are ideally just those of the phase coherent signals in the radio frequency and microwave regions of the electromagnetic spectrum, the advent of optical masers means that the concepts and techniques of electronics and microwaves are now extended to the infrared and optical regions. In fact, a whole new technology using generators, amplifiers, and mixers that work with coherent light is rapidly developing.

Although current work on infrared and optical masers is heavily concerned with obtaining oscillations in various materials and wavelengths, and comparing their properties with theoretical expectations, there is also considerable effort in pressing towards the limit of monochromaticity, directivity, and in obtaining large amounts of power, both pulsed and continuous. These developments make possible scientific experiments and technologic applications that are of considerable importance. A number of papers dealing with applications and application possibilities have appeared (*417–420*).

The many applications that have been made or proposed for the optical maser will be surveyed in this chapter. However, several applications, because they serve to amplify or illuminate topics treated earlier in this review, or because of their importance, are singled out for more detailed discussion. Two of these applications are communications, and the use of the optical maser as pump for the production of single and multiple photon transitions in various devices. Another subject, fundamental to several applications but particularly to communications and radar, is that of modulating the maser. Methods for accomplishing this are briefly summarized in the following section.

B. Modulation Methods

In the red portion of the spectrum, the frequency of light is approximately 4×10^{14} cps. A 1% band there has a width of 4×10^6 Mc, enough for 10^9 simultaneous telephone conversations. When one further considers that because of the highly directional beams that can be produced, many simultaneous channels can exist in the same frequency band without mutual interference, the problem is clearly not lack of spectrum space but of how to make use of it. In view of this, it is not surprising that considerable effort in the direction of modulating the optical maser so as to fill up the spectrum is in progress. Although the internal modulation of masers by using the Zeeman and Stark effects has been considered, most of the work reported thus far has been with external modulation schemes, i.e., Kerr cells or the electro-optical effect in ADP ($NH_4H_2PO_4$) and KDP (KH_2PO_4) crystals. Beams from optical masers have been modulated by these methods at frequencies up to about 10^4 Mc thus far, but at the cost of large modulating powers. Various methods of modulating infrared beams have been reviewed with the conclusion that the electro-optic effect in KDP appears to be the most promising method (*421*).

Possible methods for externally modulating light in the microwave region and beyond by the use of various acoustic, magnetic, and electric effects in solids have been analyzed (*423, 424*). For practical modulators, gases are not dense enough to have sufficient interaction with the microwave-optical fields and so were not considered. The successful microwave modulation of light was achieved by Kaminow (*425*) and Blumenthal (*426*) by using the electro-optic effect in KDP and ADP, respectively. KDP is transparent between 4000 Å and 13,000 Å. The tunnelling frequency in KDP for the protons in the double minimum potential, a process involved in the electro-optic effect, occurs at 6000 kMc. It may be possible, therefore, to extend the modulating frequency to much higher frequencies than the currently observed 10 kMc region (*425*). The wide band microwave modulation of light by travelling wave interaction in materials such as KDP has been discussed by a number of authors (*427–430*). A modulator using a material such as KDP in a resonant structure, the Fabry-Perot resonator, has been analyzed (*431*).

Amplitude modulation up to 80% of a light beam of several milliwatts power by means of the Kerr effect was accomplished by

Holshouser *et al.* (*432*) at 3 and 6 kMc. This represents a substantial increase in frequency over Rupp's experiment in the late 1920's (*433*) where green light was modulated at frequencies of about 10^8 cps.

In addition to the work on light modulation discussed thus far, a variety of other work in this active area is discussed in the literature (*227g, 422, 434–439*).

C. COMMUNICATION AND RADAR

The use of coherent light for communication is an obvious application and is a subject which has been analyzed by several authors (*418, 442, 443, 443a*). Among the factors which must be considered in assessing the potential of the optical maser in this application are the channel width and the transmission loss. Modulation methods for obtaining large channel widths have been considered in the previous section. The transmission loss is expected to be very small, disregarding atmospheric scattering and attenuation, because of the highly directional beams obtained with optical masers.

The formula for directional transmission of radiation is the same in optical region as in the microwave region, namely,

$$P_R = \frac{P_T G_T A_R}{4\pi D^2} = P_T \frac{A_T}{\lambda^2} \frac{A_R}{D^2}, \qquad (14.1)$$

where P_R and P_T are, respectively, the power received and transmitted, A_R and A_T are, respectively, the area of the receiving and transmitting antennas, λ is the wavelength, and D is the distance between the antennas. The relation used in (14.1), $G_T = A_T \pi^{-1}(\lambda/2\pi)^{-2}$, is a general result for antenna gain of a uniformly illuminated surface of area A_T. The factor λ^2 in the denominator reflects the fact that the beam width is limited by diffraction and that for antennas of fixed size the improvement in transmission loss with decreased wavelength comes about from this cause alone.

Equation (14.1) suggests that the received power may be increased by increasing the gain or the effective radiating aperture. This can be accomplished by bringing the light from a maser to a focus by the first lens, and allowing the light from the diffraction pattern at the focus to propagate to a second lens, an arrangement which is the optical telescope in reverse (Fig. 53). The beam width from the second lens is decreased in proportion to its diameter and the power gain is just $(f_2/f_1)^2$. For example, a 12-in. diameter telescope on the earth could produce a central spot of light only 8800 ft in diameter on the moon.

There are, however, practical limits to the beams which can be achieved. Thus, to reach the diffraction limit, an objective mirror must be well within a quarter of a wavelength of the true figure over its entire surface.

A study has been made to determine the conditions that must be fulfilled for optical systems to take full advantage of the coherent properties of light emitted by optical masers (444). However, even if optical surfaces were perfect, atmospheric scattering would limit the usable beam sharpness. In addition, the effect of molecular absorption by the atmosphere must be considered (444a). For this reason, the use of a controlled atmosphere provided by a pipe has been proposed for terrestrial communication. The scattering problem is, of course, nonexistent in communicating in free space between satellites or from one space vehicle to another. Examples of what may be expected in communicating between the earth and other places in the solar system and in interstellar communication, and comparisons of optical and microwave systems for these applications have been discussed by several authors (418, 442, 443).

Various types of receivers for light beams have been discussed: heterodyne receivers for rf-modulated light (440); homodyne detection of phase modulated light (441); automatic frequency control of optical heterodyne detection (443b), and reception of single-side band suppressed-carrier signals (443c).

Quantum effects and noise in communication systems, which are important with the advent of communication in the infrared and optical range, have been investigated (445, 445a).

Closely related to the use of optical masers in communication systems is its use in optical radar (446–448). A rudimentary optical radar has been constructed and its performance investigated (446). The requirements of a pulse-Doppler radar using an optical maser has been theoretically studied (449). It may be mentioned here that coherent light scattered from diffuse surfaces exhibits some unusual characteristics* due to the interference of coherent diffraction patterns (450–452).

D. The Optical Maser as a Pumping Source

1. Introduction

Because the optical maser is a high power and highly monochromatic light source, it is naturally suitable for optical pumping, and

* The scattered red light of the CW He-Ne maser has a granular appearance and scintillates.

for producing such multiple quantum effects as: double photon absorption, Raman emission, photon mixing, and the production of optical harmonics. These processes produce coherent radiation at new frequencies, and with suitable electromagnetic structures it is possible to develop new classes of optical devices, such as induced Raman and parametric oscillators. The various types of quantum transitions that may be induced by maser radiation, the effects produced, and their applications are summarized in Table III.

TABLE III. THE EFFECTS PRODUCED BY PHOTON PROCESSES OF VARIOUS ORDERS AND
THEIR APPLICATIONS

Type of transition	Effect	Application
Single photon	Optical pumping	Millimeter and submillimeter masers
Double photon	Two photon absorption	Produce optical maser action at a frequency higher than that of the pump, nonlinear optical properties
	Spontaneous Raman emission	Raman spectroscopy
	Induced Raman emission	Raman oscillators
Three photon	Production of sum, second harmonic, and difference frequency	Parametric oscillators, study of nonlinear optical properties
Four photon	Third harmonic production	Parametric oscillators, study of nonlinear optical properties

An attractive possibility for obtaining coherent far infrared radiation is by heterodyning the output of two optical masers. It has been suggested that a tunable source of radiation for these regions may be obtained by simply using the nonlinear field emission properties of a mercury arc or cold cathode arc (453), or just liquid cesium (454) to obtain beats. The beating process in a semiconductor which lacks inversion symmetry thus allowing the third order process has been theoretically investigated (454a).

2. Optical Pumping

Using the ruby maser as an optical pump, Devor et al. (455) obtained microwave maser action in a ruby crystal due to population inversion among the ground state sublevels produced by absorption of the light from the ruby optical maser (see Fig. 23). This experiment was also independently proposed by other investigators (456). Estimates of the expected population inversion in the ground state of several crystals, including ruby, due to optical pumping was reported earlier (457). The requirements and predicted performance of optically pumped masers have been recently analyzed (458). The significance of the ruby pumping experiment is that it points the way to obtaining maser action in multilevel systems in the submillimeter wavelength region by optical pumping, thereby bypassing the need for electron devices which are yet to be developed. However, it should be mentioned that the optical pumping of ruby proved to be difficult because of the necessity of precisely matching the energy levels in the pumped ruby crystal and in the optical maser which tend to be at somewhat different temperatures. This difficulty may be avoided and a more compact arrangement achieved if optical maser action and microwave maser action could be obtained in the same crystal. In any case, it should be noted that dielectric losses will hinder the attainment of maser action in ionic crystals in the submillimeter and far infrared regions. [Further work on microwave maser action in ruby by pumping with a ruby optical maser has been reported by Szabo (457a)].

Optical pumping with a maser to produce population inversion results in heating the lattice. However, optical pumping cycles are available which represent an energy extraction process and under suitable circumstances should result in cooling the crystal. This possibility has been theoretically studied by several people (458a, 458b).

3. Raman Emission

An intense, truly monochromatic Raman source in the red is desirable for studying the vibrations of molecules of substances which absorb in the ultraviolet, of fluorescing materials, and for low-lying frequencies. Porto and Wood (459) have investigated the use of the pulsed ruby maser as a source and have observed the usual spontaneous Raman effect in CCl_4 and C_6H_6. For example, Raman lines in C_6H_6 displaced from the source at 14,400 cm^{-1} by 849, 992, 1178, 1585, and 1606 cm^{-1} were observed by flashing a 1 joule ruby maser 50 times. Even though it was shown that the ruby maser worked as a Raman source, the authors felt that in its present form it was not very much better than other red sources. For example, the advantage of monochromaticity* was not fully realized because of the frequency dependence of the ruby maser on temperature, a difficulty which appeared in connection with the application of the ruby maser as an optical pump.

Although higher power ruby masers may be used, it is nevertheless important to optimize the coupling of the Raman radiation with the substance. Porto and Wood (459) suggested that this may be done by using a ruby maser with a detached mirror and inserting the substance directly in the optical cavity. This was essentially the arrangement, but with the ruby maser operated in the pulsed reflector mode, with which induced Raman emission in the nitrobenzene of the Kerr cell (see Fig. 31) made its appearance in an experiment by Woodbury and Ng (394). The effect was identified and observed in a number of other organic liquids including C_6H_6, C_6D_6, toluene, pyridine, cyclohexane by Eckhardt et al. (395). Induced Raman emission, which has since been observed in a number of gases, liquids, and solids (see Tables II.1 and II.2) has provided coherent radiation at many new wavelengths.

4. Optical Parametric Devices

Parametric interactions, which were studied as early as the nineteenth century by Rayleigh and others, have in recent years received a great deal of attention because of their successful utilization in low noise microwave amplifiers. An introductory treatment of parametric devices is given in Heffner (462). Quantum mechanical models for parametric interactions are discussed by Jaynes (463), Louisell (464), and Fontana (465). For a general treatment of parametric effects, especially appropriate for the optical region, see Armstrong et al. (402), and Bloembergen and Pershan (416). A simplified treatment of their theory (402) is given in Appendix IV.

The following lines of distinction have been drawn between parametric and maser devices: (1) the maser is not phase sensitive whereas phase coherence among the fields is important in parametric devices, and (2) the maser must have a population inversion, i.e., it must be at a negative temperature. Like many efforts at characterization, examples can be found where the lines of distinction seem to disappear, and the same is apparently true of the preceding criteria.

* The Raman effect has been observed by using the 6328Å CW He-Ne maser as a source (459a).

(See the discussion at the end of the papers by Heffner, *462*, and Jaynes, *463*). Nevertheless, we make the distinction that the maser utilizes single photon transitions, whereas the parametric device utilizes at least triple photon transitions.

It has been shown that in a quantum-mechanical system, the Manley-Rowe equations follow directly from the principle that at equilibrium the rate at which quanta leave a given level must equal the rate at which quanta arrive at that level (*466*). These equations govern the power flow at the various frequencies in a circuit containing a nonlinear reactance, and provide a very useful framework within which to discuss parametric processes. However, it will be sufficient here to characterize these processes in terms of the energy conservation condition,

$$\nu_1 + \nu_2 + \nu_3 = 0, \tag{14.2}$$

where ν_1, ν_2, and ν_3 are the frequencies of radiation fields. Positive signs for ν_1, ν_2, and ν_3 are equivalent to an absorption of a photon at the corresponding frequency, and negative signs indicate emission. Suppose as a first case that $\nu_1 = \nu_p$, $\nu_2 = -\nu_i$, and $\nu_3 = -\nu_s$, then from (14.2) we have $\nu_p = \nu_i + \nu_s$, the case of the regenerative parametric amplifier. This result indicates that pump power applied at ν_p, results in power flow at the signal frequency ν_s and idler frequency, $\nu_i = \nu_p - \nu_s$. The condition $\nu_2 = \nu_3 = -\nu_s$, indicates subharmonic generation, or the case of the degenerate parametric amplifier. On the other hand, if $\nu_1 = \nu_2 = \nu_p$ and $\nu_3 = -\nu_s$, then $2\nu_p = \nu_s$, which indicates harmonic generation or a special case of up conversion in the language of parametric amplifiers.

Armstrong *et al.* (*402*) have derived a macroscopic nonlinear polarization in terms of the nonlinear microscopic properties of the dielectric and incorporated this polarization into Maxwell's equations for an infinite, homogeneous, anisotropic medium. Bloembergen and Pershan (*416*) have extended the theory for a finite medium taking into account effects at the boundary. Explicit solutions to Maxwell's equations describe the power transfer between a fundamental wave and its second harmonic, or more generally, between three plane electromagnetic waves which satisfy the energy relationship for the frequencies $\omega_3 = \omega_1 + \omega_2$, and approximately satisfy the momentum relationship for wave vectors $\mathbf{k}_3 = \mathbf{k}_1 + \mathbf{k}_2 + \Delta\mathbf{k}$ where $|\Delta\mathbf{k}| \ll |\mathbf{k}_3|$. These solutions may be regarded as a generalization of the equations describing the traveling wave, parametric amplifier (*460, 461*). In fact, energy and power relationships are derived for the nonlinear dielectric which corresponds to the Manley-Rowe relations (461) in the theory of parametric amplifiers.

The most studied nonlinear interaction between light waves has been that of second harmonic production. The general analysis of Armstrong *et al.* (402) shows how it is possible, in principle, to convert all incident power into the second harmonic by the process of parametric conversion. Kingston (467) has shown how the maser beam may pump a cavity tuned at a subharmonic frequency. An important application of nonlinear interaction of light waves is the generation of submillimeter or far infrared radiation as the beat note of two optical masers (402, 453, 454, 468). According to Armstrong *et al.* (402), with peak optical power of 10 MW, 10 kW can be available at a wavelength of 0.7 mm, if perfect phase matching is obtained.

They discuss another interesting situation involving the parametric conversion between three waves where the objective is to detect a weak coherent light signal at ν_s. If a strong maser beam is applied at the pump frequency ν_p, and if the phase velocity matching is complete, all available signal power is converted to power in a wave at $\nu_s + \nu_p$. If ν_s is in the infrared and ν_p in the red, $\nu_p + \nu_s$ may be in the green or blue and detected with the high efficiency of a photomultiplier tube. This device, the parametric form of the maser photon detector, is noiseless since in the absence of a signal there would be no output. Furthermore, there is no spontaneous emission noise because the pump quanta cannot spontaneously create a quanta at $\nu_s + \nu_p$ without violating energy conservation.

Kroll (469) has considered the theory of parametric amplification in spatially extended media and has applied this theory to the design of tunable oscillators at optical frequencies. He supposes that the dielectric constant of the medium is modulated with frequency ν_p and wave vector $\mathbf{k}_p$ where a frequency range for ν_1 exists such that $|\mathbf{k}_1| + |\mathbf{k}_2| > |\mathbf{k}_p|$. Then over this range an angle and frequency will be uniquely related satisfying $\mathbf{k}_1 + \mathbf{k}_2 = \mathbf{k}_p$. By orienting a crystal of KDP with respect to a Fabry-Perot mirror system, it should be possible to obtain tunable oscillations at ν_1 and ν_2.

Thus far, the discussion of nonlinear optical effects has been entirely concerned with frequency conversion and the generation of power at these frequencies. However, Siegman has shown how an optical parametric subharmonic amplifier will function as an ideal power limiter at the fundamental (470).

E. Other Technological and Scientific Applications

This section discusses the technologic and scientific applications of the optical maser that have not been considered thus far. Although these applications are varied and do not readily lend themselves to classification, it is convenient to discuss them under the headings of the uses of focused radiation and scientific applications. Before discussing the application of focused maser beams, two technological applications using the unfocused maser beam may be mentioned. These are the uses of the ruby maser as a light source for high speed photography (*471, 472*), and a proposal for an electron accelerator using the intense radiation field of the maser for accelerating the electrons (*473*).

1. *Applications Using Focused Radiation*

Whereas communication, for example, requires well collimated beams of light, many applications based on the interaction of light and matter require the intensity that can be obtained with focussed coherent light. Before outlining some of these applications, however, we will present some relations useful for calculating the intensity and minimum beam size of focused light.

To find the power density, S, at the focal point of a lens of focal length f, we put $D = f$, and $S = P_R/A_R$ in (14.1) and obtain*

$$S = \frac{A_T P_T}{\lambda^2 f^2}. \tag{14.3}$$

Although the power density is seen to increase as f^{-2}, the general theorem in photometry that in a medium of uniform refractive index, no lens system can form an image of brightness greater than the brightest part of the source, limits S per unit solid angle to a value no greater than P_T/A_T per unit solid angle. Taking the value of 5×10^6 watts for the power output of the pulsed reflector ruby maser, we find that $S = 5 \times 10^{14}$ watts/cm². From the relation,

$$E = (120\pi S)^{1/2}, \tag{14.4}$$

which is obtained from (2.3) and (2.4), we find that this power corresponds to a field strength of 4×10^8 volts/cm!

The radius r of the focal spot is,

$$r = f\theta, \tag{14.5}$$

* A uniformly illuminated objective of area A_T is assumed.

where θ is the beam angle. In the case under consideration, θ is the diffraction limited value and is given by

$$\theta = 1.2\lambda/L, \qquad (14.6)$$

where L is the diameter of a circular aperture. Taking $f = L$, which means that the lens has an F number equal to 1, we find that the diameter of the focal spot is approximately equal to the wavelength. If a diffraction limited beam whose power is 5×10^6 watts is focused into a volume of the order of λ^3, the photon density at the focus is roughly 10^{23} photons/cm^3.

Many uses for the focused optical maser beam exist in diverse fields. It is well known that the focused maser beam can vaporize (473a) materials or punch minute holes in thin slabs of material, and therefore, should be useful in melting refractory materials, in welding, and in micromachining. The focussed maser beam, regarded as a highly brilliant light source, has been applied to high speed photomicrography (474).

The focused beam of the pulsed ruby maser has been used to ionize gases (476c, 476d), induce thermionic emission (476e), and induce emission of electrons and ions from metals (476f, 476g) and semiconductors (476h, 476i).

Some experiments of an exploratory nature in several ophthalmological laboratories have indicated that the focussed maser beam may be useful for the treatment of certain diseases of the eye. In treating the so-called detached retina, the beam is brought to a focus at the desired spot on the retina where it essentially produces a tiny spot weld. Used in the same way, the maser beam was used to disintegrate a dangerous tumor on the retina. It is also clear that the maser beam will have pathological effects upon tissue; studies on occular lesions produced this way have been made (475–476a). The optical ruby maser as a microsurgical instrument has been examined in a preliminary experiment (476b).

2. Scientific Applications

In addition to the technological applications of optical masers, there are a number of experiments possible with optical masers of fundamental interest in science. We have already discussed the use of the optical maser as a high intensity monochromatic source for optical pumping and for producing a variety of multiple photon effects. A number of other scientific applications of the optical maser are summarized below.

(1) The use of tunable optical masers as a source for high resolution spectroscopy is clearly an important area of application. The maser itself, however, has proven to be a spectroscopic device in view of the fact that transitions have been observed for the first time in an oscillating gaseous maser (260).

(2) The use of maser techniques for frequency multiplication from the radio frequency or microwave range into the visible and ultraviolet regions. Frequency multiplication up to the visible region should allow these frequencies to be directly counted and hence measured in units of the time standard. Simultaneous measurement of frequency and wavelength would yield the velocity of light. A novel way of measuring the velocity of light using the He-Ne maser has been discussed (477).

(3) Quantitative measurements of Debye-Sears frequency shifts in the light from a He-Ne maser diffracted by ultrasonic waves in liquid media has been studied (480). These shifts were measured by heterodyning the scattered and the original radiation. A similar technique has been proposed for high resolution Raman spectroscopy (417).

(4) Because of the extreme monochromaticity of the optical maser, it is anticipated that they will be used in experiments requiring measurements or comparisons of two lengths or frequencies. One such an example is an improved version of the Michelson-Morley experiment which was recently performed by Jaseja et al. (481).

(5) A novel circulatory and regenerative multiple beam interferometer making use of optical masers has been suggested for possible use in investigating with high precision various effects of motion and of fields in the propagation of light (112). Using an arrangement of four CW He-Ne gas masers operating as traveling wave devices and arranged in a ring, Macek and Davis (112b) demonstrated the sensing of rotation rate with respect to an inertial frame of reference, and improved by orders of magnitude the classical experiment of Michelson-Gale (482) and Sagnac (483).

(6) The possibility of observing the scattering of light by light by using the intense radiation from optical masers has been examined (*478, 479*).

(7) Thomson scattering of the photons from a ruby maser by a beam of electrons has been observed by Fiocco and Thompson (*484*) and was independently discussed by Hughes (*485*) and Milburn (*486*). Further work has been reported on the scattering of optical maser pulses from a nonequilibrium plasma (*487*), and the measurement of plasma density using the He-Ne maser as an interferometer (*488*). These experiments show that the optical maser should be useful for plasma diagnostics.

Other applications of the optical maser include Rayleigh scattering by gases (*489*), the determination of diffraction grating irregularities by the observation of Rowland ghosts (*490*), and the study of stimulated Brillouin scattering and the coherent generation of intense hypersonic waves (*491*).

Despite the impressive number of applications of optical masers to science and technology that have already been made, further interesting and important developments in this area may be safely anticipated.

Appendix I

TABLES OF OPTICAL MASERS AND THEIR CHARACTERISTICS

TABLE I.1. METAL IONS IN IONIC CRYSTALS[1]

Material, ion concentration[2]	Maser transition[3] (μ)	Pulse threshold[4] (joules)	Pump region[5] (μ)	Terminal maser level (μ)	τ(msec) $\Delta\nu(\text{Å})$[6]	Mode of operation[7]	Comments
Al_2O_3: Cr^{3+} [a,b] 0.052 wt% Cr_2O_3	$^2E \rightarrow {}^4A_2$ 0.6943 (R_1)	44 (300°K)	0.55–0.67 0.32–0.44	0	3.0, 4Å 300°K	P, S 300°K[b] CW, S 77°K[a]	CW$_{th}$ 850W
Al_2O_3: Cr^{3+} [c,d] 0.6 wt%	0.7009 (N_2) 0.7041 (N_1)	2300(77°K)		250 (N_2) 100 (N_1)		P	Energy levels due to Cr^{3+} pairs
Al_2O_3: Cr^{3+} [e]	$^2E \rightarrow {}^4A_2$ 0.6929(R_2)	50% greater than for R_1 line	0.55–0.67 0.32–0.44	0		P, S 300°K	R_1 line suppressed with interference filters as reflectors
CaF_2: Dy^{2+} [f,i] 0.02–0.5% [h]	$^5I_7 \rightarrow {}^5I_8$ 2.36	20(77°K)[h]	0.8–1.0[h]	111	1^g, 10^l <0.5Å[i] 77°K	P, S 77°K[l] P, No S 4°K[l] CW, SC[g] No S 77°K[f,h] 20°K[g]	CW$_{th}$ 100–800W with Dy^{2+} conc. 0.02–0.5%[h]
$CaWO_4$: Er^{3+} [j] 1.0 mole%	$^4I_{13/2} \rightarrow {}^4I_{15/2}$ 1.612	800 (77°K)	0.38 0.52	26.7		P, S	

Material	Transition (μ)					P, S	Remarks
CaF$_2$: Er^{3+} ^{k} 0.1 mole%	$^4I_{13/2} \rightarrow {}^4I_{15/2}$ 1.617	1000 (77°K)	0.35, 0.52 0.65	25	~ 20	P, S	
CaWO$_4$: Ho^{3+} ^{m,l} 0.5%	$^5I_7 \rightarrow {}^5I_8$ 2.046^l 2.059^m	80 (77°K) 250 (77°K)	0.44–0.46	44		P, S	No maser action at room temperature
CaWO$_4$:Ho^{3+} $^\zeta$ 0.5% Ho^{3+} 0.75% Er^{3+}	$^5I_7 \rightarrow {}^5I_8$ 2.0740 (77°K) 2.0707 (77°K) 2.0556 (77°K)	107 (77°K) 170 (77°K) 310 (77°K)	0.53 Er^{3+} 1.5 Er^{3+}	44	1.3,77°K, 20° K	P	Excitation of Ho^{3+} by energy transfer from E^{3+}; Lowers P$_{th}$
CaF$_2$:HO^{3+} ^{m}	$^5I_7 \rightarrow {}^5I_8$ 2.092	260 (77°K)	0.4–0.66	~ 44		P	
CaWO$_4$: Nd^{3+} $^{m-p,9}$ 0.14% ^{n} 0.5% ^{p}	$^4F_{3/2} \rightarrow {}^4I_{11/2}$ a 1.0650 b 1.0633 (77°K) c 1.066 (77°K) d 1.0576 e 1.0641 a 1.0652 (295°K) d 1.0582 (295°K)	$\sim$1.5 14 (77°K) 6 (77°K) 80 7 3 (295°K) 2 (295°K)	0.57–0.6	~ 5.0	~ 0.1, 8.0Å 77°K 77°K 295°K^n 85°K^p SC 85°K^p	P, S 77°K 295°K^n CW, No S 85°K^p SC 85°K^p	CW$_{th} \sim 1300$W SC$_{th} \sim 910$W^p
	$^4F_{3/2} \rightarrow {}^4I_{9/2}$ 0.9145	4.6 (77°K)		21.2		P 77°K^o	Maser action at 0.9μ and 1.3μ by suppressing oscillation at 1.06μ^o
	$^4F_{3/2} \rightarrow {}^4I_{13/2}$ 1.3372 1.345 1.387 (77°K) 1.3392 (295°K)	2.1 (77°K) 7.6 (77°K) 780 (77°K) 3.6 (295°K)		~ 2.5	11Å (77°K) 13Å (77°K)	P 77°K^o	

TABLE I.1.   METAL IONS IN IONIC CRYSTALS[1] *(continued)*

Material, ion concentration[2]	Maser transition[3] (μ)	Pulse threshold[4] (joules)	Pump region[5] (μ)	Terminal maser level (μ)	τ (msec) $\Delta\nu(\text{Å})$[6]	Mode of operation[7]	Comments
BaF_2: $Nd^{3+\,m}$	$^4F_{3/2} \rightarrow {}^4I_{11/2}$ 1.060	1600 (77°K)	0.57–0.6	~5.0		P	No maser action at room temperature
SrF_2: $Nd^{3+\,m,r}$	$^4F_{3/2} \rightarrow {}^4I_{11/2}$ 1.0437 1.0370	150 (77°K) 480 (295°K)	0.72–0.75 0.78–0.81	~5.0	1.3 (300°K) 1.6 (77°K)	P, S 77°K	
LaF_3: $Nd^{3+\,m}$	$^4F_{3/2} \rightarrow {}^4I_{11/2}$ a 1.0631 b 1.0399 a 1.0633	93 (77°K) 75 (77°K) 150 (295°K)	0.5–0.6	~5.0		P 77°K	
Y_2O_3: $Nd^{3+\,\eta}$ 1%	$^4F_{3/2} \rightarrow {}^4I_{11/2}$ 1.073 1.078	260 (77°K) 350 (77°K)			0.26, 4.4Å (77°K)	P, S	Crystal, 2 mm long, 2 mm in diameter
$SrMoO_4$: $Nd^{3+\,m,p,q,9}$	$^4F_{3/2} \rightarrow {}^4I_{11/2}$ a 1.0640 b 1.0652 c 1.059 (77°K) d 1.0627 e 1.0611 a 1.0643 (295°K) f 1.0576	17 70 150 (77°K) 170 500 125 45 (295°K)	0.57–0.60	~5	~3Å (77°K) SC 77°K[p] ~17Å (295°K)	P, S 77°K, 295°K[m] SC 77°K[p]	SC[th] 10 joules[p]

Material	Transition / Wavelength (µ)	Threshold	Range		P, S (°K)	Remarks
CaMoO₄:Nd³⁺ ^{m}	$^4F_{3/2} \rightarrow {}^4I_{11/2}$ 1.067 1.0673	100.0 (77°K) 360.0 (295°K)	0.57–0.59	~5	P 77°K, 295°K	
PbMoO₄:Nd³⁺ ^{m}	$^4F_{3/2} \rightarrow {}^4I_{11/2}$ 1.0586	60 (295°K)	0.57–0.58	~5	P	
SrWO₄:Nd³⁺ ^{m}	$^4F_{3/2} \rightarrow {}^4I_{11/2}$ a 1.0574 b 1.0627 c 1.0607 b 1.063	4.7 5.1 } (77°K) 7.6 180 (295°K)	0.57–0.60	~5	P 77°K, 295°K	
CaF₂: Nd³⁺ ^{s}	$^4F_{3/2} \rightarrow {}^4I_{11/2}$ 1.0457	60 (77°K)	0.7–0.8 0.56–0.58	~5	P, S	No maser action at room temperature
MgF₂: Ni²⁺ ^{t}	1.624			26.5	10(77°K) P, S 20°K, 77°K	Terminal maser level is a phonon level
LaF₃: Pr³⁺ ^{u} 1%	$^3P_0 \rightarrow {}^3H_6$ 0.5985	60 (77°K)	0.42–0.49	2.37	P, S	
CaWO₄: Pr³⁺ ^{v} 0.5 mole%	$^1G_4 \rightarrow {}^3H_4$ 1.0468	20)20, 77, 90°K	0.449 0.476 0.487	26.5	0.05(77°K) P, S 20°K 77, 90°K	No maser action at room temperature
CaF₂: Sm²⁺ ^{w} 0.01 mole%	$^5D_0 \rightarrow {}^7F_1$ 0.7082	> 21 w/cm² (20°K)	0.46–0.42 0.65–0.59	38.0	0.002, 0.8Å P, No S 20°K	Shortest radiative lifetime

TABLE I.1.   METAL IONS IN IONIC CRYSTALS[1] (*continued*)

Material, ion concentration[2]	Maser transition[3] (μ)	Pulse threshold[4] (joules)	Pump region[5] (μ)	Terminal maser level (μ)	τ (msec) $\Delta\nu$(Å)[6]	Mode of operation[7]	Comments
SrF$_2$: Sm^{2+} ^{v} 0.1 mole%	$^5D_0 \rightarrow {}^7F_1$ 0.6969		0.65–0.59	37.1	14, 0.33Å 4.2°K	P, S 4.2°K	
CaWO$_4$: Tm^{3+} ^{m,z} 0.5%	$^3H_4 \rightarrow {}^3H_6$ 1.911 1.916	60 (77°K) 73	1.7–1.8 0.46–0.48	~ 30.8		P, S	No maser action at room temperature
CaWO$_4$: Tm^{3+} $^{\zeta}$ 0.5% Tm^{3+} 0.75% Er^{3+}	$^3H_4 \rightarrow {}^3H_6$ 1.9115 1.9060	19 (77°K) 20 (77°K)	0.53 Er^{3+} 1.5 Er^{3+}	~ 30.8	≥ 0.9(77°K, 20°K)	P	Excitation of Tm^{3+} by energy transfer from Er^{3+}. Lowers P_{th}
SrF$_2$: Tm^{3+} ^{m}	$^3H_4 \rightarrow {}^3H_6$ 1.972	1600 (77°K)				P	
CaF$_2$: Tm^{2+} $^{m,\alpha}$ 0.05 mole%	$^2F_{5/2} \rightarrow {}^2F_{7/2}$ 1.1153	450 (20°K) 800 (77°K)	0.53–0.63 0.39–0.46 0.28–0.34	0	4 (4.2°K) < 0.04Å (27°K)$^{\mu}$	P, No S 4.2°K P 20, 77°K	Smallest fluorescent linewidth
CaF$_2$: U^{3+} $^{x,\beta-\epsilon}$ 0.007–0.06 mole% (conc.) 0.005 mole% (dilute)	$^4I_{11/2} \rightarrow {}^4I_{9/2}$ a 2.61$^{x,\beta,\delta}$ b 2.57$^{\delta}$ c 2.51$^{x,\delta}$ d 2.24$^{\epsilon}$	(a) 2.0(20°K) 3.28(77°K) 4.35(90°K) 1200(300°K)$^{\beta}$	0.5–0.6 0.9	(a) 16.4$^{\beta}$ (a), (c) 19.4$^{x,\delta}$	(a) 0.13 4.2°K, 20,77°K 0.095 90°K$^{\beta}$ (c) 0.14 4.2°K^{x}	(a) CW, No S 77°K (b) P 300°K$^{\delta}$ (a, c) P, S 4.2°K^{x} (d) P$^{\epsilon}$	(a), (b) concentrated crystals (c) dilute crystals (d) observed ratio of trigonal: tetragonal sites is 10:1$^{\epsilon,10}$ (a), (b), (c) typical of tetragonal sites (a) CW$_{th}$ < 2000W SC < 1150W$^{\beta}$

SrF₂: U³⁺ᵏ 0.1 mole%	$^4I_{11/2} \rightarrow {}^4I_{9/2}$ 2.407	38 (90°K) 8 (20°K)	1.0–1.3 0.4–0.6	30	∼ 0.06(90°K) 90°K	P 20°K	No maser action at 300°K
BaF₂: U³⁺ᵏ	$^4I_{11/2} \rightarrow {}^4I_{9/2}$ 2.556	12 (20°K)	1.1–1.5	94	∼0.15(20°K)	P, S 20°K	No maser action at 77°K

KEY:

P = Pulsed
S = Spiking

CW = Continuous
SC = Semi-continuous

th = Threshold
P$_{th}$ = Pulse Threshold

No S = No Spiking

REFERENCES:

^{a}(142) ^{d}(153) ^{g}(156) ^{j}(157) ^{m}(158a) ^{p}(161) ^{s}(164) ^{v}(165) ^{y}(167) ^{β}(170) ^{ε}(173) ^{λ}(175)

^{b}(150) ^{e}(154) ^{h}(156a) ^{k}(157a) ^{n}(159) ^{q}(162) ^{t}(164a) ^{w}(49) ^{z}(168) ^{γ}(171) ^{ζ}(158b) ^{μ}(224)

^{c}(152) ^{f}(155) ^{i}(156b) ^{l}(158) ^{o}(160) ^{r}(163) ^{u}(166) ^{x}(144) ^{α}(169) ^{δ}(172) ^{κ}(174) ^{η}(176)

[1] Stimulated emission has been observed in Nd³⁺, Ho³⁺, Pr³⁺, Er³⁺, and Tm³⁺ in the host crystal Ca(NbO₃)₂ (155a).

[2] Unless otherwise indicated the concentration refers to the maser ion. The designation x% refers to ratio of maser ions to host ions, which it replaces. 0.052 wt% Cr₂O₃ gives 1.6 × 10¹⁹Cr³⁺/cm³ ^{b}. 0.01 mole% Sm²⁺ gives 3 × 10¹⁸ Sm²⁺/cm³ ^{w}.

[3] Russell–Saunders (LS) notation is used except for Cr³⁺ and Ni²⁺.

[4] The pulse threshold for stimulated emission is measured as the energy input to an FT524 helical xenon flash lamp. Threshold figures depend on a number of factors: the number of active ions; the optical quality of the crystal; and the pulse duration relative to fluorescence lifetime. For materials with lifetimes small in comparison with pulse duration, the shorter the pulse duration the lower will be the measured threshold.

Crystal samples were in the form of cylinders, on the average roughly 1 in. × ¼ in., with the ends ground plane parallel or spherical, and silvered or coated with a dielectric reflecting layer.

[5] This column lists the principal pumping region, i.e., the absorption region which can be coupled into most effectively. This does not mean, in general, that the crystal cannot be pumped at other wavelengths.

[6] The values of $τ$ and $Δν$ are for the maser transition of the normal (unexcited) material. Milliseconds are understood where units are not shown.

[7] When P appears without S or No S, it means that the author has not specified whether or not there was spiking.

[8] When the lamp is excited by alternating current, the maser output will be modulated or turned on and off by the lamp. Such operation is called semi-continuous.

[9] The maser lines obtained vary from one crystal to another depending on their quality and charge compensation.

[10] The trigonal centers are U⁴⁺ ions (173a).

TABLE I.2. RARE EARTH IONS IN GLASS[1]

Material, ion concentration	Maser transition (μ)	Pulse threshold[2] (joules)	Pump region[2] (μ)	Position of terminal maser level (μ)	τ (msec) Δν(Å)[2]	Mode of operation	Comments
Ho[3+] [a] in Silicate Glass ~1 mole% Ho[3+]	$^5I_7 \to {}^5I_8$ > 1.95	3600(77°K)	0.44–0.46	—	~0.7(77°K)	P, S	Maser wavelength not well established
Nd[3+] [b,c,d,2] in Barium Crown Glass	$^4F_{3/2} \to {}^4I_{11/2}$ 1.06			~40	~0.6(300°K)[b] ~0.4(300°K)[d]	CW, S[d] 300°K	CW_th 1370W[d]
0.13–2.0 wt% Nd$_2$O$_3$	$^4F_{3/2} \to {}^4I_{9/2}$					P, S 80°K, 300°K	Stimulated emission at 0.9180μ by
6.25 wt%[d] Nd$_2$O$_3$	0.9180	700 (80°K)[c]		26.3		P, S 80°K, 300°K	suppressing 1.061μ line[c]
Yb[3+] [e,f] in Silicate Glass	$^2F_{5/2} \to {}^2F_{7/2}$ 1.015	1300 (77°K)	0.914 0.946 ~0.98	0	1.5 (77°K)	P, S	GE FT503 lamp. 29 lines from 1.0125μ to 1.0184μ

REFERENCES: [a] (178); [b] (179); [c] (180); [d] (181a); [e] (182); [f] (181).

[1] The variation of fluorescent properties with respect to variations in the compositions of oxide glasses has been reported (181b).
[2] See notes 4, 5, and 6 of Table I.1.

TABLE I.3. METALLO-ORGANIC COMPOUNDS

Material, ion concentration	Maser transition (μ)	Pulse threshold[1] (joules)	Pump Region (μ)	Position of terminal maser level (μ)	τ (msec) $\Delta\nu$ (Å)	Mode of operation	Comments
EuB$_3$ [a,b,c] in alcohol 5.2 × 10^{18} Eu^{3+}/cm^3 [a]	$^5D_0 \rightarrow {}^7F_2$ 0.6131	1800 [a,2] 125°K 750 [b,3] 125°K	0.29–0.35 0.39–0.42	~ 11.1	55 msec 16Å ~125°K	P, S	Resonators: 4 mm id frozen solution[a] Capillary cell, liquid.[b]

REFERENCES: [a] (182a); [b] (184); [c] (184a).

[1] A GE FT524 lamp was used.
[2] EuB$_3$—europium benzoylacetonate.
[3] An alcohol solution, 10^{-2} molar was used.

TABLE I.4. HELIUM-NEON[1]

Wavelength[2] (μ)	Transition[3]		Pressure (mm Hg)		Reference
	Paschen notation (Ne)	Racah notation	He	Ne	
0.5940	$3s_2-2p_8$	$5s'[1/2]_1^0-3p\,[5/2]_2$			a
0.6046	$3s_2-2p_7$	$5s'[1/2]_1^0-3p\,[3/2]_1$			a
0.6118	$3s_2-2p_6$	$5s'[1/2]_1^0-3p'[3/2]_2$			a, b
0.6293	$3s_2-2p_5$	$5s'[1/2]_1^0-3p'[3/2]_1$			a, b
0.6328	$3s_2-2p_4$	$5s'[1/2]_1^0-3p'[3/2]_2$			a
0.6351	$3s_2-2p_3$	$5s'[1/2]_1^0-3p\,[1/2]_0$			a
0.6401	$3s_2-2p_2$	$5s'[1/2]_1^0-3p'[1/2]_1$			a, b
0.7305	$3s_2-2p_1$	$5s'[1/2]_1^0-3p'[1/2]_0$			a
1.0798	$2s_5-2p_7$	$4s'[1/2]_0^0-3p\,[3/2]_1$	1–2	0.1–0.2	c
1.0844	$2s_2-2p_6$	$4s'[1/2]_1^0-3p\,[3/2]_2$	1–2	0.1–0.2	c
1.1143	$2s_4-2p_8$	$4s\,[3/2]_1^0-3p\,[5/2]_2$	1–2	0.1–0.2	c
1.1177	$2s_5-2p_9$	$4s\,[3/2]_2^0-3p\,[5/2]_3$	1	0.1	d, e
1.1390	$2s_5-2p_8$	$4s\,[3/2]_2^0-3p\,[5/2]_2$	1–2	0.1–0.2	c
1.1409	$2s_2-2p_5$	$4s'[1/2]_1^0-3p'[3/2]_1$			f
1.1523	$2s_2-2p_4$	$4s'[1/2]_1^0-3p'[3/2]_2$	1	0.1	d, e
1.1601	$2s_3-2p_3$	$4s'[1/2]_1^0-3p\,[1/2]_0$			f
1.1614	$2s_3-2p_5$	$4s'[1/2]_0^0-3p'[3/2]_1$	1	0.1	d, e
1.1767	$2s_2-2p_2$	$4s'[1/2]_1^0-3p'[1/2]_1$	1–2	0.1–0.2	c
1.1985	$2s_3-2p_2$	$4s'[1/2]_1^0-3p'[1/2]_1$	1	0.1	d, e
1.2066	$2s_5-2p_6$	$4s\,[3/2]_2^0-3p\,[3/2]_2$	1	0.1	d, e
1.5231	$2s_2-2p_1$	$4s'[1/2]_1^0-3p'[1/2]_0$	1–2	0.1–0.2	c
1.8281(v_0)		$4f\,[9/2]_4-3d\,[7/2]_4^0$ $4f\,[9/2]_5-3d\,[7/2]_4^0$	0.5	0.025	g
1.8287(v_0)		$4f\,[9/2]_4-3d\,[7/2]_3^0$	0.5	0.05	g
1.8309(v_0)		$4f\,[5/2]_2-3d\,[3/2]_2$ $4f\,[5/2]_3-3d\,[3/2]_2^0$	0.5	0.05	g
1.8408(v_0)		$4f\,[5/2]_2-3d\,[3/2]_1^0$	0.5	0.005	g
1.8596(v_0)		$4f\,[7/2]_3-3d\,[5/2]_2^0$	0.5	0.025	g
1.8602(v_0)		$4f\,[7/2]_3-3d\,[5/2]_3^0$ $4f\,[7/2]_4-3d\,[5/2]_3^0$	0.5	0.025	g
2.396[4]	$3p_4-2s_2$		0.5	0.1	k
2.784		$5s'[1/2]_0^0-4p\,[3/2]_1$	0.5	0.1	h

TABLE 1.4. HELIUM-NEON[1] *(continued)*

Wavelength[2] (μ)	Transition[3]		Pressure (mm Hg)		Reference
	Paschen notation (Ne)	Racah notation	He	Ne	
2.944		$5s\,[3/2]^0_1\text{--}4p\,[1/2]_1$	0.5	0.1	*h*
3.3179		$5s\,[3/2]^0_1\text{--}4p\,[5/2]_2$	0.5	0.1	*h*
3.3343(v_0)		$5s'[1/2]^0_1\text{--}4p'[3/2]_1$	0.5	0.1	*h, l*
3.3362(v_0)		$5s\,[3/2]^0_2\text{--}4p\,[5/2]_3$	0.5	0.1	*h, l*
3.3913	$3s_2\text{--}3p_4$	$5s'[1/2]^0_1\text{--}4p'[1/2]_1$	0.5	0.1	*h, i*
3.3922		$5s'[1/2]^0_1\text{--}4p'[3/2]_2$	0.5	0.1	*h, i*
3.4487		$5s\,[3/2]^0_1\text{--}4p\,[3/2]_1$	0.5	0.1	*h, i*
3.5846		$5s\,[3/2]^0_2\text{--}4p\,[3/2]_2$	0.5	0.1	*h, i*
3.980		$5s\,[3/2]^0_1\text{--}4p\,[1/2]_0$	0.5	0.1	*h, i*
35.602(v_c)		$7p\,[1/2]_0\text{--}6d\,[3/2]^0_1$	0.1	0.05	*j*
53.486(v_c)		$7p\,[3/2]_2\text{--}6d\,[5/2]^0_3$	0.12	0.06	*j*
54.019(v_c)		$7p\,[3/2]_1\text{--}6d\,[5/2]^0_2$	0.1	0.05	*j*
54.117(v_c)		$7p\,[5/2]_2\text{--}6d\,[7/2]^0_3$	0.1	0.05	*j*
57.355(v_c)		$7p\,[5/2]_3\text{--}6d\,[7/2]^0_4$	0.07	0.03	*j*

REFERENCES:

a—(256a)	*d*—(237)	*g*—(256b)	*j*—(260a)
b—(253a)	*e*—(13)	*h*—(260)	*k*—(260b)
c—(254)	*f*—(255)	*i*—(256)	*l*—(496)

[1] Neon is excited by collisions of the second kind with He as follows:

He $(2\,^3S_1)$ + Ne $(2p^6)$ → He $(1\,^1S)$ + Ne $(2p^5\,4s)$ + Ne $(2p^5\,4f)$

He $(2\,^1S_0)$ + Ne $(2p^6)$ → He $(1\,^1S)$ + Ne $(2p^5\,5s)$

He $(2\,^1P_1)$ + Ne $(2p^6)$ → He $(1\,^1S)$ + Ne $(2p^5\,7p)$ (tentative)

[2] The designation (v_0) means the observed wavelength reduced to vacuum, and (v_c) means the calculated wavelength in vacuum. All other wavelengths are the observed values in air.

[3] Two transitions shown for a given wavelength indicates an ambiguity in assignment.

[4] The $3p_4 \to 2s_2$ transition is normally absorptive in a He-Ne filled discharge tube. However, when mirrors are placed on boths ends of the tube, the strong oscillations at 3.39μ ($3s_2 \to 3p_4$) and 0.633μ ($2s_2 \to 2p_4$), respectively, populate the upper level and depopulate the lower level of the $3p_4 \to 2s_2$ transition. Oscillation on the $3p_4 \to 2s_4$ and $3p_2 \to 2s_5$ transitions at $2.0350\,\mu$ and $1.9577\,\mu$ have also been obtained (497).

TABLE I.5. GASES EXCITED BY DISSOCIATION

Optical maser (gas)	Maser wavelength (μ)	Maser transition[1]	Pressure (mm Hg)	Reference
Ne–O$_2$ Ar–O$_2$	0.84462	$3p^3P_2-3s^3S_1^0$ (O I)	0.35 Ne; 0.014 O$_2$ 1.3 Ar; 0.036 O$_2$	a
He–CO, Ne–CO He–CO$_2$, Ne–CO$_2$	1.0689 1.4539 0.8446	$3p^3D_3-3s^3P_2^0$ (C I) $3p^1P_1-3s^1P_1^0$ (C I) $3p^3P_2-3s^3S_1^0$ (O I)	1.0 Ne; 0.01 CO, CO$_2$ 2.0 He; 0.01 CO, CO$_2$	b,c
He–NO, Ne–NO He–NO$_2$, Ne–NO$_2$	1.3583 1.4544 0.8446	$3p^2S_{1/2}^0-3s^2P_{3/2}$ (N I) $4s^4P_{5/2}-3p^2D_{5/2}^0$ (N I) $3p^3P_2-3s^3S_1^0$ (O I)	1.0 Ne; 0.03 NO, NO$_2$ 2.0 He; 0.03 NO, NO$_2$	b
SF$_6$ He–SF$_6$	1.0455 1.0628	$4p^3P_2-4s^3S_1^0$ (S I) $4p'^1F_3-4s'^1D_2^0$ (S I)	0.03 SF$_6$ 2 He; 0.03 SF$_6$	b
Ar–Br$_2$	0.844628 (Br) 0.844638 (Br) 0.844670 (Br) 0.844679 (Br)		1.8 Ar; 0.09 Br$_2$	b

REFERENCES: a—(244); b—(244a); c—(245).
[1] The notation I refers to the un-ionized atom.

TABLE I.6. MISCELLANEOUS GASES: EXCITATION BY ELECTRON IMPACT

Gas	Wavelength (μ)	Transition[3]	Comments	Reference
Hg, He–Hg[1]	1.5295 1.813	$6p'\ ^3P^0 \to 7s\ ^3S_1$	Assignment tentative	a, b
I$_2$	3.236 3.431		Power output increased with pressure of I_2	b
Cl$_2$, He–Cl$_2$	1.9754 2.0200		0.5 mW (1.98μ) 0.5 mW (2.02μ) at 0.1 mm Hg Cl$_2$[2]	c

REFERENCES: a—(260c); b—(260d); c—(244b).

[1] Maser action in pure Hg was obtained at 1.529 and 1.813μ. The addition of He or Ne (0.1–3 mm Hg) increased the power in the 1.529μ line and decreased the power in the 1.813μ line (260d). Oscillation in Hg at additional wavelengths is reported in ref. 498.

[2] At 250W input pumping power. At 300W, the power ratio in these lines was about 2 to 1. The power output of the 1.9754μ line increased roughly linearly with power. The intensities of both lines grew with increasing He partial pressure and peaked at $\sim$ 1.5 mm Hg.

[3] The transition refers to the un-ionized atom. The maser transitions for I and Cl are given in ref. (499).

TABLE I.6a. IONIZED GASES.[1] EXCITATION BY ELECTRON IMPACT

Gas	Mode of operation	Wavelength (Å)	Reference
Hg, Singly ionized	Pulsed	5,677.2 6,149.5 7,346 10,583	a
Ar, Singly ionized	Pulsed	10 lines 4,545–5,287	b c
	CW		d

REFERENCES: a—(260g); b—(500); c—(500a); d—(501).

[1] Oscillation on approximately 60 lines in the region 0.33–0.8 μ has been seen in singly and doubly ionized Ne, Ar, Kr, and Xe (W. B. Bridges, Private communication).

TABLE I.7. SUMMARY OF OPTICAL GASEOUS MASERS COMPARING THE POWER OUTPUT AND GAIN

Gas	Wavelength (μ)	Transition	Pressure (mm Hg)	Power output[5] (mW)	Gain (%/m)	Reference
He–Ne[1]	0.6328	$5s'[1/2]^0_1 - 3p[3/2]_2$	0.5 He; 0.1 Ne	4^6	2	a
	1.1523	$4s'[1/2]_1 - 3p[3/2]_2$	1 He; 0.1 Ne	20	12	a
	1.1614	$4s'[1/2]^0 - 3p[3/2]_1$	1–2 He; 0.1–0.2 Ne	1	2	a
	1.5231	$4s'[1/2]_1 - 3'p[1/2]_0$	1–2 He; 0.1–0.2 Ne	3	6	a
	3.3913	$5s'[1/2]^0_1 - 4p[3/2]_2$	0.5 He; 0.1 Ne	10	22 db/m	a
	53.486 (v)	$7p[3/2]_2 - 6d[5/3]_3$	0.12 He; 0.06 Ne	10^{-3}	3	g
Cs[2]	3.2	$8P_{1/2} - 6D_{3/2}$	0.02	0.025	200	b
	7.18	$8P_{1/2} - 8S_{1/2}$		0.020	12	b
Ne–O$_2$[3]	0.84462	$3^3P_2 - 3^3S_1$	0.35 Ne; 0.014 O$_2$	1	3	c
Ar–O$_2$[3]	0.84462	$3^3P_2 - 3^3S_1$	1.3 Ar; 0.36 O$_2$	1	3	c
He[4]	2.0603	$7^3D - 4^3P$	8	3	5	d
Ne	1.1523	$4s'[1/2]^0_1 - 3p[3/2]_2$	0.06	1	4	a
	2.1019	$4d'[5/2]^0_2 - 4p[3/2]_2$	0.2	1	3	d
Ar	1.6941	$3d[3/2]^0_2 - 4p[3/2]_2$	0.035	0.5	3	d
	2.0616	$3d[3/2]^0_2 - 4p[3/2]_2$	0.035	1	3	d
Kr	2.1165	$4d[3/2]^0_2 - 5p[3/2]_1$	0.035	1	3	d
	2.1902	$4d[3/2]^0_2 - 5p[3/2]_2$	0.035	1	3	d
Xe	2.0261	$5d[3/2]^0_1 - 6p[3/2]_1$	0.02	1	10	d
	3.5070	$5d[7/2]^0_3 - 6p[5/2]_2$	0.03	5	48 db/m	e

He–Xe	2.0261	$5d\,[3/2]^{0}_{1}$–$6p\,[3/2]_{1}$	5 He; 0.02 Xe	10	120	a
	3.5070	$5d\,[7/2]_{3}$–$6p\,[5/2]_{2}$	1.9 He; 0.03 Xe		62 db/m	e,f

REFERENCES: a—(13); b—(262); c—(244); d—(257); e—(277a); f—(277); g—(260a).

[1] Excitation by inelastic He–Ne collisions.

[2] Excitation by optical pumping.

[3] Excitation by dissociation.

[4] Excitation by electron impact for He, Ne, Ar, Kr, He–Xe, and Xe.

[5] The values for the beam power (from one end of the maser) are the ones that have been obtained (multimode operation except for Cs). They do not represent values for optimum coupling. Except for Cs and the 3.507μ line of Xe, all systems were confocal with an active discharge length of 2 m and 7 mm i.d. A plano-spherical resonator was used for Cs and Xe (3.507μ). The active discharge was 92 cm long and 1 cm i.d. for Cs, and 60 cm long and 7 mm i.d. for Xe.

The 5.5738μ line of Xenon has been listed as very strong, but no quantitative data was given (257).

[6] The power output (in mW) in the TEM_{00} mode from one end has been measured for the $3s_2 \rightarrow 2p$ transitions: $2p_1$ (0.06), $2p_2$ (1.0), $2p_3$ (0.3), $2p_4$ (46.0), $2p_5$ (0.3), $2p_6$ (3.0), $2p_7$ (0.5), $2p_8$ (0.4) (256a). 50 mW CW power at 6328Å has been reported.

TABLE I.8. NOBLE GASES. EXCITATION BY ELECTRON IMPACT.[1]

Observed[2] wavelength (μ)	Transitions[3] (Racah Notation)	Reference	Observed[2] wavelength (μ)	Transitions[3] (Racah notation)	Reference
	Helium[4]			$4p\,[5/2]_2-3d\,[5/2]^\circ_3$	c
2.0603	7^3D-4^3P	a	8.846	$4p\,[5/2]_3-3d\,[5/2]^\circ_3$	c
				$4p\,[5/2]_3-3d\,[5/2]^\circ_2$	c
	Neon[6]		9.0890	$6s\,[3/2]^\circ_1-5p\,[1/2]_0$	c
1.1523	$4s'\,[1/2]^\circ_1-3p'[3/2]_2$	b	10.060	$4p\,[1/2]_1-3d\,[1/2]^\circ_1$	c
2.038	$4p'[3/2]_2-4s\,[3/2]^\circ_1$	c	10.9812	$4p\,[1/2]_1-3d\,[3/2]^\circ_2$	c
	$4p'[1/2]_1-4s\,[3/2]^\circ_1$	c	11.865	$5p\,[1/2]_1-5s'[1/2]^\circ_0$	c
2.1019	$4d'[5/2]^\circ_2-4p\,[3/2]_2$	a	12.820	$5p'[1/2]_1-4d\,[3/2]^\circ_1$	c
2.542	$4d\,[1/2]^\circ_1-4p\,[3/2]_2$	c	13.757	$7s'\,[1/2]^\circ_1-6p'[3/2]_2$	c
2.755	$4d\,[3/2]^\circ_1-4p\,[1/2]_0$	c		$4d'[5/2]^\circ_3-4f\,[5/2]_3$	c
2.967	$4d\,[3/2]^\circ_1-4p'[3/2]_1$	c	14.93	No assignment	c
2.981	$4d\,[3/2]^\circ_2-4p'[3/2]_1$	c	16.63	$5p\,[3/2]_2-4d\,[5/2]^\circ_2$	c
3.028	$4d\,[3/2]^\circ_2-4p'[1/2]_1$	c	16.676	$5p\,[3/2]_2-4d\,[5/2]^\circ_3$	c
	$4d\,[3/2]^\circ_2-4p'[3/2]_2$	c	16.897	$5p\,[3/2]_2-4d\,[5/2]^\circ_2$	c
3.380	$7s'\,[1/2]^\circ_0-5p'[3/2]_1$	c	16.943	$5p\,[5/2]_2-4d\,[7/2]^\circ_3$	c
	$7s'\,[1/2]^\circ_0-5p'[1/2]_1$	c	17.156	$5p'[3/2]_2-4d'[5/2]^\circ_3$	c
3.7747	$4p'[1/2]_0-3d\,[3/2]^\circ_1$	c	17.189	$5p'[3/2]_2-4d'[3/2]^\circ_2$	c
5.40	$5d\,[1/2]^\circ_1-5p\,[3/2]_1$	b	17.802	$5p\,[1/2]_1-4d'[3/2]^\circ_2$	c
	$5d\,[7/2]^\circ_3-5p\,[3/2]_2$	b	17.838	$5p\,[3/2]_1-4d'[5/2]^\circ_2$	c
5.4046	$4p'[1/2]_0-3d'[3/2]^\circ_1$	c	17.884	$5p\,[5/2]_3-4d\,[7/2]^\circ_4$	c
5.662	$4p\,[1/2]_0-3d\,[3/2]^\circ_1$	c	18.397	$5p\,[5/2]_2-4d\,[5/2]^\circ_2$	c
7.330	$6s\,[3/2]^\circ_2-5p\,[5/2]_3$	c	20.482	$6p\,[1/2]_1-5d\,[1/2]^\circ_1$	c
7.427	$6s'[1/2]^\circ_0-5p'[1/2]_1$	c	21.752	$6p\,[1/2]_0-5d\,[3/2]^\circ_1$	c
	$5p'[1/2]_1-4d\,[3/2]^\circ_2$	c	22.836	$5p\,[1/2]_1-4d\,[3/2]^\circ_2$	c
7.4794	$4p\,[3/2]_2-3d\,[5/2]^\circ_3$	c	25.415	$6p'[1/2]_0-5d'[3/2]^\circ_1$	c
7.495	$6s\,[3/2]^\circ_2-5p\,[5/2]_2$	c	28.064	$6p\,[3/2]_1-5d\,[1/2]^\circ_0$	c
7.6164	$4p\,[3/2]_1-3d\,[5/2]^\circ_2$	c	31.55	$6p\,[3/2]_2-5d\,[5/2]^\circ_3$	c
7.6505	$4p\,[5/2]_2-3d\,[7/2]^\circ_3$	c	31.928(v)	$6p\,[3/2]_1-5d\,[5/2]^\circ_2$	f
7.7012	$4p'[3/2]_2-3d'[5/2]^\circ_3$	c	32.02	$6p\,[5/2]_2-5d\,[7/2]^\circ_3$	c
7.740	$4p\,[5/2]_2-3d\,[3/2]^\circ_2$	c	32.52	$6p'[3/2]_2-5d'[5/2]^\circ_3$	c
7.7654	$4p'[1/2]_1-3d'[3/2]^\circ_2$	c	33.83	$6p'[3/2]_1-5d'[5/2]^\circ_2$	c
7.781	$6s\,[3/2]^\circ_2-5p\,[3/2]_1$	c		$6p\,[5/2]_3-5d\,[7/2]^\circ_4$	c
7.8364	$6s\,[3/2]^\circ_2-5p\,[3/2]_2$	c	34.55	$6p'[1/2]_1-5d'[3/2]^\circ_2$	c
8.0085	$4p'[3/2]_1-3d'[5/2]^\circ_2$	c	34.679(v)	$6p\,[5/2]_2-5d\,[5/2]^\circ_2$	f
8.0615	$4p'[5/2]_3-3d\,[7/2]^\circ_4$	c	37.231(v)	$7p'[1/2]_0-6d'[3/2]^\circ_1$	f
8.337	$4p\,[5/2]_2-3d\,[5/2]^\circ_2$	c	41.741(v)	$6p\,[1/2]_1-5d\,[3/2]^\circ_2$	f

TABLE I.8. NOBLE GASES. EXCITATION BY ELECTRON IMPACT.[1] *(continued)*

Observed[2] wavelength (μ)	Transitions[3] (Racah Notation)	Reference	Observed[2] wavelength (μ)	Transitions[3] (Racah Notation)	Reference
	Argon		7.2150	$6p\,[1/2]_1-6s\,[3/2]^{\circ}_2$	c
1.6180	$5s\,[3/2]^{\circ}_2-4p'[3/2]_2$	a, b	7.799	No assignment	c
1.6941	$3d\,[3/2]^{\circ}_2-4p\,[3/2]_2$	a, b	12.140	$4d'[3/2]^{\circ}_2-4f\,[3/2]_1$	c
1.793	$3d\,[1/2]^{\circ}_1-4p\,[3/2]_2$	a, b		$4d'[3/2]^{\circ}_2-4f\,[3/2]_2$	c
	$3d\,[1/2]^{\circ}_0-4p\,[3/2]_1$	a, b	15.039	$5d'[3/2]_2-5f\,[5/2]_3$	c
2.0616	$3d\,[3/2]^{\circ}_2-4p'[3/2]_2$	a, b		$5d'[3/2]_2-5f\,[5/2]_2$	c
2.142	No assignment	c	26.936	$4d'[3/2]^{\circ}_2-4f\,[5/2]_3$	c
2.205	$3d\,[1/2]^{\circ}_0-4p'[3/2]_1$	c			
	$3d\,[1/2]^{\circ}_1-4p'[3/2]_2$	c			
2.312	$3d\,[1/2]^{\circ}_1-4p'[1/2]_1$	c			
2.395	$3d\,[1/2]^{\circ}_1-4p'[1/2]_1$	c		**Krypton**	
2.502	$6d'[3/2]^{\circ}_2-6p\,[1/2]_1$	c	1.6900	$4d\,[1/2]^{\circ}_1-5p\,[1/2]_1$	a, b
2.549	$5p\,[1/2]_0-5s\,[3/2]^{\circ}_1$	c	1.6936	$4d\,[5/2]^{\circ}_2-5p\,[3/2]_1$	a, b
	$5p\,[5/2]_3-3d\,[7/2]^{\circ}_3$	c	1.7843	$4d\,[1/2]^{\circ}_0-5p\,[1/2]_1$	a, b
2.562	$5p'[1/2]_0-5s'[1/2]^{\circ}_0$	c	1.8185	$4d'[5/2]^{\circ}_2-5p'[3/2]_2$	a, b
2.682	$5p\,[3/2]_1-3d\,[5/2]^{\circ}_2$	c	1.9211	$8s\,[3/2]^{\circ}_2-6p\,[5/2]_2$	a, b
2.736	$5p'[1/2]_1-3d'[3/2]^{\circ}_2$	c	2.1165	$4d\,[3/2]^{\circ}_2-5p\,[3/2]_1$	a, b
2.823	$5p'[3/2]_2-5s'[1/2]^{\circ}_0$	c	2.1902	$4d\,[3/2]^{\circ}_2-5p\,[3/2]_2$	a, b
	$5p.[3/2]_2-5s\,[3/2]^{\circ}_2$	c	2.5234	$4d\,[1/2]^{\circ}_0-5p\,[3/2]_2$	b
2.882	$5p\,[5/2]_3-5s\,[3/2]^{\circ}_2$	c	2.626	$7p\,[3/2]_2-4d'[5/2]^{\circ}_2$	c
	$5p\,[3/2]_2-3d\,[5/2]^{\circ}_3$	c		$4d\,[1/2]^{\circ}_0-5p\,[3/2]_1$	c
2.928	$5p\,[1/2]_0-3d\,[3/2]^{\circ}_1$	c	2.865	$6p\,[5/2]_3-6s\,[3/2]^{\circ}_2$	c
2.980	$5p\,[5/2]_2-5s\,[3/2]^{\circ}_1$	c		$6p\,[5/2]_2-6s\,[3/2]^{\circ}_2$	c
3.042	$5p\,[5/2]_2-3d\,[5/2]^{\circ}_3$	c	2.985	$6p'[3/2]_2-6s'[1/2]^{\circ}_1$	c
3.096	$5p\,[5/2]_3-3d\,[5/2]^{\circ}_3$	c		$6p'[1/2]_1-5d\,[5/2]^{\circ}_2$	c
3.135	$5p\,[1/2]_1-5s\,[3/2]^{\circ}_2$	c	3.050	$6p'[3/2]_1-5d\,[5/2]^{\circ}_2$	c
4.916	$5d\,[5/2]^{\circ}_2-4f\,[7/2]_3$	c	3.0673	$6p\,[1/2]_1-6s\,[3/2]^{\circ}_2$	c
	$6p'[3/2]_2-4d'[3/2]^{\circ}_2$	c	3.151	$6p'[1/2]_0-5d\,[3/2]^{\circ}_1$	c
5.1216	$5d\,[7/2]^{\circ}_3-4f\,[9/2]_4$	c	3.341	$4d\,[1/2]_1-5p\,[1/2]_0$	g
	$6p\,[5/2]_3-4d\,[7/2]^{\circ}_3$	c	3.466	$7s\,[3/2]^{\circ}_2-6p\,[1/2]_1$	c
5.4677	$5d\,[7/2]^{\circ}_4-4f\,[9/2]_5$	c	3.488	$6p'[1/2]_1-7s\,[3/2]^{\circ}_2$	c
	$5d\,[7/2]^{\circ}_4-4f\,[9/2]_4$	c		$6p'[1/2]_1-5d\,[3/2]^{\circ}_1$	c
5.8468	$6p\,[1/2]_0-6s\,[3/2]^{\circ}_1$	c	4.3748	$5d\,[3/2]^{\circ}_2-6p\,[3/2]_2$	c
6.050	$4d\,[1/2]^{\circ}_1-5p\,[5/2]_2$	c	4.875	$4d\,[3/2]^{\circ}_1-5p'[3/2]_1$	c
6.940	$6p'[1/2]_1-6s'[1/2]^{\circ}_0$	c		$5d\,[5/2]^{\circ}_2-6p\,[5/2]_3$	c
	$4d\,[3/2]^{\circ}_1-5p'[3/2]_1$	c	5.2965	No assignment	c

TABLE I.8. NOBLE GASES. EXCITATION BY ELECTRON IMPACT.[1] *(continued)*

Observed[2] wavelength (μ)	Transitions[3] (Racah Notation)	Reference	Observed[2] wavelength (μ)	Transitions[3] (Racah Notation)	Reference
5.302	$5d\,[3/2]^{\circ}_{1}$–$6p\,[1/2]_{0}$	c	3.2748(v)	$5d\,[3/2]^{\circ}_{2}$–$6p\,[1/2]_{1}$	e
	$5d\,[3/2]^{\circ}_{2}$–$6d\,[5/2]_{2}$	c	3.3667	$5d\,[5/2]^{\circ}_{2}$–$6p\,[3/2]_{1}$	b
5.5740[5]	$5d\,[7/2]^{\circ}_{3}$–$6p\,[5/2]_{2}$	c	3.434	$7p\,[5/2]_{2}$–$7s\,[3/2]^{\circ}_{2}$	c
5.5860	$6d\,[7/2]^{\circ}_{4}$–$4f\,[9/2]_{5}$	c	3.5070	$5d\,[7/2]^{\circ}_{3}$–$6p\,[5/2]_{2}$	b
5.6299	$6d\,[3/2]_{2}$–$4f\,[5/2]_{3}$	c	3.6525	$7p\,[1/2]_{1}$–$7s\,[3/2]^{\circ}_{2}$	c
7.058	$4f\,[7/2]_{4}$–$5d\,[7/2]^{\circ}_{4}$	c	3.6788	$5d\,[1/2]^{\circ}_{1}$–$6p\,[1/2]_{1}$	b
	$4f\,[7/2]_{3}$–$5d\,[7/2]^{\circ}_{4}$	c	3.6849	$5d\,[5/2]^{\circ}_{2}$–$6p\,[3/2]_{2}$	b
			3.8697(v)	$5d\,$–$6p$	e
	Xenon		3.8940	$5d\,[7/2]^{\circ}_{3}$–$6p\,[5/2]_{3}$	b
1.5104(v)	$5d\,[3/2]^{\circ}_{1}$–$6p\,[1/2]_{1}$	e	3.9955	$5d\,[1/2]^{\circ}_{0}$–$6p\,[1/2]_{1}$	b
1.7331(v)	$5d\,[3/2]^{\circ}_{1}$–$6p\,[5/2]_{2}$	e	4.1527	$5d\,$–$7p$	e
2.0261	$5d\,[3/2]^{\circ}_{1}$–$6p\,[3/2]_{1}$	a	4.6109	$5d\,$–$6p$	e
2.1379(v)	$5d\,[3/2]^{\circ}_{1}$–$6p\,[3/2]_{2}$	e	5.5738	$5d\,[7/2]^{\circ}_{4}$–$6p\,[5/2]_{3}$	b
2.3193	$5d\,[5/2]^{\circ}_{3}$–$6p\,[5/2]_{2}$	b	7.3147	$5d\,[3/2]^{\circ}_{2}$–$6p\,[3/2]_{1}$	b
2.4831(v)	$5d\,[5/2]^{\circ}_{2}$–$6p\,[5/2]_{3}$	e	9.0040	$5d\,[3/2]^{\circ}_{2}$–$6p\,[3/2]_{2}$	b
2.6269	$5d\,[5/2]^{\circ}_{2}$–$6p\,[5/2]_{2}$	f	9.7002	$5d\,[1/2]^{\circ}_{1}$–$6p\,[3/2]_{1}$	b
2.6511	$5d\,[3/2]^{\circ}_{2}$–$6p\,[1/2]_{0}$	b	11.297	$5d'[5/2]^{\circ}_{0}$–$4f\,[9/2]_{4}$	c
2.6608(v)	$5d'[3/2]^{\circ}_{2}$–$6p'[1/2]_{0}$	e	12.263	$5d\,[1/2]^{\circ}_{0}$–$6p\,[3/2]_{1}$	f
2.8389(v)	$5d\,[5/2]^{\circ}_{2}$–$6p\,[5/2]_{3}$	e	12.913	$5d\,[1/2]^{\circ}_{0}$–$6p\,[3/2]_{2}$	f
3.1078(v)	$5d\,[5/2]^{\circ}_{3}$–$6p\,[3/2]_{2}$	e	18.514	$5d'[3/2]^{\circ}_{2}$–$4f\,[5/2]_{3}$	c

REFERENCES: a—(257); b—(13); c—(260); d—(256); e—(259); f—(260a); g—(496).

[1] Pressures in mm Hg used were Ne—0.05, Ar—0.05, Kr—0.03, and Xe—0.02. Excitation may occur through electron impact of atoms in the ground state or in the lowest s states, or it may occur through processes of recombination and cascade (260). The addition of He to Xe improved maser action—presumably by increasing the density of high energy electrons (257, 259).

[2] The designation (v) means the observed wavelength reduced to vacuum. All other wavelengths are the observed value in air.

[3] The spectrometers used in Ref. c (260) were of three different types and with different accuracies. When several observed wavelengths which were nearly alike were assigned to the same transition, only the wavelength determined with the most accurate spectrometer is shown in Table I.8. Two transitions shown for a given wavelength indicates an ambiguity in assignment.

[4] L–S notation.

[5] It is possible that this wavelength belongs to the extremely strong xenon lines at 5.5780μ rather than the krypton line. Xenon is generally present in krypton as an impurity. However, no xenon had been deliberately introduced into the system at anytime (260).

Relative transition probabilities have been calculated for Ne (256c, 256e, 272b), Ar (256e), Kr (256e), and Xe (256d, 256e).

[6] Additional maser transitions are given in refs. 496 and 502. The longest wavelength reported thus far is 85.05μ (502).

TABLE I.9. MOLECULES,[4] EXCITATION BY ELECTRON IMPACT

Wavelength (μ) and transition	Relative intensity[1]	Reference
N_2 $B^3\pi_g - A^3\ \Sigma_u^{+\,[2]}$		a
2–1 band		
0.86835	0.1	
0.86912	1	
0.86980	1	
0.87044	1	
0.87099	0.2	
1–0 band		
0.88440	0.005	
0.88478	0.04	
0.88523	0.03	
0.88563	0.07	
0.88625	0.05	
0.88711	0.3	
0.88790	1	
0.88865	1	
0.88927	1	
0.88989	0.4	
0.89093	0.06	
0–0 band		
1.04493	0.006	
1.04612	0.01	
1.04723	0.1	
1.04800	1	
1.04909	0.06	
1.04948	0.4	
1.05052	0.08	
0–1 band		
1.2303	0.01	
1.2312	1	
1.2319	0.04	
1.2334	0.1	
1.2347	0.06	
$C^3\pi_u - B^3\pi_g$ [3]		b
0.3–0.4		

REFERENCES: a—($260e$); b—($260f$).

[1] Intensities are given relative to the strongest line in each group.

[2] Discharge column 7 mm i.e., 40 cm long. Gas pressure 4 mm Hg. The discharge was pulsed at 20 kV at 35A, with a pulse duration of 1μ and a repetition rate of 50–150 cps. The peak power output was 0.5 W for all lines.

[3] A plasma 48 in long was excited with 100-150 kV pulses of submicrosecond duration ($260b$). Peak power output for all lines (in the second positive group) was of the order of 10W. The gain at 4 mm Hg was approximately 60dB/m.

[4] Oscillation has been observed in a number of lines in the $B^1\Sigma - A^1\pi$ band of **CO**, 0.5591–0.6614μ (503) and in the $\Sigma_u^+ - \Sigma_g^+$ bands of **CO_2** with centers at 10.41μ and 9.40μ (504).

TABLE I.10. p-n JUNCTION DIODES

Material	Wavelength (μ)	Pulse threshold[1] (amp/cm²)	Bandwidth (Å)[2]	Comments
GaAs[a-c,3] Donor and acceptor concentration ~ 10^{18}/cm³	~ 0.9020 ~ 0.8425 ~ 0.8370	10^5 (295°K)[e] 10^4 (77°K) 700 (4.2°K)	250 (295°K) ~ 150 (77°K) 100 (4.2°K)	CW_{th} ~ 410 amp/cm² (77°K)[d] ~ 75 amp/cm² (1.9°K)[f]
GaAs[f] ~ 10^{16}/cm³	0.8240	10^3 (77°K)	~ 28 (77°K)	Due to exciton recombination
GaAs$_{1-x}$P$_x$[h] Donor concentration > 10^{18}/cm³	0.7100	1.1×10^4 (300°K)	125 (77°K)	μ depends on composition[4]
In$_x$Ga$_{1-x}$As[i]	2.07 1.77	3×10^4 (1.9°K)[5] (14kG)	~ 500 (1.9°K) ~ 500 (1.9°K)	μ depends on composition[4] 2.07μ, x = 0.75 1.77μ, x = 0.25
InAs[j]	3.1500 3.1120	1.6×10^4 (77°K)[5] 1.3×10^4 (4.2°K)	3800 (77°K) 1100 (4.2°K)	Magnetically tunable between 3.1168 and 3.1125μ. CW (4.2°K)[k]
InP[l]	~ 0.9100 ~ 0.9030	5.8×10^3 (77°K)[m] 1.3×10^3 (4.2°K)	~ 160 (77°K) ~ 810 (4.2°K)	CW_{th} ~ 60 amp/cm at 2°K, and ~ 150 amp/cm at 20°K[m]
InP$_{0.49}$As$_{0.51}$[p] Donor conc. 1.4×10^{19}/cm^{-3}	1.602	6–13×10^3 (77°K)	600 (77°K)	No stimulated emission obtained from InP$_{0.18}$As$_{0.82}$
InSb[n]	5.18	1.4×10^3 (1.7°K, 31kG)[5]	~ 650 (1.7°K)	CW_{th} ~ 1,400 amp/cm² at 27kG and 2°K[q]. Magnetically tunable

REFERENCES:

[a](287)	[e](297a)	[i](290c)	[m](290g)	[q](290i)
[b](288)	[f](297)	[j](290a)	[n](290f)
[c](289)	[g](287c)	[k](290e)	[o](290d)
[d](289a)	[h](290)	[l](290b)	[p](290h)

[1] The current pulses are typically several μsec duration at a repetition rate of several hundred pulses per second.

[2] Bandwidth of maser transition below threshold.

[3] Power output for GaAs maser: cw at 2°K, $\sim$ 10 mW at 40 ma input; pulsed operation at 4.2°K, 280 W peak at an input of 190 amp, average power $\sim$ 30 mW. The best average power output has been about 1 W.

[4] By varying the composition, it may be possible to tune $GaAs_{1-x}P_x$ from 0.64μ to 0.84μ[o], and $In_xGa_{1-x}As$ from 0.84μ to 3.1μ.[i]

[5] Magnetic field reduces threshold.

Appendix II

TABLE II.1. INDUCED RAMAN FREQUENCIES OF LIQUIDS

Compound	Frequency Shift[1] (cm^{-1})	Tabulated frequency shift (cm^{-1})	Reference
Acetone	2921 ± 7	2922	b
Benzene	3064 ± 4	3064	a
	990 ± 2	991.6	
	2 × (992 ± 2) ∗		
1-Bromonaphthalene	1368 ± 4	1363	a
Cyclohexane	2852 ± 1	2853	a
Cyclohexanone	2863 ± 7	2897	b
	2945 ± 5	2949	
Deuterated benzene	944.3 ± 1	944.7	a
C_6D_6	2 × (944 ± 1)		
Ethyl benzene	1002 ± 10	1000	b
Metaxylene	2933 ± 10	2916	b
Nitrobenzene	1344 ± 2	1345	a
	2 × (1346 ± 2)		
	3 × (1340 ± 5)		
Orthoxylene	2913	2916	b
	2922		
	2933		
	730	733	
Paraxylene	2998 ± 14	3008	b
Piperidine	2933	2935	b
	2936		
	2940		
	2943		
Pyridine	992 ± 2	991	a
	2 × (992 ± 5)		
1, 1, 2, 2-Tetrachloro-ethane	2984	2985	b
Toluene	1004 ± 4	1002	a

REFERENCES: a—(395); b—(395a).

[1] These results were obtained with a Q-spoil ruby maser. The shifts were measured from 14,402 cm^{-1} (6943 Å). The uncertainty is due to the linewidth of the maser radiation.

TABLE II.2. INDUCED RAMAN FREQUENCIES OF GASES (395h)

Gas	Frequency shift[1] (cm^{-1})	Assignment	Temperature $(°K)$	Pressure (psi)
Deuterium				
$Q(1) = 2991.39$ cm^{-1}	-2990.3 ± 3.4	$-Q(1)$	140	10^3
$S_0(0) = 179.86$ cm^{-1}	2812.7 ± 14	$Q(1) - S_0(0)$	155	550
	2899.7 ± 3.4	unknown	155	550
	2991.1 ± 0.7	$+ Q(1)$	140	10^3
	4981.6 ± 0.6	$+ 2Q(1)$	140	10^3
Hydrogen				
$Q(1) = 4155.21$ cm^{-1}	-8404.1 ± 0.2	$- 2Q(1)$		
	-4153.1 ± 4.2	$- Q(1)$		
	4155.0 ± 0.4	$+ Q(1)$	300	500
	8310.3 ± 0.4	$+ 2Q(1)$		
	$12464.9 + 3.2$	$+ 3Q(1)$		
	15545.9	$+ 4Q(1)$		
Methane				
ν_1 band $= 2916.5$ cm^{-1}	2915.5 ± 0.7	$- \nu_1$		
	2915.1 ± 0.9	$+ \nu_1$	300	1.4×10^3
	5829.9 ± 0.5	$+ 2\nu_1$		

[1] These results were obtained with a Q-spoil ruby maser. The shifts were measured from 14405.3 ± 0.4 for the D_2 lines, from 14404.1 ± 0.2 for the H_2 lines, and from 14404.4 ± 0.2 for the methane lines.

Appendix III

THEORY OF SPONTANEOUS AND INDUCED TRANSITIONS IN RESONATORS AND IN FREE SPACE

In this appendix, the equations of motion of the modes of a resonator driven by spontaneous emission are derived. Expressions are obtained for the spontaneous and induced emission rates in a resonator as well as in an unbounded medium.

A. HAMILTONIAN FORM OF THE FIELD EQUATIONS*

In a lossless or nearly lossless resonator, the field represented by the vector potential $\mathbf{A}$ can be expanded in terms of the normal modes,

$$\mathbf{A} = \sum_m q_m(t)\mathbf{A}_m(\mathbf{r}), \tag{III.1}$$

where $q_m(t)$ is a scalar function of time. $\mathbf{A}_m$ has to satisfy the boundary conditions and the equations,

$$\nabla^2 \mathbf{A}_m + \frac{\omega_m{}^2}{v^2}\mathbf{A}_m = 0, \tag{III.2}$$

$$\operatorname{div} \mathbf{A}_m = 0, \tag{III.3}$$

where ω_m are the eigenfrequencies of the resonator. For a reason which will appear subsequently, $\mathbf{A}_m$ is normalized as follows:

$$\int \mathbf{A}_m \cdot \mathbf{A}_n \, dV = 4\pi v^2 \delta_{mn}. \tag{III.4}$$

$v = c/\epsilon^{1/2}$ is the velocity of light in the inactive or host material filling the resonator, where ϵ is the dielectric constant, and the permeability is taken as unity. If the medium is anisotropic, it suffices here to regard ϵ as an average value.

---

* Sections A and B are based on Heitler (*494*).

The energy in mode m is calculated from the relation,

$$H_m = \frac{\epsilon}{8\pi} \int \mathbf{E}_m{}^2 \, dV + \frac{1}{8\pi} \int \mathbf{H}_m{}^2 \, dV, \tag{III.5}$$

where the electric and magnetic field intensities are given by

$$\mathbf{E}_m = -\frac{\dot{q}_m(t)}{c} \mathbf{A}_m(\mathbf{r}), \qquad \mathbf{H}_m = q_m(t) \nabla \times \mathbf{A}_m(\mathbf{r}). \tag{III.6}$$

The first integral in (III.5), $\int \mathbf{A}_m(\mathbf{r}) \cdot \mathbf{A}_m(\mathbf{r}) \, dV$, is evaluated by (III.4). The second integral can be transformed by the relation,

$$\int \nabla \times \mathbf{A}_m \cdot \nabla \times \mathbf{A}_m \, dV = \int_s \mathbf{A}_m \times \nabla \times \mathbf{A}_m \cdot d\mathbf{s} + \int \mathbf{A}_m \cdot \nabla \times \nabla \times \mathbf{A}_m \, dV. \tag{III.7}$$

The surface integral, which is proportional to the Poynting vector, vanishes because of the boundary conditions. Furthermore, since $\nabla \times \nabla \times \mathbf{A}_m = \text{grad div } \mathbf{A}_m - \nabla^2 \mathbf{A}_m$, the second integral reduces to $(\omega_m/v)^2 \int \mathbf{A}_m \cdot \mathbf{A}_m \, dV$ from (III.2). Then the energy in mode m is

$$H_m = \tfrac{1}{2}\omega_m^2 q_m^2 + \tfrac{1}{2}\dot{q}_m^2 . \tag{III.8}$$

From the orthogonality of the modes the total energy in the radiation field, H_{rad}, is simply

$$H_{\text{rad}} = \sum_m H_m . \tag{III.9}$$

Thus, the classical radiation field may be regarded as a collection of independent harmonic oscillators of unit mass. Hamilton's equations of motion in terms of these normal coordinates are

$$\frac{\partial H_m}{\partial q_m} = -\dot{p}_m , \qquad \frac{\partial H_m}{\partial p_m} = \dot{q}_m = p_m . \tag{III.10}$$

Equations (III.8) and (III.10) give

$$\ddot{q}_m + \omega_m^2 q_m = 0, \tag{III.11}$$

which is the dynamical equation of an undamped, freely oscillating mode.

B. Quantization of the Field

To obtain a quantum description of the electromagnetic field, p_m and q_m are regarded as the Hermitian operators of the harmonic oscillator of unit mass. The matrix elements of these operators are

$$q(J_m, J_m \pm 1) = q^*(J_m \pm 1, J_m) = \sqrt{\frac{\hbar}{2\omega_m}} \begin{cases} \sqrt{J_m + 1} \\ \sqrt{J_m} \end{cases}, \qquad \text{(III.12)}$$

$$p(J_m, J_m \pm 1) = p^*(J_m \pm 1, J_m) = \pm i \sqrt{\frac{\hbar\omega_m}{2}} \begin{cases} \sqrt{J_m + 1} \\ \sqrt{J_m} \end{cases}. \qquad \text{(III.13)}$$

These matrix elements connect radiation states for which the number of photons, J_m, of a given mode change by ± 1. The eigenvalues of the energy operator (III.8) are given by

$$W_m = \hbar\omega_m(J_m + \tfrac{1}{2}). \qquad \text{(III.14)}$$

In this method of quantizing the radiation field, the energy does not vanish when $J_m = 0$. Apart from this zero point energy, the energy in a given mode is simply the number of photons in that mode.

To the first order in e/c the interaction of a single electron with the radiation field is given by

$$H_{\text{Int}} = -\frac{e}{mc} \mathbf{p} \cdot \mathbf{A}, \qquad \text{(III.15)}$$

where $\mathbf{p}$ is the momentum operator of the electron. The matrix element of H_{Int} formed with the combined wave function for the electron and the radiation field of the mth mode is

$$-\frac{e}{mc} q(J_m, J_m \pm 1) \int \psi_2^* \mathbf{p} \cdot \mathbf{A}_m \psi_1 \, dV,$$

where ψ is the electronic wave function. Thus, although the matrix element for the absorption of a photon vanishes when $J_m = 0$, that for emission does not and represents the case of spontaneous emission.

C. The Equations of Motion for the Driven Normal Modes*

In the following treatment of the interaction of atoms with the radiation field of a resonator, the field will be represented by classical variables rather than by quantum operators. Nevertheless, the semi-classical theory to be formulated here takes into account spontaneous transitions and is shown to lead to the Einstein A coefficient. From (III.8) and (III.15) we obtain,

$$\ddot{q}_m + \omega_m^2 q_m = \frac{e}{mc} \mathbf{p} \cdot \mathbf{A}_m, \tag{III.16}$$

which is the equation for the forced vibration of a harmonic oscillator. The effect of losses in the resonator walls and host dielectric may be represented by adding on the left side of (III.16) the term $\gamma_m \dot{q}_m$, where γ_m is the damping rate. If these losses are small, their effect in coupling the modes may be neglected. Now the driving force at the ith maser atom in the electric dipole approximation may be represented by $(\omega_m/c)\mu^i \cdot \mathbf{A}(\mathbf{r}^i)$, where μ^i is the sum of an induced part, μ_i^i, and a spontaneous part, μ_s^i. Then the equations of motion including damping may be written as

$$\ddot{q}_m + \gamma_m \dot{q}_m + \omega_m^2 q_m = \sum_i (\mu_i^i + \mu_s^i)(4\pi)^{1/2} f_m^i \omega_m / \epsilon^{1/2}, \tag{III.17}$$

where

$$\mu \cdot \mathbf{A}_m(\mathbf{r}^i) = (4\pi c^2)^{1/2} \mu f_m^i / \epsilon^{1/2}. \tag{III.18}$$

The orthogonality of the f_m^i is expressed by

$$\sum_i (f_m^i f_n^i)^2 = \frac{N}{V} \xi_m \delta_{mn}, \tag{III.19}$$

or by $\int f_m f_n \, dV = \xi_m \delta_{mn}$. ξ_m is an average of the square of the cosine of the angle between the vectors μ and $\mathbf{A}(\mathbf{r})$, and N is the total number of maser atoms filling the resonator volume V.

In the case of an isotropic medium $\xi_m = 1/3$. The factor $\epsilon^{-1/2}$ which appears in (III.18) is suppressed in the subsequent analysis with the understanding that $f_m^i \to f_m^i/\epsilon^{1/2}$, and $\xi_m \to \xi_m/\epsilon$. The final results,

---

* Sections C to E are based on Wagner and Birnbaum (42).

however, are the same if $\mu^2 \rightarrow \mu^2/\epsilon$ and the f_m^i and ξ_m are left unchanged.

Equation (III.17) expresses the fact that every maser atom in an excited state drives each cavity mode. However, since μ_s^i is a fluctuating quantity and its phase is unspecified, we characterize its effect on the fields in the resonator by giving the spectral density. This quantity, i.e., the total noisy dipole moment per unit frequency interval for all the atomic systems in the cavity, is from a formula of Ekstein and Rostoker (*492*) given by

$$| \mu_s(\omega) |^2 = 2\mu^2 N_2 \{ T/\pi [1 + T^2(\omega - \omega_a)^2] \}, \qquad \text{(III.20)}$$

where $\mu^2 = |(1 \mid \mu \mid 2)|^2$, N_2 is the number of atoms in level 2, and $\mu_s(\omega)$ is the Fourier transform of μ_s. We assume here that the atomic line is homogeneously broadened and has a Lorentzian shape.

The dipole induced in each atom because of an electric field oscillating as $e^{-i\omega t}$ is from lowest order perturbation theory, for frequencies not too far from resonance,

$$\langle \mu_i^i(\omega) \rangle = \sum_n i\omega_m \frac{(4\pi)^{1/2}\mu^2}{\hbar} q_n f_n^i T \frac{(N_1 - N_2)}{N_0} \frac{1}{1 - iT(\omega - \omega_a)}, \qquad \text{(III.21)}$$

where $\mu_i^i(\omega)$ is the Fourier transform of μ_i^i. The factor $(N_1 - N_2)/N_0$, which is the probability that an atom be found in state 1 minus the probability that the atom be found in state 2, arises because μ_i^i is due to induced upward and downward transitions.

The populations, which are obtained by solving the rate equations, depend on the induced emission rate [(8.6) and (8.7)]. Although the induced rate depends on position via the energy density (see III.29), and consequently so does N_2 and N_1, the population distribution is assumed here to be independent of position.

The admittance of each mode to the spontaneous dipole of the ith atom is obtained from (III.17) by making the substitution $q_m = q(\omega)e^{-i\omega t}$, and eliminating the induced moment μ_i^i by substituting (III.21), with the result

$$\frac{q_m(\omega)}{\mu_s^i(\omega)} = \frac{-(2\pi)^{\frac{1}{2}}f_m^i\omega_m}{\omega^2 - \omega_m^2 + i\omega\gamma_m - i\omega_m^2\xi_m\mu^2 T(N_2 - N_1)/\hbar V[1 - iT(\omega - \omega_a)]}. \qquad \text{(III.22)}$$

The terms containing $\langle f_m^i f_n^i \rangle$ vanish because of the orthogonality of the modes. The last term in the denominator of (III.22) represents the effect of the maser atoms on the dispersion and damping of the mth mode.

It has been shown in Chapter IV how starting with (III.22) one may compute the spectral distribution of the coherent and incoherent power of a maser. We will indicate here how the oscillation frequency ω_{os} may be obtained from (III.22). Assuming that oscillation will occur at that frequency for which the real part of the denominator is zero, we have

$$2(\omega_{os} - \omega_m) + \frac{\gamma_m T(\omega_{os} - \omega_a)}{1 + T^2(\omega_{os} - \omega_a)^2} = 0, \qquad \text{(III.23)}$$

In obtaining (III.23) we have made the approximation $\omega^2 - \omega_m{}^2 = 2\omega_m(\omega - \omega_m)$, and have used the threshold relation,

$$K_m = 4\pi\mu^2(N_2 - N_1)T\xi_m/\hbar V = \gamma_m/\omega_m .$$

For ω_{os} near ω_a, $T^2(\omega_{os} - \omega_a)^2$ may be neglected in comparison with one, and (4.27) is obtained.

D. Spontaneous Emission Rates

For the ith system, the spontaneous emission rate, according to a formula by Weber (493), may be written in the form,

$$\Gamma_{21}^s = \frac{16\pi^2\mu^2}{h} \sum_m \int \text{Im}[\omega_m f_m^i q_m(\omega)/\mu_s^i(\omega)]S(\omega)\, d\omega , \qquad \text{(III.24)}$$

where Im means taking the imaginary part of the complex expression, and

$$S(\omega) = T/\pi[1 + T^2(\omega - \omega_a)^2].$$

On substituting for $q_m(\omega)/\mu_s^i$ and averaging over all the atoms, we obtain

$$\Gamma_{21}^s = \frac{16\pi^2\mu^2}{hV} \sum_m \int \xi_m\omega_m S(\omega)\, d\omega$$

$$\times \left\{ \frac{\Gamma_m(\omega)}{[2(\omega - \omega_m) + \omega_m K_m(\omega)T(\omega - \omega_a)]^2 + \Gamma_m^2(\omega)} \right\}, \qquad \text{(III.25)}$$

where $K_m(\omega)$, the reciprocal Q of the maser atoms for the mth mode, is given by

$$K_m(\omega) = \frac{8\pi^3\mu^2\xi_m(N_2 - N_1)}{hV} S(\omega). \qquad \text{(III.26)}$$

$\Gamma_m(\omega)$ is the total cavity loss rate including that due to the maser atoms, and is defined by

$$\Gamma_m(\omega) = \gamma_m - \omega_m K_m(\omega).$$

The expression in the curley brackets is the response of the coupled resonator and atomic system. Clearly the spontaneous emission rate depends in a pronounced way on the cavity loss rate and the material in the cavity. When $\omega_m = \omega_a$, (III.25) for a single mode reduces to*

$$\Gamma_{21}^s(m) = \frac{8\pi^2\mu^2\xi_m T\omega_a}{hV(1 + \Gamma_m T/2)}. \qquad \text{(III.27)}$$

When $\Gamma_m T \gg 1$, the spontaneous emission rate is directly proportional to the cavity Q ($Q_m = \omega_a/\Gamma_m$).

In the optical region, $\gamma_m T \ll 1$ and the spontaneous emission will excite all the modes contained within the atomic line. Since the wavelength in the optical region is very small compared with the dimensions of the resonator, the sum over modes in (III.25) can be approximated by the integral $\int p(\omega_m)\, d\omega_m$. The quantity $p(\omega_m) = \omega^2 V/(2\pi v)^3$ is the number of radiation oscillators per unit angular frequency interval per unit solid angle, Ω, and with direction of polarization specified by $\mathbf{e}$. The result obtained by integrating over ω and ω_m, is*

$$\Gamma_{21}^s = \frac{64\pi^4\mu^2 v^3\langle\xi_m\rangle}{hv^3} \qquad \text{(III.28)}$$

where

$$\langle\xi_m\rangle = \frac{1}{8\pi}\sum\int \xi(\theta, \phi, \mathbf{e})\, d\Omega,$$

and $\xi(\theta, \phi, \mathbf{e}) = (\mathbf{\mu} \cdot \mathbf{e}/\mu)^2$. The angles θ and ϕ specify the direction of propagation, and the sum is over the two directions of polarization. On performing the summation and integration, the value $\langle\xi_m\rangle = \frac{1}{3}$ is obtained, and (III.28) becomes the usual formula for the Einstein A coefficient (2.12).

---

*Provided $T\omega_m K_m(\omega)/2 \ll 1$, and the frequency dependence of $\Gamma_m(\omega)$ can be neglected.

E. INDUCED TRANSITION RATES

The rate of induced transitions between two atomic levels is given by the general formula obtained from lowest order perturbation theory,

$$\Gamma^i_{12} = \frac{16\pi^4\mu^2}{h^2} \sum_m \int (f^i_m)^2 W_m(\omega)S(\omega) \, d\omega, \qquad \text{(III.29)}$$

where $W_m(\omega)$ is the energy per unit angular frequency interval in the mth mode. Consider the case that $W_m(\omega)$ represents nearly monochromatic radiation with a bandwidth $\delta\omega \ll \Delta\omega$. On averaging (III.29) over all the atoms in the resonator, we obtain for the average induced rate for a single mode,

$$\Gamma^i_{12}(m) = \frac{8\pi^3\mu^2\xi_m}{h^2 V} W_m S(\nu), \qquad \text{(III.30)}$$

where $W_m = \int W_m(\omega) \, d\omega$. The coefficient of $W_m V^{-1} S(\nu)$ is the Einstein B coefficient.

To obtain the induced rate in an unbounded medium, the sum over modes is replaced by $\int p(\nu_m) \, d\nu_m$. Then noting that

$$\int W_m(\nu)p(\nu_m) \, d\nu_m = W(\nu, \theta, \phi, \mathbf{e}),$$

the induced emission rate may be written in the form,

$$\Gamma^i_{12} = \frac{8\pi^3\mu^2}{h^2} \int\int \xi(\theta, \phi, \mathbf{e})S(\nu)w(\nu, \theta, \phi, \mathbf{e}) \, d\Omega \, d\nu. \qquad \text{(III.31)}$$

$w(\nu, \theta, \phi, \mathbf{e})$ is the energy density per unit frequency interval per unit solid angle in the direction specified by θ and ϕ, and with direction of polarization $\mathbf{e}$. If the medium is isotropic, (III.31) reduces to (2.2).

Consider now the case that the energy density is due to the fluctuating dipoles in a single resonator mode, viz.

$$W_m(\omega) = \omega_m^2 \, | \, q_m(\omega) \, |^2 \, ,$$

where $q_m(\omega)$ is given by (III.22). On evaluating the integral in (III.29) and taking $\gamma_m T/2 \ll 1$, and $(1 - K_m Q_m) \ll 1$, the induced transition rate becomes

$$\Gamma^i_{12}(\omega) = \left\{ \frac{4\pi\omega_m^2\mu^2\xi_m T N_2}{V^2\gamma_m} \frac{1}{[1 - K_m Q_m + T^2(\omega_m - \omega_a)^2]} \right\} \frac{16\pi^4\mu^2\xi_m}{h^2} S(\omega_m), \qquad \text{(III.32)}$$

where the term in the brackets is the energy density, $w_m = \int w_m(\omega) d\omega$.

Clearly the induced transition rate becomes very large when the threshold condition is reached, i.e., when $K_m Q_m \simeq 1 + T^2(\omega_m - \omega_a)^2$.

The total power in a given mode due to spontaneous and induced transitions is

$$P_m = \hbar\omega_a[N_2\Gamma_{12}^i(m) + (N_2 - N_1)\Gamma_{12}^i(m)]. \qquad \text{(III.33)}$$

Upon substituting the expressions for the induced and spontaneous rates, we find that

$$P_m = \frac{4\pi N_2 \mu^2 \omega_a^2 T}{V} \frac{\xi_m}{1 - K_m Q_m + T^2(\omega_m - \omega_a)^2} \qquad \text{(III.34)}$$

where $\gamma_m T/2 \ll 1$ and $(1 - K_m Q_m) \ll 1$. However, (III.34) may be also obtained directly from

$$P_m = \gamma_m \omega_m^2 \int |q_m(\omega)|^2 d\omega .$$

Thus, as expected, the total power in a given mode is simply the energy dissipated in the resonator losses.

Appendix IV

Interactions between Electromagnetic Waves in a Nonlinear Dielectric

The problem of electromagnetic wave propagation in anisotropic media with nonlinear polarizability has been treated in detail by Armstrong *et al.* (*402*). We will summarize their results for second harmonic generation and parametric amplification to illustrate the essential features of the interactions between light waves in a non-linear medium.

A. The Inhomogeneous Wave Equation

The dielectric displacement **D** for a nonlinear medium can be put in the form

$$\mathbf{D} = \epsilon\mathbf{E} + 4\pi\mathbf{P}, \qquad (\text{IV.1})$$

where ϵ is the linear dielectric tensor, and $4\pi\mathbf{P}$ is the nonlinear polarization source term. The nonlinear polarizations at the second harmonic and fundamental frequencies, for example, are given by

$$
\begin{aligned}
\mathbf{P}(2\omega) &= \chi(2\omega = \omega + \omega)\colon \mathbf{E}_1\mathbf{E}_2\,, \\
\mathbf{P}(\omega) &= 2\chi(\omega = 2\omega - \omega)\colon \mathbf{E}_2\mathbf{E}_1\,,
\end{aligned}
\qquad (\text{IV.2})
$$

where χ is a third order tensor relating the three vectors. A general expression for the nonlinear polarization in component form is given by (13.6).

Maxwell's equations are

$$\nabla\times\mathbf{H} = \frac{1}{c}\frac{\partial\mathbf{D}}{\partial t}\,, \qquad \nabla\times\mathbf{E} = -\frac{1}{c}\frac{\partial\mathbf{B}}{\partial t}\,, \qquad (\text{IV.3})$$

261

where for simplicity the magnetic permeability will be taken as a scalar linear quantity. Equations (IV.3) in combination with (IV.1) lead to the inhomogeneous wave equations,

$$\nabla \times \nabla \times \mathbf{E} + \frac{1}{c^2} \frac{\partial^2(\epsilon \mathbf{E})}{\partial t^2} = -\frac{4\pi}{c^2} \frac{\partial^2 \mathbf{P}}{\partial t^2}. \tag{IV.4}$$

Solutions to this equation may be obtained in the form

$$\begin{aligned}
\mathbf{E}_n &= \mathrm{Re}[\mathbf{e}_n A_n(z) e^{i(k_n z - \omega_n t)}], \\
&= \mathbf{e}_n \rho_n(z) \cos[k_n z - \omega_n t + \phi_n(z)],
\end{aligned} \tag{IV.5}$$

where $\mathbf{e}_n$ is a unit vector defining the direction of polarization, and k_n is the wave vector.

The right-hand side of (IV.4) put equal to zero is the homogeneous wave equation and can be satisfied in a linear medium with $\rho(z)$ and $\phi(z)$ independent of z. However, in a nonlinear medium this amplitude and phase will change due to interaction or coupling between waves of different frequencies. Now in physically realizable situations the relative change in the amplitude per wavelength is small, since the nonlinear susceptibility is very small compared to the linear part. Thus terms in the second derivative of the amplitude may be neglected, i.e., $\partial^2 \rho / \partial z^2 \ll k \partial \rho / \partial z$.

B. SECOND HARMONIC GENERATION

By substituting (IV.2) and (IV.5) in (IV.4), the following set of coupled equations are obtained which govern second harmonic generation:

$$\frac{d\rho_1}{dz} = -\frac{2\omega^2 K}{k_1} \rho_1 \rho_2 \sin\theta, \tag{IV.6}$$

$$\frac{d\rho_2}{dz} = \frac{4\omega^2 K}{k_2} \rho_1^2 \sin\theta, \tag{IV.7}$$

$$\frac{d\theta}{dz} = \Delta k - 4\omega^2 K \left(\frac{\rho_2}{k_1} - \frac{\rho_1^2}{\rho_2 k_2}\right) \cos\theta, \tag{IV.8}$$

where

$$\theta = 2\phi_1(z) - \phi_2(z) + \Delta kz, \qquad \Delta k = 2k_1 - k_2, \tag{IV.9}$$

and

$$K = \frac{2\pi}{c^2} \mathbf{e}_2 \cdot \chi(2\omega) : \mathbf{e}_1\mathbf{e}_1 = \frac{2\pi}{c^2} \mathbf{e}_1 \cdot \chi(\omega) : \mathbf{e}_2\mathbf{e}_1 . \tag{IV.10}$$

The right sides of (IV.6) and (IV.7) are, respectively, directly proportional to $P(\omega)$ and $P(2\omega)$. For simplicity, we have omitted factors such as $\cos^2 \alpha_1$ where α_1 is the angle between the propagation vector and the direction of energy flow. In isotropic media $\alpha = 0$, and in most crystals the values of $\cos^2 \alpha$ are close to unity. Substitution of (IV.6) and (IV.7) into (IV.8) leads to

$$\frac{d\theta}{dz} = \varDelta k + \frac{\cos\theta}{\sin\theta} \frac{d}{dz} \ln (\rho_1^2 \rho_2). \tag{IV.11}$$

When the fundamental and second harmonic have equal phase velocities, $2k_1 = k_2$ and $\varDelta k = 0$, and (IV.11) can be integrated immediately. If the amplitude of the second harmonic is initially zero, $\rho_2(0) = 0$, then the solution to (IV.11) shows that θ must be equal to $\pi/2$, i.e., the nonlinear polarization is 90° out of phase with E. The out of phase component of P does not change the phase, $\varDelta\phi = 2\phi_1(z) - \phi_2(z)$, but causes a growth in the amplitude of ρ_1. The component of nonlinear polarization in phase with the field changes the phase, $\varDelta\phi(z)$.

Equations (IV.6) and (IV.7) with $\rho_2(0) = 0$ and $\sin\theta = 1$, can be integrated exactly with the result

$$\begin{aligned} \rho_1 &= \rho_1(0) \operatorname{sech} (z/l), \\ \rho_2 &= \rho_1(0) \tanh (z/l), \end{aligned} \tag{IV.12}$$

where l is a characteristic interaction length defined by

$$l^{-1} \approx 2\omega^2 K k_1^{-1} \rho_1(0). \tag{IV.13}$$

In this distance about 75 % of the fundamental power will have been converted to the second harmonic. Since $\chi \approx 6 \times 10^{-10}$ esu for KDP, one finds in this case that $l = 20$ cm for a field strength $E = 30$ kV/cm in the incident beam. If the medium is lossy with an absorption coefficient k, then for significant power conversion it is necessary that $k \ll l^{-1}$. In practice, however, the conversion will be limited by the distance over which phase matching can be maintained.

The usual experimental situation is that of imperfect phase matching, in which case ρ_1 can be regarded as a constant since the conversion of ρ_1 to ρ_2 will be very small. Then if $\rho_2(0) = 0$, the approximate solutions to (IV.8) and (IV.7) are

$$\theta = \Delta kz/2 + \pi/2,$$
$$\rho_2(z) = [4\rho_1(0)/\Delta kl] \sin (\Delta kz/2).$$
$$\text{(IV.14)}$$

The amplitude of $\rho_2(z)$ thus varies sinusoidally with z with a period that depends on the amount of mismatch.

C. Parametric Amplification

In a manner analogous to that indicated for second harmonic generation, the amplitude and phase equations for three interacting waves may be obtained in the form*

$$\frac{d\rho_1}{dz} = - \frac{\omega_1^2 K}{k_1} \rho_2\rho_3 \sin \theta, \qquad \text{(IV.15)}$$

$$\frac{d\rho_2}{dz} = - \frac{\omega_2^2 K}{k_2} \rho_3\rho_1 \sin \theta, \qquad \text{(IV.16)}$$

$$\frac{d\rho_3}{dz} = \frac{\omega_3^2 K}{k_3} \rho_1\rho_2 \sin \theta, \qquad \text{(IV.17)}$$

$$\frac{d\theta}{dz} = \Delta k + K\left(\frac{\omega_3^2}{k_3} \frac{\rho_1\rho_2}{\rho_3} - \frac{\omega_2^2}{k_2} \frac{\rho_3\rho_1}{\rho_2} - \frac{\omega_1^2}{k_1} \frac{\rho_2\rho_3}{\rho_1}\right) \cos \theta, \quad \text{(IV.18)}$$

where

$$\theta = \Delta kz + \phi_3(z) - \phi_2(z) - \phi_1(z), \qquad \Delta k = k_3 - k_2 - k_1. \quad \text{(IV.19)}$$

If (IV.15), (IV.16), and (IV.17) are multiplied, respectively, by ρ_1, ρ_2, and ρ_3 and divided by ω_1^2/k, etc., the right-hand sides except

---

* Coupled amplitude equations adapted to nonlinear effects in resonator modes rather than travelling waves have been given by Bloembergen and Shen (370b).

for sign, become equal. One then obtains the Manley-Rowe equations, essentially, for a three frequency parametric device, viz.

$$\frac{v_1}{\omega_1}\frac{d\rho_1^2}{dz} + \frac{v_3}{\omega_3}\frac{d\rho_3^2}{dz} = 0, \qquad \frac{v_2}{\omega_2}\frac{d\rho_2^2}{dz} + \frac{v_3}{\omega_3}\frac{d\rho_3^2}{dz} = 0. \qquad \text{(IV.20)}$$

A simple case of physical interest is that of a very strong pumping signal at ω_1 converting a signal from frequency ω_2 to ω_3. Then if $\rho_1(0) \gg \rho_2(0) > 0$ and $\rho_3(0) = 0$, and for perfect phase matching, $\Delta k = 0$, the amplitude of the electric field becomes

$$\rho_3(z) = (\omega_3/\omega_2)^{1/2}\rho_2(0)\sin(\pi z/l), \qquad \text{(IV.21)}$$

where the interaction length for this process is given by

$$l^{-1} = \pi^{-1}K\omega_2\omega_3(k_2k_3)^{-1/2}\rho_1(0). \qquad \text{(IV.22)}$$

For $\omega_3 > \omega_2$ there is power gain in the conversion of a photon to a higher frequency. This result is also obtained from the second of the Manley-Rowe relation (IV.20), which gives the optimum conversion. If there are initially equal numbers of photons at ω_1 and ω_2 and none at ω_3, solutions for $\rho_1 = \rho_2$ and ρ_3 are obtained which are similar to second harmonic generation.

D. Induced Raman Emission

Induced Raman emission may be dealt with as a special case of parametric amplification. Consider the situation in which one quantum $\hbar\omega_1$ is absorbed and a smaller one $\hbar\omega_2$ is emitted, while the energy of the atomic system is raised by $\hbar(\omega_1 - \omega_2)$. For definiteness, suppose that the wave at ω_1 is polarized along x and that at ω_2 is polarized along y. Then the nonlinear polarizations at ω_1 and ω_2 may be written as*

$$P_y(\omega_2) = (\chi' - i\chi'')_{yyxx}E_{2y}(\omega_2)E_{1x}^*(\omega_1)E_{1x}(\omega_1), \qquad \text{(IV.23)}$$

$$P_x(\omega_1) = (\chi' - i\chi'')_{xxyy}E_{1x}(\omega_1)E_{2y}^*(\omega_2)E_{2y}(\omega_2), \qquad \text{(IV.24)}$$

where the tensor elements $\chi' - i\chi''$ are functions of ω_1 and ω_2. Since $\chi(\omega_2)$ is negative corresponding to emission at ω_2, and $P(\omega_2)$ is always 90° out of phase with $E(\omega_2)$, there is gain at ω_2 without any requirement for phase matching.

* Nonlinear absorption in which two quanta take part simultaneously leads to an absorption coefficient proportional to the intensity [see (13.4)].

Appendix V

PHYSICAL CONSTANTS AND CONVERSION FACTORS

PHYSICAL CONSTANTS[1]

Constant	Symbol	Value	Estimated error limit*	Unit	
				Système international (MKSA)	Centimeter-gram-second (CGS)
Speed of light in vacuum	c	2.997925	3	$\times\ 10^8$ m s^{-1}	$\times\ 10^{10}$ cm s^{-1}
Elementary charge	e	1.60210	7	$\times\ 10^{-19}$ C	10^{-20} cm$^{1/2}$g$^{1/2}$†
		4.80298	20	—	10^{-10} cm$^{3/2}$g$^{1/2}$s^{-1}‡
Avogadro constant	N_A	6.02252	28	$\times\ 10^{23}$ mole^{-1}	10^{23} mole^{-1}
Electron rest mass	m_e	9.1091	4	$\times\ 10^{-31}$ kg	10^{-28} g
Proton rest mass	m_p	1.67252	8	$\times\ 10^{-27}$ kg	10^{-24} g
Planck constant	h	6.6256	5	$\times\ 10^{-34}$ J s	10^{-27} erg s
	$\hbar$	1.05450	7	$\times\ 10^{-34}$ J s	10^{-27} erg s
Fine structure constant	α	7.29720	10	$\times\ 10^{-3}$ —	10^{-3}
Bohr magneton	μ_B	9.2732	6	$\times\ 10^{-24}$ J T^{-1}	10^{-21} erg G^{-1}†
Normal volume perfect gas	V_0	2.24136	30	$\times\ 10^{-2}$ m^3 mole^{-1}	10^4 cm^3 mole^{-1}
Boltzmann constant	k	1.38054	18	$\times\ 10^{-23}$ J °K^{-1}	10^{-16} erg °K^{-1}
Stefan-Boltzmann constant	σ	5.6697	29	$\times\ 10^{-8}$ W m^{-2} °K^{-4}	10^{-5} erg cm^{-2} s^{-1}°K^{-4}

* Based on 3 standard deviation; applied to last digits in preceding column. †Electromagnetic system. ‡Electrostatic system.

KEY: C—coulomb; J—joule; W—watt; T—tesla; G—gauss.

[1] From *Natl. Bur. Standards Tech. News Bull.* (October, 1963), and based on a report by E. R. Cohen and J. W. M. DuMond, *in* "Proceedings of the Second International Conference on Nuclidic Masses" (W. H. Johnson, ed.). Springer, Vienna, 1964.

TABLE OF CONVERSION FACTORS FOR VARIOUS UNITS OF FREQUENCY, WAVELENGTH, AND ENERGY*

	Energy eV	Wavelength Å	Wavelength μ	Wave number cm⁻¹	Frequency megacycles	Temperature °K
Energy eV	1	12,398	1.2398	8.066	2.418×10^8	11,606
Wavelength Å	12,398	1	10^{-4}	10^8	3×10^{12}	1.439×10^8
Wavelength μ	1.2398	10^4	1	10^4	3×10^8	1.439×10^4
Wave number cm⁻¹	1.2398×10^{-4}	10^8	10^4	1	3×10^4	1.439
Frequency megacycles	4.135×10^{-9}	3×10^{12}	3×10^8	3.336×10^{-5}	1	4.79×10^{-11}
Temperature °K	8.616×10^{-5}	1.439×10^8	1.439×10^4	0.695	2.084×10^4	1

1 eV = 1.602×10^{-12} erg = 23.053 kcal/mole.

* Note that to convert to wavelength it is necessary to divide the conversion factor by the number of the other units and vice versa. More accurate conversion factors may be obtained from the fundamental constants and the following expressions for the energy: eVc^{-1} 10^8, hc/λ, $h\nu$, and kT.

Principal Symbols

A Einstein A coefficient, also power absorption coefficient of mirror

B Einstein B coefficient

D separation of interferometer mirrors

E electric field intensity

g degeneracy of a state

J number of photons

k absorption coefficient

k_n wave vector

K_m reciprocal of material Q

L diameter or width ($2L$ in Chapter VI)

n population density, also refractive index

N population

p total number of modes within the full atomic line width

P power

P_ν power per unit frequency interval

q axial mode number

q_m field amplitude

Q cavity Q

R power reflection coefficient

S power flow per unit area

$S(\nu)$ normalized shape factor of the atomic resonance

T the inverse angular line width, or temperature, or power transmission coefficient of mirror

TEM_{mnq} mode designation

v velocity of light in medium

V volume

w energy density

$w(\nu)$ energy density per unit frequency interval

W energy, also net pumping rate

α negative absorption coefficient

γ damping rate

Γ rate, superscripts s, i, and l mean: s — spontaneous; i — induced; l — lattice

η quantum efficiency

θ angle between propagation direction of a plane wave in the resonator and axis of resonator

σ absorption cross section

ϕ fraction of excited atoms which decay by emitting the desired radiation, also single pass phase shift

$\Delta\phi$ single pass phase shift measured from the resonance value ϕ_0

χ susceptibility

τ_c damping time of resonator

τ_{21} radiative lifetime

ω angular frequency, $\omega = 2\pi\nu$

λ wavelength in medium

μ dipole matrix element

$|\mu_{12}|$ dipole matrix element

ν frequency

$\Delta\nu$ line width, half width at half amplitude

ν_{os} oscillation frequency of maser

ξ_m geometrical factor giving coupling of dipole and electric field

References

1. Schawlow, A. L., and Townes, C. H., *Phys. Rev.* **112**, 1940 (1958).
2. Weber, J., *Rev. Mod. Phys.* **31**, 681 (1959).
3. Singer, J. R., *Advan. Electron. Electron Phys.* **15**, 73 (1961).
4. Singer, J. R., "Masers." Wiley, New York, 1959.
5. Troup, G. J., "Masers and Lasers." Methuen Monographs. Wiley, New York, 1963.
6. Vuylsteke, A. A., "Elements of Maser Theory." Van Nostrand, Princeton, New Jersey, 1960.
7. Kaiser, W., *Physica Status Solidii* **2**, 1117 (1962).
8. Townes, C. H., ed., "Quantum Electronics." Columbia Univ. Press, New York, 1960.
9. Singer, J. R., ed., "Advances in Quantum Electronics." Columbia Univ. Press, New York, 1961.
10. P. Grivet and N. Bloembergen, eds., "Quantum Electronics: Proceedings of the Third International Congress, Paris, 1963." Columbia Univ. Press, New York, 1964.
11. Chang, W. S. C., ed., "Lasers and Applications." Engineering Station, Ohio State Univ., Columbus, Ohio, 1961.
11a. Fox, J., ed., "Proceedings of the Symposium on Optical Masers," Microwave Research Inst. Symp. Ser., Vol. XIII. Polytechnic Press of the Polytechnic Inst. of Brooklyn, New York, 1963.
12. Heavens, O. S., *Appl. Opt.* Suppl. on Optical Masers, p. 1 (1962); "Optical Masers." Wiley, New York, 1964.
13. Bennett, W. R., Jr., *Appl. Opt.* Suppl. on Optical Masers, p. 24 (1962).
14. Yariv, A., and Gordon, J. P., *Proc. IEEE* **51**, 4 (1963).
15. Lengyel, B. A., "Lasers." Wiley, New York, 1962.
16. Kassel, S., *Proc. IEEE* (*Corres.*) **51**, 216 (1963).
17. Kemble, E. C., "The Fundamental Principles of Quantum Mechanics," Section 54. Dover, New York.
18. Condon, E. U., and Shortley, G. H., "The Theory of Atomic Spectra," Chapter IV. Cambridge Univ. Press, London and New York, 1957.
19. Kastler, A., *Ann. Phys.* (*N.Y.*) **7**, 57 (1962).
20. Lax, M., *J. Chem. Phys.* **20**, 1752 (1952).
21. Dexter, D. L., *Solid State Phys.* **6**, 360 (1958).
22. Mitchell, A. C. G., and Zemansky, M. W., "Resonance Radiation and Excited Atoms." Cambridge Univ. Press, London and New York, 1961.
23. Ditchburn, R. W., "Light," p. 460. Wiley (Interscience), New York, 1957.
24. Genzel, L., Hopp, H., and Weber, R., *Z. Physik* **154**, 13 (1959).
25. Kaiser, W., Spitzer, W. G., Kaiser, R. H., and Howarth, L. E., *Phys. Rev.* **127**, 1950 (1962).

25a. Rowntree, R. F., and Chang, W. S. C., *in* "Lasers and Applications" (W. S. C. Chang, ed.), p. 35. Engineering Experiment Station, Ohio State Univ., Columbus, Ohio, 1963.

25b. Hadni, A., Wyncke, B., Strimer, P., Descamps, E., and Claudel, J., *in* "Quantum Electronics: Proceedings of the Third International Congress, Paris, 1963" (P. Grivet and N. Bloembergen, eds.), Vol. 1, p. 731. Columbia Univ. Press, New York, 1964.

26. Breene, R. G., "The Shift and Shape of Spectral Lines." Pergamon Press, New York, 1961.

27. Yajima, T., *J. Phys. Soc. Japan* **16**, 1594 (1961).

28. Dieke, G. H., *in* "Advances in Quantum Electronics" (J. Singer, ed.), p. 164. Columbia Univ. Press, New York, 1961.

29. Dexter, D. L., *Solid State Phys.* **6**, 353 (1958).

29a. Silsbee, R. H., *Phys. Rev.* **128**, 1726 (1962).

29b. McCumber, D. E., and Sturge, M. D., *J. Appl. Phys.* **34**, 1682 (1962).

30. Yatsiv, S., *Physica* **28**, 521 (1962).

31. Kiel, A., *Phys. Rev.* **126**, 1292 (1962).

32. Shimoda, K., *Appl. Opt.* **1**, 303 (1962).

33. Lamb, W. E., Jr., *in* "Lectures in Theoretical Physics" (W. E. Britten and B. W. Downs, ed.), p. 435. Wiley (Interscience), New York, 1960.

34. Senitzky, I. R., *Phys. Rev.* **111**, 3 (1958); **115**, 227 (1959); **119**, 1807 (1960); **123**, 1525 (1961); **127**, 1638 (1962); **128**, 2864 (1962).

35. Jaynes, E. T., and Cummings, F. W., *Proc. IEEE* **51**, 89 (1963).

36. Gordon, J. P., Zeiger, H. J., and Townes, C. H., *Phys. Rev.* **99**, 1264 (1955).

37. Shimoda, K., Wang, T. C., and Townes, C. H., *Phys. Rev.* **102**, 1308 (1956).

38. Kastler, A., *Appl. Opt.* **1**, 17 (1962).

38a. Fleck, J. A., Jr., *J. Appl. Phys.* **34**, 2997 (1963).

39. Vil'ner, L. D., Rautian, S. G., and Khaikin, A. S., *Opt. Spectr.* (*U.S.S.R.*) (*Engl. Transl.*) **12**, 240 (1962).

40. Kagan, Yu. M., Perel', V. I., and Chaika, M. P., *Opt. Spectr.* (*U.S.S.R.*) (*Engl. Transl.*) **12**, 234 (1962).

40a. Jacobs, H., Holmes, D. A., Hatkin, L., and Brand, F. A., *J. Appl. Phys.* **34**, 2617 (1963).

41. Smiley, V. N., *Proc. IEEE* **51**, 120 (1963).

42. Wagner, W. G., and Birnbaum, G., *J. Appl. Phys.* **32**, 1185 (1961).

43. Bennett, W. R., Jr., *Phys. Rev.* **126**, 580 (1962).

44. Condell, W. J., and Mandelberg, H. I., *Appl. Opt.* **1**, 771 (1962).

45. Davis, L. W., *Proc. IEEE* **51**, 76 (1963).

46. Geusic, J. E., and Scovil, H. E. D., *Bell System Tech. J.* **41**, 1371 (1962).

46a. Prokhorov, A. M., *Opt. Spectr.* (*USSR*) (*Engl. Transl.*) **14**, 38 (1963).

46b. Rigrod, W. W., *J. Appl. Phys.* **34**, 2602 (1963).

46c. Fain, V. M., and Khanin, Ya. J., *Soviet Phys.—JETP* (*Engl. Transl.*) **14**, 1069 (1962).

46d. McCumber, D. E., *Phys. Rev.* **130**, 675 (1963).

46e. Lamb, W. E., Jr., *Phys. Rev.* (to be published).

46f. Haken, H., and Sauermann, H., *Z. Physik* **173**, 261 (1963).

46g. McFarlane, R. A., Bennett, W. R., Jr., and Lamb, W. E., Jr., *Appl. Phys. Letters* **2**, 189 (1963).

46h. Szöke, A., and Javan, A., *Phys. Rev. Letters* **10**, 521 (1963).

47. Kotik, J., and Newstein, M. C., *J. Appl. Phys.* **32**, 178 (1962).

48. Lugovoy, V. N., *Radiotekhn. i Electron.* (English translation in "Radio Engineering and Electronic Physics" published by AIEE) 16, 1518 (1961).

49. Kaiser, W., Garrett, C. G. B., and Wood, D. L., *Phys. Rev.* 123, 766 (1961).

50. Szabo, A., and Lipsett, F. R., *Proc. IRE (Corres.)* 50, 1690 (1962).

51. Wagner, W. G., and Birnbaum, G., *in* "Advances in Quantum Electronics" (J. Singer, ed.), p. 328. Columbia Univ. Press, New York, 1961.

52. Tang, C. L., and Statz, H., *Phys. Rev.* 128, 1013 (1962).

53. Tang, C. L., Statz, H., and deMars, G., *J. Appl. Phys.* 34, 2289 (1963).

54. Maiman, T. H., *Brit. Commun. Electron.* 7, 674 (1960); *Nature* 187, 493 (1960).

55. Collins, R. J., Nelson, D. F., Schawlow, A. L., Bond, W., Garrett, C. G. B., and Kaiser, W., *Phys. Rev. Letters* 5, 303 (1960).

56. Statz, H., and deMars, G., *in* "Quantum Electronics" (C. H. Townes, ed.), p. 530. Columbia Press, New York, 1960.

57. Sinnett, D. M., *J. Appl. Phys.* 33, 1578 (1962).

58. Makhov, G., *J. Appl. Phys.* 33, 202 (1962).

59. Dunsmuir, R., *J. Electron. Control* 10, 453 (1961).

60. Kaiser, W., Garrett, C. G. B., and Wood, D. L., *Phys. Rev.* 123, 766 (1962).

61. Sorokin, P. P., Stevenson, M. J., Lankard, J. R., and Pettit, G. D., *Phys. Rev.* 127, 503 (1962).

62. Statz, H., Luck, C., Shafer, C., and Ciftan, M., *in* "Advances in Quantum Electronics" (J. Singer, ed.), p. 342. Columbia Univ. Press, New York, 1961.

63. Hellwarth, R. W., *Phys. Rev. Letters* 6, 9 (1961).

64. Post, E. J., *Appl. Opt.* 1, 165 (1962).

65. Kaplan, J. E., and Zier, R., *J. Appl. Phys.* 33, 2372 (1962).

66. Pao, Yoh-Han, *J. Opt. Soc. Am.* 52, 871 (1962).

67. Chester, R. F., and Bolef, D. I., *Proc. IRE (Corres.)* 45, 1287 (1957).

68. Feher, G., Gordon, J. P., Buehler, E., Gere, E. A., and Thurmond, C. D., *Phys. Rev.* 109, 221 (1958).

69. Hellwarth, R. W., *in* "Advances in Quantum Electronics" (J. Singer, ed.), p. 334. Columbia Univ. Press, New York, 1961.

70. Wagner, W. G., and Lengyel, B. A., *J. Appl. Phys.* 34, 2040 (1963).

70a. Wang, C. C., *Proc. IEEE (Corres.)* 51, 1767 (1964).

71. Bloembergen, N., and Pound, R. V., *Phys. Rev.* 95, 8 (1954).

72. Dicke, R. H., *Phys. Rev.* 93, 99 (1954).

73. Bloom, S., *J. Appl. Phys.* 28, 800 (1957).

74. Greifinger, C., and Birnbaum, G., *IRE Trans. Electron Devices* 6, 288 (1959).

75. Bevensee, R. M., *Proc. IEEE (Corres.)* 51, 215 (1963).

76. Singer, J. R., and Wang, S., *Phys. Rev. Letters* 6, 351 (1961).

77. Kemp, J. C., *Phys. Rev. Letters* 7, 21 (1961).

78. Yariv, A., *J. Appl. Phys.* 31, 740 (1960).

79. Kemp, J. C., *J. Appl. Phys.* 30, 1451 (1959).

80. Bellman, R., Birnbaum, G., and Wagner, W. G., *J. Appl. Phys.* 34, 780 (1963).

80a. Frantz, L. M., and Nodvik, J. S., *J. Appl. Phys.* 34, 2346 (1963).

80b. Schulz-DuBois, E. O., *Bell System Tech. J.* 63, 625 (1964).

81. Prokhorov, A. M., *Soviet Phys.—JETP (Engl. Transl.)* 7, 1140 (1958).

82. Dicke, R. H., U. S. Patent 2,851,652 (1958).

83. Fox, A. G., and Li, T., *Bell System Tech. J.* 40, 453 (1961).

84. Boyd, G. D., and Gordon, J. P., *Bell System Tech. J.* 40, 489 (1961); Boyd, G. D., *in* "Advances in Quantum Electronics" (J. Singer, ed.), p. 318. Columbia Univ. Press, New York, 1961.

85. Boyd, G. D., and Kogelnik, H., *Bell System Tech. J.* **41**, 1347 (1962).
86. Goubau, G., and Schwering, F., *IRE Trans. Antennas Propagation* **9**, 248 (1961).
87. Schwering, F., *Arch. Elek. Übertragung* **15**, 555 (1961).
88. Fox, A. G., and Li, T., *Proc. IEEE* **51**, 80 (1963).
89. Soohoo, R. F., *Proc. IEEE* **51**, 70 (1963).
89a. Barone, S. R., *J. Appl. Phys.* **34**, 831 (1963).
89b. Beyer, J. B., and Scheibe, E. H., *IRE Trans. Antennas Propagation* **10**, 349 (1962).
90. Kogelnik, H., and Rigrod, W. W., *Proc. IRE (Corres.)* **50**, 220 (1962).
91. Rigrod, W. W., *Appl. Phys. Letters* **2**, 51 (1963).
91a. Polanyi, T. G., and Watson, W. R., *J. Appl. Phys.* **34**, 553 (1963).
92. Tang, C. L., *Appl. Opt.* **1**, 768 (1962).
92a. Fox, A. G., Li, T., and Morgan, S. P., *J. Appl. Opt.* **2**, 544 (1963).
93. Ready, J. F., and Hardwick, D. L., *Proc. IRE (Corres.)* **50**. 2484 (1962).
94. Herriott, D. R., *J. Opt. Soc. Am.* **52**, 31 (1962).
95. Rigrod, W. W., and Rustako, A. J., Jr., *J. Appl. Phys.* **34**, 967 (1963).
95a. Zimmerer, R. W., *Proc. IEEE (Corres.)* **51**, 475 (1963).
96. Koppelmann, G., *Z. Physik* **173**, 241 (1963).
96a. Culshaw, W., *Advan. Electron. Electron Phys.* **15**, 197 (1961).
97. Carson, J. R., Mead, S. P., and Schelkunoff, S. A., *Bell System Tech. J.* **15**, 310 (1936).
98. Schelkunoff, S. A., "Electromagnetic Waves." Van Nostrand, Princeton, New Jersey, 1943.
99. Ramo, S., and Whinnery, J. R., "Fields and Waves in Modern Radio, " p. 349. Wiley, New York (third printing), 1946.
100. Snitzer, E., *J. Opt. Soc. Am.* **51**, 491 (1961).
101. Snitzer, E., and Osterberg, H., *J. Opt. Soc. Am.* **51**, 499 (1961).
102. Snitzer, E., in "Advances in Quantum Electronics" (J. Singer, ed.), p. 348. Columbia Univ. Press, New York, 1961.
102a. Bird, V. R., Carpenter, D. R., McDermott, P. S., and Powell, R. L., in "Lasers and Applications" (W. S. C. Chang, ed.), p. 147. Engineering Station, Ohio State Univ., Columbus, Ohio, 1963.
102b. Kaplan, R. A., *Proc. IEEE (Corres.)* **51**, 1144 (1963).
103. Evtuhov, V., and Neeland, J. K., in "Quantum Electronics: Proceedings of the Third International Congress, Paris, 1963" (P. Grivet and N. Bloembergen, eds.), Vol. II, p. 1405. Columbia Univ. Press, New York, 1964.
104. Collins, R. J., and Giordmaine, J. A., in "Quantum Electronics: Proceedings of the Third International Congress, Paris, 1963" (P. Grivet and N. Bloembergen, eds.), Vol. II, p. 1239. Columbia Univ. Press, New York, in press.
105. Okaya, A., and Barash, L. F., *Proc. IRE* **50**, 2081 (1962).
106. Born, M., and Wolf, E., "Principles of Optics," Section 7.6.8. Pergamon Press, New York, 1959.
107. Kleinman, D. A., and Kisliuk, P. P., *Bell System Tech. J.* **41**, 453 (1962).
108. Gould, G., Jacobs, S., Rabinowitz, P., and Schultz, T., *Appl. Opt.* **1**, 533 (1962).
109. Peck, E., *J. Opt. Soc. Am.* **51**, 253 (1961).
110. Rabinowitz, P., Jacobs, S. F., Schultz, T., and Gould G., *J. Opt. Soc. Am.* **52**, 452 (1962).
111. Bergstein, L., Kahn, W., and Shulman, C., *Proc. IRE (Corres.)* **50**. 1833 (1962).
112. Rosenthal, A. H., *J. Opt. Soc. Am.* **52**, 1143 (1962).
112a. Clark, P. O., *Proc. IEEE (Corres.)* **51**, 949 (1963).

112b. Macek, W. M., and Davis, D. T. M., Jr., *Appl. Phys. Letters* **2**, 67 (1963).

113. Walsh, P., and Kemeny, G., *J. Appl. Phys.* **34**, 956 (1963).

113a. Ross, D., *Proc. IEEE* (*Corres.*) **51**, 468 (1963).

114. Garrett, C. G. B., Kaiser, W., and Bond, W. L., *Phys. Rev.* **124**, 1807 (1962).

114a. Birnbaum, M., Stocker, T., and Welles, S. J., *Proc. IEEE* (*Corres.*) **52**, 746 (1964).

115. Snitzer, E., *J. Appl. Phys.* **32**, 36 (1961).

116. Yariv, A., *Proc. IEEE* **51**, 1723 (1963).

116a. Rigrod, W. W., *J. Appl. Phys.* **34**, 2602 (1963).

116b. White, A. D., Gordon, E. I., and Rigden, J. D., *Appl. Phys. Letters* **2**, 91 (1963).

116c. White, J. A., *Appl. Phys. Letters* **3**, 107 (1963).

117. Bloembergen, N., *Phys. Rev. Letters* **2**, 84 (1959).

117a. deFigueiredo, R. P., *in* "Quantum Electronics: Proceedings of the Third International Congress, Paris, 1963" (P. Grivet and N. Bloembergen, eds.), Vol. II, p. 1353. Columbia Univ. Press, New York, 1964.

117b. Fink, E. L., and Ellison, G. N., *Proc. IEEE* (*Corres.*) **51**, 951 (1963).

117c. Gold, L., *in* "Quantum Electronics: Proceedings of the Third International Congress, Paris, 1963" (P. Grivet and N. Bloembergen, eds.), Vol. II, p. 1155. Columbia Univ. Press, New York, 1964.

117d. Vali, V., and Vali, W., *Proc. IEEE* (*Corres.*) **51**, 182 (1963).

117e. Neissel, J. P., Tonks, L., Vali, V., and Vali, W., *Proc. IEEE* **51**, 1247 (1963).

117f. Marcuse, D., *Bell Syst. Tech. J.* **41**, 1557 (1962).

117g. Marcuse, D., *Proc. IEEE* **51**, 849 (1963).

117h. Becker, C. H., *Z. Physik* **172**, 125 (1963).

118. Porter, J. F., Jr., *J. Appl. Phys.* **32**, 825 (1961).

119. Brown, M. R., and Shand, W. A., *Phys. Rev. Letters* **11**, 366 (1963).

120. Penner, S. S., *J. Quant. Spectry. Radiative Transfer* **1**, 163 (1961).

121. Bloembergen, N., *Phys. Rev.* **104**, 324 (1956).

122. Basov, N. G., and Prokhorov, A. M., *Soviet Phys. JETP* (*Engl. Transl.*) **1**, 184 (1955).

123. Maiman, T. H., *Phys. Rev.* **123**, 1145 (1961).

123a. Stitch, M. L., *J. Appl. Phys.* **32**, 1994 (1961).

123b. Stepanov, B. I., and Samson, A. M., *Opt. Spectr.* (*U.S.S.R.*) (*Engl. Transl.*) **14**, 34 (1963).

124. Barker, W. A., and Keating, J. D., *Appl. Opt.* **1**, 335 (1962).

125. Scovil, H. E. D., and Schulz-DuBois, E. O., *Phys. Rev. Letters* **2**, 262 (1959).

126. Edgerton, H. E., *in* "Advances in Quantum Electronics" (J. Singer, ed.), p. 276. Columbia Univ. Press, New York, 1961.

127. Buck, A., Erickson, R., and Barnes, F., *J. Appl. Phys.* **34**, 2115 (1963).

128. Marshak, I. S., *Appl. Opt.* **2**, 793 (1963).

128a. Emmett, J. L., and Schawlow, A. L., *Appl. Phys. Letters* **2**, 204 (1963).

129. Stevenson, M. J., Reuter, W., Braslau, N., Sorokin, P. P., and Landon, A. J., *J. Appl. Phys.* **34**, 500 (1963).

129a. Church, C. H., Haun, R. D., Jr., Osial, T. A., and Somers, E. V., *Appl. Opt.* **2**, 451 (1963).

130. Kiss, Z. J., Lewis, H. R., and Duncan, R. C., *Appl. Phys. Letters* **2**, 93 (1963).

130a. Keck, P. H., Redmann, J. J., White, C. E., and de Kinder, R. E., Jr., *Appl. Opt.* **2**, 827 (1963).

131. Colgate, S. A., and Trivelpiece, A. W., *in* "Advances in Quantum Electronics" (J. Singer, ed.), p. 288. Columbia Univ. Press, New York, 1961.

131a. Derr, V. E., and Gallagher, J. J., *in* "Quantum Electronics: Proceedings of the Third International Congress, Paris, 1963" (P. Grivet and N. Bloembergen, eds.), Vol. I, p. 817. Columbia Univ. Press, New York, 1964.

132. Lamb, W. E., Jr., *Phys. Rev.* **70**, 308 (1946).

133. Miles, P. A., and Edgerton, H. E., *J. Appl. Phys.* **32**, 2490 (1961).

134. Ciftan, M., Luck, C. F., Shafer, C. G., and Statz, H., *Proc. IRE* **49**, 960 (1961).

135. Boyd, G. D., Collins, R. J., Porto, S. P. S., Yariv, A., and Hargreaves, W. A., *Phys. Rev. Letters* **8**, 269 (1962).

136. Tomiyasu, K., *Proc. IRE* (*Corres.*) **50**, 2488 (1962).

136a. Schuldt, S. B., and Aagard, R. L., *Appl. Opt.* **2**, 509 (1963).

137. Bowness, C., Missio, D., and Rogala, T., *Proc. IRE* **50**, 1704 (1962).

138. Fried, D. L., and Eltgroth, P., *Proc. IRE* (*Corres.*) **50**, 2489 (1962).

139. Bowness, C., Missio, D., and Rogala, T., *Proc. IEEE* (*Corres.*) **51**, 254 (1963).

139a. Ackerman, J. A., *Proc. IEEE* (*Corres.*) **51**, 1032 (1963).

140. Devlin, G. E., McKenna, J., May, A. D., and Schawlow, A. L., *Appl. Opt.* **1**, 11 (1962).

141. Svelto, O., *Appl. Opt.* **1**, 745 (1962).

141a. McKenna, J., *Appl. Opt.* **2**, 303 (1963).

141b. Svelto, O., and DiDomenico, M., Jr., *Appl. Opt.* **2**, 431 (1963).

142. Nelson, D. F., and Boyle, W. S., *Appl. Opt.* **1**, 181 (1962).

142a. Keck, P. H., Redmann, J. J., White, C. E., and Bowen, D. C., *Appl. Opt.* **2**, 833 (1963).

143. Kremen, J., *Appl. Opt.* **1**, 773 (1962).

144. Sorokin, P. P., and Stevenson, M. J., *in* "Advances in Quantum Electronics" (J. Singer, ed.), p. 65. Columbia Univ. Press, New York, 1961.

145. Kaiser, W., Garrett, C. G. B., and Wood, D. L., *Phys. Rev.* **123**, 766 (1961).

146. Yariv, A., Porto, S. P. S., and Nassau, K., *J. Appl. Phys.* **33**, 2519 (1962).

147. Li, T., and Sims, S. D., *Proc. IRE* **50**, 464 (1962).

148. Aagard, R. L., Hardwick, D. L., and Ready, J. F., *Appl. Opt.* **1**, 537 (1962).

149. Newman, R., *J. Appl. Phys.* **34**, 437 (1963).

150. Maiman, T. H., Hoskins, R. H., D'Haenens, I. J., Asawa, C. K., and Evtuhov, V., *Phys. Rev.* **123**, 1151 (1961).

151. Collins, R. J., Nelson, D. F., Schawlow, A. L., Bond, W., Garrett, C. G. B., and Kaiser, W., *Phys. Rev. Letters* **5**, 303 (1960).

152. Schawlow, A. L., and Devlin, G. E., *Phys. Rev. Letters* **6**, 96 (1961).

153. Wieder, I., and Sarles, L. R., *Phys. Rev. Letters* **6**, 95 (1961).

154. McClung, F. J., Schwarz, S. E., and Meyers, F. J., *J. Appl. Phys.* **33**, 3139 (1962).

155. Kiss, Z. J., and Duncan, R. C., Jr., *Proc. IRE* (*Corres.*) **50**, 1531 (1962).

155a. Ballman, A. A., Porto, S. P. S., and Yariv, A., *J. Appl. Phys.* **34**, 3155 (1963).

156. Johnson, L. F., *Proc. IRE* (*Corres.*) **50**, 1691 (1962).

156a. Yariv, A., *Proc. IRE* (*Corres.*) **50**, 1699 (1962).

156b. Kiss, Z. J., *Appl. Phys. Letters* **3**, 145 (1963).

157. Kiss, Z. J., and Duncan, R. C., Jr., *Proc. IRE* (*Corres.*) **50**, 1531 (1962).

157a. Pollock, S. A., *Proc. IEEE (Corres.)* **51**, 1793 (1963).
158. Johnson, L. F., Boyd, G., and Nassau, K., *Proc. IRE (Corres.)* **50**, 87 (1962).
158a. Johnson, L. F., *J. Appl. Phys.* **34**, 897 (1963).
158b. Johnson, L. F., Van Uitert, L. G., Rubin, J. J., and Thomas, R. A., *Phys. Rev.* **133**, A494 (1964).
159. Johnson, L. F., and Nassau, K., *Proc. IRE (Corres.)* **49**, 1704 (1961).
160. Johnson, L. F., and Thomas, R. A., *Phys. Rev.* **131**, 2038 (1963).
161. Johnson, L. F., Boyd, G. D., Nassau, K., and Soden, R. R., *Phys. Rev.* **126**, 1406 (1962).
162. Johnson, L. F., and Soden, R. R., *J. Appl. Phys.* **33**, 757 (1962).
163. Kariss, Ya. E., and Feofilov, P. P., *Opt. Spectr. (U.S.S.R.) (Engl. Transl.)* **14**, 89 (1963).
164. Johnson, L. F., *J. Appl. Phys.* **33**, 756 (1962).
164a. Johnson, L. F., Dietz, R. E., and Guggenheim, H. J., *Phys. Rev. Letters* **11**, 318 (1963).
165. Yariv, A., Porto, S. P. S., and Nassau, K., *J. Appl. Phys.* **33**, 2519 (1962).
166. Solomon, R., and Mueller, L., *Appl. Phys. Letters* **3**, 135 (1963).
167. Sorokin, P. P., Stevenson, M. J., Lankard, J. R., and Pettit, G. D., *Phys. Rev.* **127**, 503 (1962).
168. Johnson, L. F., Boyd, G. D., and Nassau, K., *Proc. IRE (Corres.)* **50**, 86 (1962).
169. Kiss, Z. J., and Duncan, R. C., Jr., *Proc. IRE (Corres.)* **50**, 1532 (1962).
170. Boyd, G. D., Collins R. J., Porto, S. P. S., Yariv, A., and Hargreaves, W. A., *Phys. Rev. Letters* **8**, 269 (1962).
171. Sorokin, P. P., and Stevenson, M. J., *Phys. Rev. Letters* **5**, 557 (1961).
172. Wittke, J. P., Kiss, Z. J., Duncan, R. C., Jr., and McCormick, J. J., *Proc. IEEE* **51**, 56 (1963).
173. Porto, S. P. S., and Yariv, A., *J. Appl. Phys.* **33**, 1620 (1962).
173a. Title, R. S., Sorokin, P. P., Stevenson, M. J., Pettit, G. D., Scardefield, J. E., and Lankard, J. R., *Phys. Rev.* **128**, 62 (1962).
174. Porto, S. P. S., and Yariv, A., *Proc. IRE (Corres.)* **50**, 1543 (1962).
175. Porto, S. P. S., and Yariv, A., *Proc. IRE (Corres.)* **50**, 1542 (1962).
176. Hoskins, R. H., and Soffer, B. H., *Appl. Phys. Letters* **4**, 22 (1964).
177. Gandy, H. W., and Ginther, R. J., *Appl. Phys. Letters* **1**, 25 (1962).
178. Gandy, H. W., and Ginther, R. J., *Proc. IRE (Corres.)* **50**, 2113 (1962).
179. Snitzer, E., *Phys. Rev. Letters* **7**, 444 (1962).
180. Maurer, R. D., *Appl. Opt.* **2**, 87 (1963).
181. Etzel, H. W., Gandy, H. W., and Ginther, R. J., *Appl. Opt.* **1**, 534 (1962).
181a. Young, C. G., *Appl. Phys. Letters* **2**, 151 (1963).
181b. Maurer, R. D., *in* "Proceedings of the Symposium on Optical Masers" (J. Fox, ed.), p. 451. Microwave Research Inst. Symp. Ser., Vol. XIII. Polytechnic Press of the Polytechnic Inst. of Brooklyn, New York, 1963.
182. Gandy, H. W., and Ginther, R. J., *Proc. IRE (Corres.)* **50**, 2114 (1962).
182a. Lempicki, A., and Samelson, H., *Physics Letters* **4**, 133 (1963).
182b. Lempicki, A., and Samelson, H., *Appl. Phys. Letters* **2**, 159 (1963).
182c. Bhaumik, M. L., Lyons, H., and Fletcher, P. C., *J. Chem. Phys.* **38**, 568 (1963).
183. Wolff, N. E., and Pressley, R. J., *Appl. Phys. Letters* **2**, 152 (1963).

184. Schimitschek, E. J., *Appl. Phys. Letters* **3**, 117 (1963).

184a. Lempicki, A., and Samelson, H., *in* "Proceedings of the Symposium on Optical Masers" (J. Fox, ed.), p. 347. Microwave Research Inst. Symp. Ser., Vol. XIII. Polytechnic Press of the Polytechnic Inst. of Brooklyn, New York, 1963.

185. Brock, E. G., Csavinszky, P., Hormats, E., Nedderman, H. C., Stirpe, D., and Unterleitner, F., *J. Chem. Phys.* **35**, 759 (1961).

186. Morantz, D. J., White, B. G., and Wright, A. J. C., *J. Chem. Phys.* **37**, 2041 (1962).

187. Pringsheim, P., "Fluorescence and Phosphorescence." Wiley (Interscience), New York, 1949.

188. McClure, D. S., *Solid State Phys.* **9**, 400 (1959).

189. Runciman, W. A., *Rept. Progr. Phys.* **21**, 30 (1958).

190. McClure, D. S., and Kiss, Z., *in* "Proceedings of the Symposium on Optical Masers" (J. Fox, ed.), p. 357. Microwave Research Inst. Symp. Ser., Vol. XIII. Polytechnic Press of the Polytechnic Inst. of Brooklyn, New York, 1963.

191. Low, W., *in* "Advances in Quantum Electronics" (J. Singer, ed.), p. 138. Columbia Univ. Press, New York, 1961.

192. El'yashevich, M. A., "Spectra of the Rare Earths," Books 1 and 2. Translated from a publication of the State Publishing House of Technical-Theoretical Literature, Moscow, 1953. Atomic Energy Commission, Office of Technical Information.

193. Dieke, G. H., *in* "Advances in Quantum Electronics" (J. Singer, ed.), p. 164. Columbia Univ. Press, New York, 1961.

194. Dieke, G. H., and Crosswhite, H. M., *Appl. Opt.* **2**, 695 (1963).

195. Sugano, S., *Appl. Opt.* **1**, 295 (1962).

195a. Troup, G. J., *in* "Advances in Quantum Electronics" (J. Singer, ed.), p. 85. Columbia Univ. Press, New York, 1961.

196. Bond, W. L., *Rev. Sci. Instr.* **33**, 372 (1962).

196a. Nassau, K., *in* "Proceedings of the Symposium on Optical Masers" (J. Fox, ed.), p. 451. Microwave Research Inst. Symp. Ser., Vol. XIII. Polytechnic Press of the Polytechnic Inst. of Brooklyn, New York, 1963.

197. Snitzer, E., *47th Ann. Meeting Opt. Soc. Am.* p. 20 (1962).

198. Theissing, H. H., Caplan, P. J., Ewanizky, T., and de Lhery, G., *Appl. Opt.* **2**, 291 (1963).

199. Schawlow, A. L., *in* "Advances in Quantum Electronics" (J. Singer, ed.), p. 50. Columbia Univ. Press, New York, 1961.

200. Wieder, I., and Sarles, L. R., *in* "Advances in Quantum Electronics" (J. Singer, ed.), p. 214. Columbia Univ. Press, New York, 1961.

201. Sugano, S., and Tanabe, Y., *J. Phys. Soc. Japan* **13**, 880 (1958).

202. Sugano, S., and Tsujikawa, I., *J. Phys. Soc. Japan* **13**, 899 (1958).

203. Varsanyi, F., Wood, D. L., and Schawlow, A. L., *Phys. Rev. Letters* **3**, 544 (1959).

204. D'Haenens, I. J., and Asawa, C. K., *J. Appl. Phys.* **33**, 3201 (1962).

205. Maiman, T. H., *Phys. Rev. Letters* **4**, 564 (1960).

206. Schawlow, A. L., Piksis, A. H., and Sugano, S., *Phys. Rev.* **122**, 1469 (1961).

207. Schawlow, A. L., and Devlin, G. E., reported in P. P. Kisliuk and W. S. Boyle, *Proc. IRE* **49**, 1635 (1961).

208. Wittke, J. P., *J. Appl. Phys.* **33**, 2333 (1962).

209. Abella, I. D., and Cummins, H. Z., *J. Appl. Phys.* **32**, 1177 (1961).
210. Burns, G., and Nathan, M. I., *J. Appl. Phys.* **34**, 703 (1963).
211. Schawlow, A. L., Wood, D. L., and Clogston, A. M., *Phys. Rev. Letters* **3**, 271 (1959).
211a. Kisliuk, P., Schawlow, A. L., and Sturge, M. D., *in* "Quantum Electronics: Proceedings of the Third International Congress, Paris, 1963" (P. Grivet and N. Bloembergen, eds.), Vol. I, p. 725. Columbia Univ. Press, New York, 1964.
212. Kaiser, W., Sugano, S., and Wood, D. L., *Phys. Rev. Letters* **6**, 605 (1961).
213. Chen, D., *Proc. IRE (Corres.)* **51**, 227 (1963).
214. Cook, J. C., *Proc. IRE (Corres.)* **49**, 1570 (1961).
215. Nelson, D. F., and Collins, R. J., *in* "Advances in Quantum Electronics" (J. Singer, ed.), p. 79. Columbia Univ. Press, New York, 1961.
216. D'Haenens, I. J., and Evtuhov, V., *in* "Quantum Electronics: Proceedings of the Third International Congress, Paris, 1963" (P. Grivet and N. Bloembergen, eds.), Vol. II, p. 1131. Columbia Univ. Press, New York, 1964.
216a. Aagard, R. L., *J. Appl. Phys.* **33**, 2842 (1962).
216b. Aagard, R. L., *Proc. IRE (Corres.)* **50**, 2374 (1962).
217. Sage, S. J., *Appl. Opt.* **1**, 173 (1962).
218. Masters, J. I., and Ward, J. H., *Proc. IEEE (Corres.)* **51**, 221 (1963).
219. Flowers, W., and Jenney, J., *Proc. IEEE (Corres.)* **51**, 858 (1963).
219a. Nelson, D. F., and McCumber, D. E., *in* "Quantum Electronics: Proceedings of the Third International Congress, Paris, 1963" (P. Grivet and N. Bloembergen, eds.), Vol. II, p. 1037. Columbia Univ. Press, New York, 1964.
220. Kisliuk, P. P., and Boyle, W. S., *Proc. IRE* **49**, 1635 (1961).
221. Dieke, G. H., and Hall, L. A., *J. Chem. Phys.* **27**, 464 (1957).
222. Garrett, C. G. B., Kaiser, W., and Wood, D. L., *in* "Advances in Quantum Electronics" (J. Singer, ed.), p. 77. Columbia Univ. Press, New York, 1961.
223. Wood, D. L., and Kaiser, W., *Phys. Rev.* **126**, 2079 (1962).
224. Kiss, Z. J., *Appl. Phys. Letters* **2**, 61 (1963).
225. McClung, F. J., and Hellwarth, R. W., *J. Appl. Phys.* **33**, 828 (1962).
226. McClung, F. J., and Hellwarth, R. W., *Proc. IEEE* **51**, 46 (1963).
226a. Sooy, W. R., Congleton, R. S., Dobratz, B. E., and Ng, W. K., *in* "Quantum Electronics: Proceedings of the Third International Congress, Paris, 1963" (P. Grivet and N. Bloembergen, eds.), Vol. II, p. 1103. Columbia Univ. Press, New York, 1964.
227. Marshall, F. R., and Roberts, D. L., *Proc. IRE (Corres.)* **50**, 2108 (1962).
227a. Helfrich, J. L., *J. Appl. Phys.* **34**, 1000 (1963).
227b. TRG-134 series, "Research Properties of Laser Devices." T. R. G., Syosset, New York.
227c. Sorokin, P. P., Luzzi, J. J., Lankard, J. R., and Pettit, G. D., *IBM J. Res. Develop.* **8**, 182 (1964).
227d. Grant, D. G., *Proc. IEEE* **51**, 604 (1963).
227e. DeMaria, A. J., Gagosz, R., and Barnard, G., *J. Appl. Phys.* **34**, 453 (1963).
227f. DeMaria, A. J., and Gagosz, R., *Proc. IRE (Corres.)* **50**, 1522 (1962).
227g. DeMaria, A. J., *J. Appl. Phys.* **34**, 2984 (1963).
228. Collins, R. J., and Kisliuk, P. P., *J. Appl. Phys.* **33**, 2009 (1962).
229. Basov, N. G., Zuev, V. S., and Krujuhov, P. G., *Appl. Opt.* **1**, 767 (1962).

230. Nedderman, H. C., Kiang, Y. C., and Unterleitner, F. C., *Proc. IRE (Corres.)* **50**, 1687 (1962).

231. Kaiser, W., and Lessing, H., *Appl. Phys. Letters* **2**, 206 (1963).

232. Koester, C. J., Woodcock, R. F., Snitzer, E., and Teager, H. M., *47th Ann. meeting Opt. Soc. Am.* p. 19 (1962).

233. Fabrikant, V. A., Doctoral dissertation, Physics Inst. P. N. Lebedev, Academy of Sciences U.S.S.R., 1939.

234. Lamb, W. E., Jr., and Retherford, R. C., *Phys. Rev.* **79**, 549 (1950).

235. Sanders, J. H., *Phys. Rev. Letters* **3**. 86 (1959).

236. Javan, A., *Phys. Rev. Letters* **3**, 87 (1959).

237. Javan, A., Bennett, W. R., Jr., and Herriott, D. R., *Phys. Rev. Letters* **6**, 106 (1961).

238. Basov, N. G., and Krokhin, O. N., *Appl. Opt.* **1**, 213 (1962).

239. Fabrikant, V. A., *Zhur. Eksperim. i Teor. Fiz.* **41**, 524 (1961); *Soviet Phys. JETP (Engl. Transl.)* **14**, 375 (1962).

239a. Allen, L., and Heavens, O. S., *Physics Letters* **2**, 35 (1962).

240. Massey, H. S. W., and Burhop, E. H. S., "Electronic and Ionic Impact Phenomena." Oxford Univ. Press (Clarendon), London and New York, 1952.

241. Bennett, W. R., Jr., *Ann. Phys. (N.Y.)* **18**, 367 (1962).

241a. Moore, C. E., "Atomic Energy Levels," Vol. I. *Natl. Bur. Standards (U.S.) Cir.* **467**, 1949.

242. Holstein, T., *Phys. Rev.* **72**, 1212 (1947); **83**, 1159 (1951).

243. Muller, M. W., Sher, A., Solomon, R., and Dow, D. G., *Appl. Phys. Letters* **2**, 86 (1963).

244. Bennett, W. R., Jr., Faust, W. L., McFarlane, R. A., and Patel, C. K. N., *Phys. Rev. Letters* **8**, 470 (1962).

244a. Patel, C. K. N., McFarlane, R. A., and Faust, W. L., *Phys. Rev.* **133**, A1244 (1964).

244b. Paananen, R. A., Tang, C. L., and Horrigan, F. A., *Appl. Phys. Letters* **3**, 154 (1963).

245. Boote, H. A. H., and Clunie, D. M., *Nature* **197**, 173 (1963).

246. Singer, J. R., and Gorog, I., *Bull. Am. Phys. Soc.* [2] **7**, 14 (1962).

247. Rautian, S. G., and Sobel'man, I. I., *Soviet Phys. JETP (Engl. Transl.* **14**, 1433 (1962).

248. Zare, R. N., and Herschbach, D. R., *Proc. IEEE* **51**, 173 (1963).

249. Polanyi, J. C., *J. Chem. Phys.* **34**, 347 (1961).

250. Garvin, D., Broida, H. P., and Kostkowski, H. J., *J. Chem. Phys.* **32**, 880 (1960).

251. Charters, P. E., and Polanyi, J. C., *Can. J. Chem.* **38**, 1742 (1960).

252. Polanyi, J. C., *J. Chem. Phys.* **31**, 1338 (1959).

253. White, A. D., and Rigden, J. D., *Proc. IRE (Corres.)* **50**, 1697 (1962).

253a. Bloom, A. L., *Appl. Phys. Letters* **2**, 101 (1963).

254. McFarlane, R. A., Patel, C. K. N., Bennett, W. R., Jr., Faust, W. L., *Proc. IRE (Corres.)* **50**, 2111 (1962).

255. Rigden, J. D., and White, A. D., *Proc. IEEE (Corres.)* **51**, 943 (1963).

256. Bloom, A. L., Bell, W. E., and Rempel, R. E., *Appl. Opt.* **2**, 317 (1963).

256a. White, A. D., and Rigden, J. D., *Appl. Phys. Letters* **2**, 211 (1963).

256b. McFarlane, R. A., Faust, W. L., and Patel, C. K. N., *Proc. IEEE (Corres.)* **51**, 468 (1963).

256c. Koster, G. F., and Statz, H., *J. Appl. Phys.* **32**, 2054 (1961).

256d. Tang, C. L., *Proc. IEEE* (*Corres.*) **51**, 219 (1963).

256e. Statz, H., Tang, C. L., and Koster, G. F., *J. Appl. Phys.* **34**, 2625 (1963).

257. Patel, C. K. N., Bennett, W. R., Jr., Faust, W. L., and McFarlane, R. A., *Phys. Rev. Letters* **9**, 102 (1962).

258. Patel, C. K. N., *in* "Lasers and Applications" (W. S. C. Chang, ed.), p. 49. Engineering Experiment Station, Ohio State University, Columbus, Ohio, 1963.

259. Faust, W. L., McFarlane, R. A., Patel, C. K. N., and Garrett, C. G. B., *Appl. Phys. Letters* **1**, 85 (1962).

260. Faust, W. L., McFarlane, R. A., Patel, C. K. N., and Garrett, C. G. B., *Phys. Rev.* **133**, A1476 (1964).

260a. Patel, C. K. N., Faust, W. L., McFarlane, R. A., and Garrett, C. G. B., *Appl. Phys. Letters* **4**, 18 (1964).

260b. Gerritsen, H. J., and Gœdertier, P. V., *Appl. Phys. Letters* **4**, 20 (1964).

260c. Paananen, R. A., Tang, C. L., Horrigan, F. A., and Statz, H., *J. Appl. Phys.* **34**, 3148 (1963).

260d. White, A. D., and Rigden, J. D., *Nature* **198**, 774 (1963).

260e. Mathias, L. E. S., and Parker, J. T., *Appl. Phys. Letters* **3**, 16 (1963).

260f. Heard, H. G., *Bull. Am. Phys. Soc.* **9**, 65 (1964).

260g. Bell, E. W., *Appl. Phys. Letters* **4**, 34 (1964).

261. Rabinowitz, P., Jacobs, S., and Gould, G., *Appl. Opt.* **1**, 513 (1962).

262. Jacobs, S., and Rabinowitz, P., *in* "Quantum Electronics: Proceedings of the Third International Congress, Paris, 1963" (P. Grivet and N. Bloembergen, eds.), Vol. I, p. 489. Columbia Univ. Press, New York, 1964.

263. Ablekov, V. K., Pesiu, M. S., and Fabelins, I. L., *Zhur. Eksperim. i Teor. Fiz.* **39**, 892 (1960); *Soviet Phys. JETP* (*Engl. Transl.*) **12**, 618 (1961).

264. Bennett, W. R., Jr., *Bull. Am. Phys. Soc.* [2] **7**, 15 (1962).

265. Bennett, W. R., Jr., *in* "Advances in Quantum Electronics" (J. Singer, ed.), p. 28. Columbia Univ. Press, New York, 1961.

266. Javan, A., *in* "Advances in Quantum Electronics" (J. Singer, ed.), p. 18. Columbia Univ. Press, New York, 1961.

267. Powers, J. K., and Harned, B. W., *Proc. IEEE* (*Corres.*) **51**, 605 (1963).

268. Luck, C. F., Paananen, R. A., and Statz, H., *Proc. IRE* **49**, 1954 (1961).

269. Killpatrick, J., Gustafson, H., and Wold, L., *Proc. IRE* (*Corres.*) **50**, 1521 (1962).

270. Brangaccio, D. J., *Rev. Sci. Instr.* **33**, 921 (1962).

271. Rigrod, W. W., Kogelnik, H., Brangaccio, D., and Herriott, D. R., *J. Appl. Phys.* **33**, 743 (1962).

271a. Byerly, E. H., Goldsmith, J., and McMahan, W. H., *Proc. IEEE* (*Corres.*) **51**, 360 (1963).

272. George, N., *Proc. IEEE* (*Corres.*) **51**, 1152 (1963).

272a. Bennett, W. R., Jr., and Kindlmann, *Rev. Sci. Instr.* **33**, 601 (1962).

272b. Koster, G. F., and Statz, H., *J. Appl. Phys.* **32**, 2054 (1961).

272c. Boot, H. A. H., Clunie, D. M., and Thorn, R. S. A., *Nature* **198**, 774 (1963).

273. Statz, H., Paananen, R., and Koster, G. F., *J. Appl. Phys.* **33**, 2319 (1962).

274. Paananen, R., Tang, C. L., and Statz, H., *Proc. IEEE* **51**, 63 (1963).

275. Culshaw, W., Kanneland, J., and Lopez, F., *Phys. Rev.* **128**, 1747 (1962); Culshaw, W., and Kanneland, J., *Phys. Rev.* **133**, A691 (1964).

276. Patel, C. K. N., Faust, W. L., and McFarlane, R. A., *Appl. Phys. Letters* **1**, 84 (1962).

276a. Aisenberg, S., *Appl. Phys. Letters* **2**, 187 (1963).

277. Paananen, R. A., and Bobroff, D. C., *Appl. Phys. Letters* **2**, 99 (1963).

277a. Bridges, W. B., *Appl. Phys. Letters* **3**, 45 (1963).

277b. Fork, R. L., and Patel, C. K. N., *Appl. Phys. Letters* **2**, 180 (1963).

278. Bernard, M. G. A., and Duraffourg, G., *Physica Status Solidii* **1**, 469, (1961).

279. Basov, N. G., Krokhin, O. N., and Popov, Ju. M., *in* "Advances in Quantum Electronics" (J. Singer, ed.), p. 496. Columbia Univ. Press, New York, 1962.

280. Dumke, W. P., *Phys. Rev.* **127**, 1559 (1962).

281. Lax, B., *in* "Quantum Electronics" (C. H. Townes, ed.), p. 428. Columbia Univ. Press, New York, 1960; also *in* "Advances in Quantum Electronics." (J. Singer, ed.), p. 465. Columbia Univ. Press, New York, 1961.

281a. Basov, N. G., Krokhin, O. N., and Popov, Yu. M., *Soviet Phys.—Usp. (Engl. Transl.)* **3**, 702 (1961).

281b. Lax, M., *Science* **141**, 1247 (1963).

282. Shockley, W., *Bell System Tech. J.* **28**, 435 (1949): also "Electrons and Holes in Semiconductors," p. 308. Van Nostrand, Princeton, New Jersey, 1950.

283. Letter by J. Bardeen, *Sci. American* **208**, 12 (1963).

284. Keyes, R. J., and Quist, T. M., *Proc. IRE (Corres.)* **50**, 1822 (1962).

285. Pankove, J. I., *Phys. Rev. Letters* **9**, 283 (1962).

285a. Keyes, R. W., *Proc. IEEE* **51**, 602 (1963).

285b. Yariv, A., and Leite, R. C. C., *in* "Quantum Electronics: Proceedings of the Third International Congress, Paris, 1963" (P. Grivet and N. Bloembergen, eds.), Vol. II, p. 1873. Columbia Univ. Press, New York, 1964.

285c. Lasher, G. J., *IBM J. Res. Dev.* **7**, 58 (1963).

286. Nathan, M. I., and Burns, G., *Appl. Phys. Letters* **1**, 89 (1962).

286a. Moll, J. L., and Gibbons, J. F., *IBM J. Res. Develop.* **7**, 157 (1963).

286b. Cheroff, G., Stern, F., and Triebwasser, S., *Appl. Phys. Letters* **2**, 173 (1963).

286c. Nasledov, N., Rogachev, A. A., Ryvkin, S. M., and Tsarenkov, B. V., *Fiz. Tverd. Tela* **4**, 1062 (1962).

287. Hall, R. N., Fenner, G. E., Kingsley, J. D., Soltys, T. J., and Carlson, R. O., *Phys. Rev. Letters* **9**, 366 (1962).

287a. Nelson, D. F., Gershenzon, M., Ashkin, A., d'Asaro, L. A., and Sarace, J. C., *Appl. Phys. Letters* **2**, 182 (1963).

287b. Galeeher, F. L., Wright, G. B., Krag, W. E., Quist, T. M., and Zeiger, H. J., *Phys. Rev. Letters* **10**, 472 (1963).

287c. Wilson, D. K., *Appl. Phys. Letters* **3**, 127 (1963).

288. Nathan, M. I., Dumke, W. P., Burns, G., Dill, F. H., and Lasher, G., *Appl. Phys. Letters* **1**, 62 (1962).

289. Quist, T. M., Rediker, R. H., Keyes, R. J., Krag, W. E., Lax, B., McWhorter, A. L., and Zeiger, H. J., *Appl. Phys. Letters* **1**, 91 (1962).

289a. Pilkuhn, M., Rupprecht, H., and Woodall, J., *Proc. IEEE (Corres.)* **51**, 1243 (1963).

290. Holonyak, Jr., N., and Bevacqua, S. F., *Appl. Phys. Letters* **1**, 82 (1962).

290a. Melngailes, I., *Appl. Phys. Letters* **2**, 176 (1963).

290b. Weiser, K., and Levitt, R. S., *Appl. Phys. Letters* **2**, 178 (1963).

290c. Melngailes, I., Straus, A. J., and Rediker, R. H., *Proc. IEEE (Corres.)* **51** 1154 (1963).

290d. Holonyak, Jr., N., Bevacqua, S. F., Bielan, C. V., and Lubowski, S. J., *Appl. Phys. Letters* **3**, 47 (1963).

290e. Melngailes, I., and Rediker, R. H., *Appl. Phys. Letters* **2**, 202 (1963).

290f. Phelan, R. J., Calawa, A. R., Rediker, R. H., Keyes, R. J., and Lax, B., *Appl. Phys. Letters* **3**, 143 (1963).

290g. Burns, G., Levitt, R. S., Nathan, M. I., and Weiser, K., *Proc. IEEE (Corres.)* **51**, 1148 (1963).

290h. Alexander, F. B., Bird, V. R., Carpenter, D. R., Manley, G. W., McDermott, P. S., Peloke, J. R., Quinn, H. F., Riley, R. J., and Yetter, L. R., *Appl. Phys. Letters* **4**, 13 (1963).

290i. Phelan, R. J., Jr., and Rediker, R. H., *Proc. IEEE (Corres.)* **52**, 91 (1964).

291. Burns, G., Laff, R. A., Blum, S. E., Dill, F. H., Jr., and Nathan, M. I., *IBM J. Res. Develop.* **7**, 62 (1962).

292. Laff, R. A., Dumke, W. P., Dill, F. H., Jr., and Burns, G., *IBM J. Res. Develop.* **7**, 63 (1963).

293. McWhorter, A. L., Zeiger, H. J., and Lax, B., *J. Appl. Phys.* **34**, 235 (1963).

294. Yariv, A., and Leite, R. C. C., *Appl. Phys. Letters* **2**, 55 (1963).

295. Bond, W. L., Cohen, B. G., Leite, R. C. C., and Yariv, A., *Appl. Phys. Letters* **2**, 57 (1963).

295a. Ashkin, A., and Gershenzon, M., *J. Appl. Phys.* **34**, 2116 (1963)

295b. Leite, R. C. C., and Yariv, A., *Proc. IEEE* **51**, 1035 (1963).

295c. Collins, R. E., "Field Theory and Guided Modes," Chapter II. McGraw-Hill, New York, 1960.

295d. Lax, B., *Solid State Design* **4**, 26 (1963).

296. Burns, G., and Nathan, M. I., *IBM J. Res. Develop.* **7**, 72 (1963).

297. Howard, W. E., Fang, F. F., Dill, Jr., F. H., and Nathan M. I., *IBM J. Res. Develop.* **7**, 74 (1963).

297a. Burns, G., Dill, Jr., F. H., and Nathan, M. I., *Proc. IEEE (Corres.)* **51**, 947 (1963).

297b. Burns, G., and Nathan, M. I., *Proc. IEEE (Corres.)* **51**, 471 (1963).

297c. Stevenson, M. J., Axe, J. D., and Lankard, J. R., *IBM J. Res. Develop.* **7** 155 (1963).

297d. Fenner, G. E., and Kingsley, J. D., *J. Appl. Phys.* **34**, 3204 (1964).

297e. Kingsley, J. D., Fenner, G. E., Hall, R. N., *in* "Lasers and Applications" (W. S. C. Chang, ed.), p. 76. Engineering Experiment Station, Ohio State University, Columbus, Ohio, 1963.

297f. Sorokin, P. P., Axe, J. D., and Lankard, J. R., *J. Appl. Phys.* **34**, 2553 (1963).

297g. Nathan, M. I., Fowler, A. B., and Burns, G., *Phys. Rev. Letters* **11**, 152 (1963).

297h. Garfinkel, M., and Engeler, W. E., *IEEE Solid State Device Res. Conf., Michigan State Univ., East Lansing, Michigan, June, 1963.*

297i. Feinleib, J., Groves, S., Paul, W., and Zallen, R., *Phys. Rev.* **131**, 2070 (1963).

297j. Ryan, F. M., and Miller, R. C., *Appl. Phys. Letters* **3**, 162 (1963).

297k. Fenner, G. E., *J. Appl. Phys.* **34**, 2955 (1963).

297l. Meyerhofer, D., and Braunstein, R., *Appl. Phys. Letters* **3**, 171 (1963).

298. Glick, A. L., *Proc. IRE (Corres.)* **50**, 1835 (1962).

299. Li, T., and Sims, S. D., *Appl. Opt.* **1**, 325 (1962).

300. Koozekanani, S., Debye, P. P., Krutchkoff, A., and Ciftan, M., *Proc. IRE (Corres.)* **50**, 207 (1962).

300a. Leite, R. C. C., and Porto, S. P. S., *Proc. IEEE* **51**, 606 (1963).

301. Damon, E. K., and Flynn, J. T., *Appl. Opt.* **2**, 163 (1963).

302. Cook, J. J., Flowers, W. L., and Arnold, C. B., *Proc. IRE (Corres.)* **50**, 1693 (1962).

302a. Herriott, D. R., *Appl. Opt.* **2**, 865 (1963).

303. Forrester, A. T., Gudmundsen, R. A., and Johnson, P. O., *Phys. Rev.* **99**, 1691 (1955).

304. Brown, R. H., and Twiss, R. Q., *Nature* **177**, 27; **178**, 1046 (1956); *Proc. Roy. Soc.* **A248**, 199 and 222 (1958).

305. Forrester, A. T., *J. Opt. Soc. Am.* **51**, 253 (1961); also *in* "Advances in Quantum Electronics" (J. Singer, ed.), p. 233. Columbia Univ. Press, New York, 1961.

306. Smith, A. W., and Williams, G. W., *J. Opt. Soc. Am.* **52**, 337 (1962).

307. Oliver, B. M., *Proc. IRE (Corres.)* **49**, 1960 (1961).

308. Haus, H. A., and Townes, C. H., *Proc. IRE (Corres.)* **50**, 1544 (1962).

309. Oliver, B. M., *Proc. IRE (Corres.)* **50**, 1545 (1962).

310. Serber, R., and Townes, C. H., *in* "Quantum Electronics" (C. H. Townes, ed.), p. 233. Columbia Univ. Press, New York, 1960.

311. Javan, A., Ballik, E. A., and Bond, W. L., *J. Opt. Soc. Am.* **52**, 96 (1962).

311a. Jaseja, T. S., Javan, A., and Townes, C. H., *Phys. Rev. Letters* **10**, 165 (1963).

312. McMurtry, B. J., *Appl. Opt.* **2**, 767 (1963).

313. McMurtry, B. J., and Siegman, A. E., *Appl. Opt.* **1**, 51 (1962).

314. Lucy, R. F., *Proc. IEEE* **51**, 162 (1963).

315. Gaddy, O. L., and Holshouser, D. F., *Proc. IRE (Corres.)* **50**, 207 (1962); *Proc. IEEE* **51**, 153 (1963).

316. Gaddy, O. L., and Holshouser, D. F., *Proc. IRE (Corres.)* **50**, 1525 (1962).

316a. Wittwer, N. C., *Appl. Phys. Letters* **2**, 194 (1963).

316b. Petroff, M. D., Spetzler, H. A., and Bjørnerud, E. K., *Proc. IEEE (Corres.)* **51**, 614 (1963).

316c. Gilbert, K. D., McClees, H. C., Lindsay, P. A., and Park, S. F., *Proc. IEEE (Corres.)* **51**, 1148 (1963).

317. Harris, S. E., and Siegman, A. E., *IRE Trans. Electron Devices* **9**, 322 (1962).

318. Inaba, H., and Siegman, A. E., *Proc. IRE (Corres.)* **50**, 1823 (1962).

319. Kibler, L. U., *Proc. IRE (Corres.)* **50**, 1834 (1962).

320. Riesz, R. P., *Rev. Sci. Instr.* **33**, 994 (1962).

321. Lucovsky, G., Lasser, M. E., and Emmons, R. B., *Proc. IEEE* **51**, 1661 (1963).

322. Svelto, O., Coleman, P. D., DiDomenico, M., Jr., and Pantell, R. H., *J. Appl. Phys.* **34**, 3182 (1963).

322a. Lucovsky, G., Schwarz, R. F., and Emmons, R. B., *Proc. IEEE* **51**, 613 (1963).

322b. Patel, C. K. N., and Sharpless, W. M., *Proc. IEEE (Corres.)* **52**, 107 (1964).

323. Saito, S., Kurokawa, K., Fujii, Y., Kimura, T., and Uno, Y., *Proc. IRE (Corres.)* **50**, 2369 (1962).

324. Sommers, Jr., H. H., *Proc. IEEE* **51**, 140 (1963).

325. Bernard, M., *Appl. Phys. Letters* **2**, 9 (1963).

325a. Pershan, P. S., and Bloembergen, N., *Appl. Phys. Letters* **2**, 117 (1963).

326. Dayhoff, E. S., and Kessler, B., *Appl. Opt.* **1**, 339 (1962).

327. Broei, J. C., Durand, M., and Orszag, A., *Compt. Rend.* **253**, 2215 (1961).

328. Clark, G. L., Wuerker, R. F., and York, C. M., *J. Opt. Soc. Am.* **52**, 878 (1962).

329. Kurtz, M. C., *J. Soc. Motion Picture Television Engrs.* **68**, 16 (1959).

330. Clark, G. L., *IRE WESCON Conv. Record, Part 5*, p. 189 (1958).

330a. Wolf, E., *in* "Proceedings of the Symposium on Optical Masers" (J. Fox, ed.), p. 29. Microwave Research Inst. Symp. Ser., Vol. XIII. Polytechnic Press of the Polytechnic Inst. of Brooklyn, New York, 1963.

331. Mandel, L., and Wolf, E., *Proc. Phys. Soc. (London)* **80**, 894 (1962).

332. Born, M., and Wolf, E., "Principles of Optics," Chapter X. Pergamon Press, New York, 1959.

333. Neugebauer, H. E., *J. Opt. Soc. Am.* **52**, 470 (1962).

334. Mandel, L., *J. Opt. Soc. Am.* **51**, 797 (1961).

335. Glauber, R. J., *Phys. Rev. Letters* **10**, 84 (1963).

336. Glauber, R. J., *Phys. Rev.* **130**, 2529 (1963).

337. Mandel, L., and Wolf, E., *Phys. Rev.* **124**, 1696 (1961).

338. Mandel, L., and Wolf, E., *Phys. Rev. Letters* **10**, 276 (1963).

339. Sudarshan, E. C. G., *Phys. Rev. Letters* **10**, 277 (1963).

340. Bellisio, J. A., Freed, C., and Haus, H. A., *Appl. Phys. Letters* **4**, 5 (1964).

341. Golay, M. J. E., *Proc. IRE (Corres.)* **49**, 958 (1961).

342. Nelson, D. F., and Collins, R. J., *J. Appl. Phys.* **32**, 2739 (L) (1961).

343. Hercher, M., *Appl. Opt.* **1**, 25 (1962).

344. Berkley, D. A., and Wolga, G. J., *Phys. Rev. Letters* **9**, 479 (1962).

345. Kisliuk, P., and Walsh, D. J., *Appl. Opt.* **1**, 45 (1962).

346. Weisman, D., *Appl. Opt.* **1**, 672 (1962).

347. Michel, A. E., and Walker, J. E., *J. Appl. Phys.* **34**, 2492 (1963).

348. Morokuma, T., Neflen, K. F., Lawrence, T. R., and Klucher, T. M., *J. Opt. Soc. Am.* **53**, 394 (1963).

349. Magyar, G., and Mandel, L., *Nature* **198**, 255 (1963).

349a. Mandel, L., *Phys. Rev.* **134**, A10 (1964).

350. Evtuhov, V., and Neeland, J. K., *Appl. Opt.* **1**, 517 (1962).

350a. Stickley, C. M., *Proc. IEEE* **51**, 848 (1963).

351. Ciftan, M., Krutchkoff, A., and Koozekanani, S., *Proc. IRE (Corres.)* **50**, 84 (1962).

352. Duncan, R. C., Jr., Kiss, Z. J., and Wittke, J. P., *J. Appl. Phys.* **33**, 2568 (1962).

353. Dayhoff, E. S., *Proc. IRE (Corres.)* **50**, 1684 (1962).

354. Stickley, C. M., *Appl. Opt.* **2**, 855 (1963).

355. Hughes, T. P., and Young, K. M., *Nature* **196**, 332 (1962).

356. Tonks, L., *J. Appl. Phys.* **33**, 1980 (1962).

356a. Boersch, H., Herziger, G., Maslowski, S., and Weber, H., *Phys. Letters* **4**, 86 (1963).

357. Olt, R. D., *Appl. Opt.* **1**, 25 (1962).

358. Collins, R. J., and Nelson, D. F., *Proc. Meeting Intern. Commission on Optics, London, 1961.*

359. Kaiser, W., and Keck, M. J., *J. Appl. Phys.* **33**, 762 (1962).

360. Lipsett, M. S., and Strandberg, M. W. P., *Appl. Opt.* **1**, 343 (1962).

361. Abella, I. D., and Townes, C. H., *Nature* **192**, 957 (1961).

362. Masters, J. I., and Parrent, G. B., Jr., *Proc. IRE (Corres.)* **50**, 230 (1962).

362a. Stoicheff, B. P., and Szabo, A., *Appl. Opt.* **2**, 811 (1963).

363. Bostick, H. A., and O'Connor, J. R., *Proc. IRE (Corres.)* **50**, 219 (1962).

364. Gandy, H. W., *Proc. IRE (Corres.)* **50**, 2375 (1962).

365. Mallory, W. R., *Proc. IEEE* **51**, 850 (1963).

365a. Shimoda, K., *in* "Proceedings of the Symposium on Optical Masers" (J. Fox, ed.), p. 95. Microwave Research Inst. Symp. Ser., Vol. XIII. Polytechnic Press of the Polytechnic Inst. of Brooklyn, New York, 1963.

366. Johnson, R. E., McMahan, W. H., Oharek, F. J., and Shepard, A. P., *Proc. IRE (Corres.)* **49**, 1942 (1961).

366a. Birnbaum, M., Stocker, T., and Welles, S. J., *Proc. IEEE* **51**, 854 (1963).

366b. Birnbaum, M., and Stocker, T. L., *Appl. Phys. Letters* **3**, 164 (1963).

367. Koozekanani, S., Ciftan, M., and Krutchkoff, A., *Appl. Opt.* **1**, 372 (1962).

368. Baker, J. A., and Peters, C. W., *Appl. Opt.* **1**, 674 (1962).

369. Skinner, J. G., and Geusic, J. E., *in* "Quantum Electronics: Proceedings of the Third International Congress, Paris, 1963" (P. Grivet and N. Bloembergen, eds.), Vol. II, p. 1437. Columbia Univ. Press, New York, 1964.

369a. Collins, S. A., and White, G. R., *Appl. Opt.* **2**, 448 (1963).

369b. Okaya, A., *Proc. IEEE (Corres.)* **51**, 1033 (1963).

370. Kogelnik, H., and Patel, C. K. N., *Proc. IRE (Corres.)* **50**, 2365 (1962).

370a. Birnbaum, M. and Stocker, T., *J. Appl. Phys. (Communs.)* **34**, 3414 (1963).

370b. Bloembergen, N., and Shen, Y. R., *Phys. Rev.* **133**, A37 (1964).

371. Goeppert-Mayer, M., *Ann. Physik* [5] **9**, 273 (1931).

372. Breit, G., and Teller, E., *Astrophys. J.* **91**, 215 (1940).

373. Wheeler, J., *J. Opt. Soc. Am.* **37**, 813 (1947).

374. Hughes, V., and Grabner, L., *Phys. Rev.* **79**, 829 (1950).

375. Ramsay, N., "Molecular Beams," Chapter V. Oxford Univ. Press (Clarendon), London and New York, 1956.

376. Winter, J. M., *Ann. Phys. (N.Y.)* **4**, 49 (1959).

377. Kaiser, W., and Garrett, C. G. B., *Phys. Rev. Letters* **7**, 229 (1961).

378. Abella, I. D., *Phys. Rev. Letters* **9**, 453 (1962).

379. Peticolas, W. L., Goldsborough, J. P., and Rieckhoff, K. E., *Phys. Rev. Letters* **10**, 43 (1963).

379a. Singh, S., and Stoicheff, B. P., *J. Chem. Phys.* **38**, 2032 (1963).

380. Porter, J. F., Jr., *Phys. Rev. Letters* **7**, 414 (1961).

381. Kleinman, D. A., *Phys. Rev.* **125**, 87 (1962).

382. Braunstein, R., *Phys. Rev.* **175**, 475 (1962).

383. Javan, A., *Phys. Rev.* **107**, 1579 (1957).

384. Kontorovich, V. M., and Prokhorov, A. M., *Zhur. Eksperim. i Teor. Fiz.* **33**, 1428 (1947).

385. Clogston, A. M., *Phys. Chem. Solids* **4**, 271 (1958).

386. Yatsiv, S., *Phys. Rev.* **113**, 1522, 1538 (1959).

387. Butcher, P. N., *in* "Quantum Electronics" (C. H. Townes, ed.), p. 189. Columbia Univ. Press, New York, 1960.

388. Williams, R. C., *Phys. Rev.* **126**, 1011 (1962).

389. Wells, W. H., *J. Appl. Phys.* **33**, 1851 (1962).

390. Javan, A., *J. Phys. Radium* **19**, 806 (1958).

391. Winter, J. M., *J. Phys. Radium* **19**, 202 (1958).

392. Autler, S. H., and Townes, C. H., *Phys. Rev.* **100**, 703 (1955).

393. Yajima, T., *J. Phys. Soc. Japan* **16**, 1709 (1962).

394. Woodbury, E. J., and Ng, W. K., *Proc. IRE (Corres.)* **50**, 2367 (1962).

395. Eckhardt, G., Hellwarth, R. W., McClung, F. J., Schwarz, S. E., and Weiner, D., *Phys. Rev. Letters* **9**, 455 (1962).

395a. Geller, M., Bortfield, D. P., and Sooy, W. R., *Appl. Phys. Letters* **3**, 36 (1963).

395b. Geller, M., Bortfield, D. P., Sooy, W. R., and Woodbury, E. J., *Proc. IEEE (Corres.)* **51**, 1236 (1963).

395c. Zeiger, H. J., and Tannenwald, P. E., *in* "Quantum Electronics: Proceedings of the Third International Congress, Paris, 1963" (P. Grivet and N. Bloembergen, eds.), Vol. II, p. 1589. Columbia Univ. Press, New York, 1964.

395d. Hellwarth, R. W., *Phys. Rev.* **130**, 1850 (1963).

395e. Terhune, R. W., *Solid State Design* **4**, 38 (1963).

395f. Garmire, E., Pandarese, F., and Townes, C. H., *Phys. Rev. Letters* **11**, 160 (1963).

395g. Zeiger, H. J., Tannenwald, P. E., Kern, S., and Hereqdeen, R., *Phys. Rev. Letters* **11**, 419 (1963).

395h. Minck, R. W., Terhune, R. W., and Raclo, W. G., *Appl. Phys. Letters* **3**, 181 (1963).

395i. Eckhardt, G., Bortfield, D. P., and Geller, M., *Appl. Phys. Letters* **3**, 137 (1963).

395j. Bloembergen, N., and Shen, Y. R., *Phys. Rev. Letters* **12**, 504 (1964).

396. Franken, P. A., Hill, A. E., Peters, C. W., and Weinrich, G., *Phys. Rev. Letters* **7**, 118 (1961).

396a. Franken, P. A., and Ward, J. F., *Rev. Mod. Phys.* **35**, 23 (1963).

397. Bass, M., Franken, P. A., Hill, A. E. Peters, C. W., and Weinrich, G., *Phys. Rev. Letters* **8**, 18 (1962).

398. Smith, A. W., and Braslau, N., *IBM J. Res. Develop.* **6**, 361 (1962).

399. Terhune, R. W., Maker, P. D., and Savage, C. M., *Phys. Rev. Letters* **8**, 404 (1962).

399a. Bond, W. L., *Bell System Tech. J.* **22**, 1 (1943).

399b. Maker, P. D., Terhune, R. W., and Savage, C. M., *in* "Quantum Electronics: Proceedings of the Third International Congress, Paris, 1963" (P. Grivet and N. Bloembergen, eds.), Vol. II, p. 1559. Columbia Univ. Press, New York, 1964.

400. Lax, B., Mavroides, J. G., and Edwards, D. F., *Phys. Rev. Letters* **8**, 166 (1962).

401. Kleinman, D. A., *Phys. Rev.* **128**, 1761 (1962).

402. Armstrong, J. A., Bloembergen, N., Ducuing, J., and Pershan, P. S., *Phys. Rev.* **127**, 1918 (1962).

402a. Pershan, P., *Phys. Rev.* **130**, 919 (1963).

403. Loudon, R., *Proc. Phys. Soc.* **80**, 952 (1962).

404. Bloembergen, N., *Proc. IEEE* **51**, 124 (1963).

405. Kleinman, D. A., *Phys. Rev.* **126**, 1977 (1962).

406. Giordmaine, J. A., *Phys. Rev. Letters* **8**, 19 (1962).

407. Maker, P. D., Terhune, R. W., Nisenoff, M., and Savage, C. M., *Phys. Rev. Letters* **8**, 21 (1962).

408. Franken, P. A., Hill, A. E., and Peters, C. W., to be published.

409. Terhune, R. W., Maker, P. D., and Savage, C. M., *Appl. Phys. Letters* **2**, 54 (1963)

410. Miller, R. C., and Savage, A. C., *Phys. Rev.* **128**, 2175 (1962).

411. Savage, A. C., and Miller, R. C., *Appl. Opt.* **1**, 661 (1962).

412. Boyne, H. S., and Martin, W. C., *J. Opt. Soc. Am.* **52**, 880 (1962).

413. Abella, I. D., *Proc. IRE (Corres.)* **50**, 1824 (1962).

414. Vachaspati, *Phys. Rev.* **128**, 664 (1962).

414a. Armstrong, J. A., Nathan, M. I., and Smith, A. W., *Appl. Phys. Letters* **3**, 68 (1963).

414b. Garfinkel, M., and Engeler, W. E., *Appl. Phys. Letters* **3**, 178 (1963).

414c. Adams, N. I., and Shoefer, P. P., *Appl. Phys. Letters* **3**, 19 (1963).

414d. Ashkin, A., Boyd, G. D., and Dziedzic, J. M., *Phys. Rev. Letters* **11**, 14 (1963).

415. Bass, M., Franken, P. A., Ward, J. F., and Weinrich, G., *Phys. Rev. Letters* **9**, 446 (1962).

415a. Niebuhr, K. E., *Appl. Phys. Letters* **2**, 136 (1963).

416. Bloembergen, N., and Pershan, P. S., *Phys. Rev.* **128**, 606 (1962).

416a. Ducuing, J., and Bloembergen, N., *Phys. Rev. Letters* **10**, 474 (1963).

417. Townes, C. H., *in* "Advances in Quantum Electronics" (J. Singer, ed.), p. 3. Columbia Univ. Press, New York, 1961.

418. Oliver, B. M., *Proc. IRE* **50**, 135 (1962).

419. Dacey, G. C., *Science* **135**, 71 (1962).

420. Franken, P., *Intern. Sci. Technol.* October, p. 62 (1962).

421. Moss, T. S., *Infrared Phys.* **2**, 129 (1962).

422. Renton, C. A., *Proc. IEEE* (*Corres.*) **52**, 93 (1964); Filinski, I., *Phys. Rev.* **107**, 1193 (1957).

423. Pershan, P. S., and Bloembergen, N., *in* "Advances in Quantum Electronics" (J. Singer, ed.), p. 187. Columbia Univ. Press, New York, 1961.

424. Bloembergen, N., Pershan, P. W., and Wilcox, L. R., *Phys. Rev.* **120**, 2014 (1960).

425. Kaminow, I. P., *Phys. Rev. Letters* **6**, 528 (1961).

426. Blumenthal, R. H., *Proc. IRE* **50**, 452 (1962).

427. Kaminow, I. P., and Liu, J., *Proc. IEEE* **51**, 132 (1963).

428. Rigrod, W. W., and Kaminow, I. P., *Proc. IEEE* **51**, 137 (1963).

429. Peters, C. J., *Proc. IEEE* **51**, 147 (1963).

430. White, R. M., and Enderly, C. E., *Proc. IEEE* (*Corres.*) **51**, 214 (1963).

431. Gordon, I. E., and Rigden, J. D., *Bell System Tech. J.* **42**, 155 (1963).

432. Holshouser, D. F., von Foerster, H., and Clark, G. L., *J. Opt. Soc. Am.* **51**, 1360 (1961).

433. Rupp, E., *Z. Physik* **47**, 72 (1928).

434. Cummins, H. Z., and Knable, N., *Proc. IEEE* (*Corres.*) **51**, 1246 (1963).

435. Buhrer, C. F., *Proc. IEEE* (*Corres.*) **51**, 1151 (1963).

436. Harris, S. E., McMurtry, B. J., and Siegman, A. E., *Appl. Phys. Letters* **1**, 37 (1962).

437. Pankove, J. I., and Berkeyheiser, J. E., *Proc. IRE* (*Corres.*) **50**, 1976 (1962).

438. Harris, S. E., *Appl. Phys. Letters* **2**, 47 (1963).

439. Kaminow, I. P., *Appl. Phys. Letters* **2**, 41 (1963).

440. Blattner, D. J., and Sterzer, F., *RCA Rev.* **23**, 407 (1962).

441. Rabinowitz, P., Jacobs, S., Targ, R., and Gould, G., *Proc. IRE* (*Corres.*) **50**, 2365 (1962).

442. Schwartz, R. N., and Townes, C. H., *Nature* **190**, 205 (1961).

443. Luck, D. G. C., *RCA Rev.* **22**, 359 (1961).

443a. Megla, G. K., *Appl. Opt.* **2**, 311 (1963).

443b. Rabinowitz, P., La Tourette, S., and Gould, G., *Proc. IEEE* **51**, 857 (1963).

443c. Bloom, L. R., and Buhrer, C. F., *Proc. IEEE* **51**, 610 (1963).

444. Rosenthal, J. E., *Appl. Opt.* **1**, 169 (1962).

444a. Long, R. K., *Proc. IEEE* (*Corres.*) **51**, 859 (1963).

445. Gordon, J. P., *Proc. IRE* **50**, 1898 (1962).

445a. Ross, M., *Proc. IEEE* (*Corres.*) **51**, 602 (1963).

446. Buddenhagen, D. A., Lengyel, B. A., McClung, F. J., and Smith, G. F., *IRE Intern. Conv. Record, Pt. 5* p. 285 (1961).

447. Katzman, M., and Frost, E., *Proc. IRE (Corres.)* **49**, 1684 (1961).

448. Rubin, M. D., *Proc. IRE (Corres.)* **50**, 471 (1962).

449. Biernson, G., and Lucy, R. F., *Proc. IEEE* **51**, 202 (1963).

450. Rigden, J. D., and Gordon, E. I., *Proc. IRE (Corres.)* **50**, 2367 (1962).

451. Oliver, B. M., *Proc. IEEE (Corres.)* **51**, 220 (1963).

452. Langmuir, R. V., *Appl. Phys. Letters* **2**, 29 (1963).

453. Lainé, D. C., *Nature* **191**, 796 (1961).

454. Froome, K. D., *Nature* **192**, 859 (1961).

454a. Mahan, G. D., and Hopfield, J. J., *J. Appl. Phys.* **34**, 1535 (1963).

455. Devor, D. P., D'Haenens, I. J., and Asawa, C. K., *Phys. Rev. Letters* **8**, 432 (1962).

456. Ready, J. F. and Chen, D., *Proc. IRE (Corres.)* **50**, 329 (1962).

457. Theissing, H. H., Caplan, P. J., Dieter, F. A., and Rabbiner, N., *Phys. Rev. Letters* **3**, 460 (1959).

457a. Szabo, A., *Proc. IEEE* **51**, 1037 (1963).

458. Hsu, H., and Tittel, F. K., *Proc. IEEE* **51**, 185 (1963).

458a. Yatsiv, S., *in* "Advances in Quantum Electronics" (J. Singer, ed.), p. 200. Columbia Univ. Press, New York, 1960.

458b. Tsujikawa, I., and Murao, T., *J. Phys. Soc. Japan* **18**, 503 (1963).

459. Porto, S. P. S., and Wood, D. L., *J. Opt. Soc. Am.* **52**, 251 (1962).

459a. Kogelnik, H., and Porto, S. P. S., *J. Opt. Soc. Am.* **53**, 1446 (1964).

460. Tien, P., and Suhl, H., *Proc. IRE* **46**, 700 (1958).

461. Louisell, W. H., "Coupled Mode and Parametric Electronics." Wiley, New York, 1960.

462. Heffner, H., *in* "Quantum Electronics" (C. H. Townes, ed.), p. 269. Columbia Univ. Press, New York, 1960.

463. Jaynes, E. T., *in* "Quantum Electronics" (C. H. Townes, ed.), p. 289. Columbia Univ. Press, New York, 1961.

464. Louisell, W. H., Yariv, A., and Siegman, A. E., *Phys. Rev.* **124**, 1646 (1961).

465. Fontana, J. R., Pantell, R. H., and Smith, R. G., *J. Appl. Phys.* **33**, 2085 (1962).

466. Weiss, M. T., *Proc. IRE* **45**, 1012 (1957).

467. Kingston, R. H., *Proc. IRE (Corres.)* **50**, 472 (1962).

468. Gandhi, O. P., *Proc. IRE (Corres.)* **50**, 1829 (1962).

469. Kroll, N. M., *Phys. Rev.* **127**, 1207 (1962); *Proc. IEEE* **51**, 110 (1963).

470. Siegman, A. E., *Appl. Opt.* **1**, 739 (1962).

471. Yajima, T., Shimizu, F., and Shimoda, K., *Appl. Opt.* **1**, 770 (1962).

472. Ellis, A. T., and Fourney, M. E., *Proc. IEEE (Corres.)* **51**, 942 (1963).

473. Shimoda, K., *Appl. Opt.* **1**, 33 (1962).

473a. Ready, J. F., *Appl. Phys. Letters* **3**, 11 (1963).

474. Courtney-Pratt, J. S., *Bell Lab. Record* **39**, *April* (1961).

475. Zaret, M. M., Breinin, G. M., Schmidt, H., Ripps, H., and Siegel, I. M., *Science* **134**, 1525 (1961).

476. Solon, L. R., Aronson, R., and Gould, G., *Science* **134**, 1506 (1961).

476a. Goldman, L., Blaney, D. J., Kindel, Jr., D. J., and Franke, E. K., *J. Invest. Dermatol.* **40**, in press (1963).

476b. Saks, N. M., and Roth, C. A., *Science* **141**, 46 (1963).

476c. Damon, E. K., and Townlson, R. G., *J. Appl. Opt.* **2**, 546 (1963).

476d. Meyerand, R. G., and Haught, A. F., *Phys. Rev. Letters* **11**, 401 (1963).

476e. Verber, C. M., and Adelman, A. H., *Appl. Phys. Letters* **2**, 220 (1963).

476f. Lichtman, D., and Ready, J. F., *Phys. Rev. Letters* **10**, 342 (1963).

476g. Lichtman, D., and Ready, J. F., *Appl. Phys. Letters* **3**, 115 (1963).

476h. Hornig, R. E., and Woolston, J. R., *Appl. Phys. Letters* **2**, 138 (1963).

476i. Hornig, R. E., *Appl. Phys. Letters* **3**, 8 (1963).

477. Sinclair, D. C., and Givens, M. P., *47th Ann. Meeting Opt. Soc. Am.* p. 20 (1962).

478. McKenna, J., and Platzman, P. M., *Phys. Rev.* **129**, 2354 (1963).

479. Harntyunian, V. M., Harntyunian, F. R., Ispirian, K. A., and Tumanian, V. A., *Phys. Letters* **6**, 175 (1963).

480. Cummins, H., Knable, N., Gampel, L., and Yeh, Y., *Appl. Phys. Letters* **2**, 62 (1963).

481. Jaseja, T. S., Javan, A., Murray, J., and Townes, C. H., *Phys. Rev.* **133**, A1221 (1964).

482. Michelson, A. A., and Gale, G. H., *Astrophys. J.* **61**, 140 (1945).

483. Sagnac, G., *Compt. Rend.* **157**, 708 (1913); *J. Phys. (Paris)* [5] **4**, 177 (1921).

484. Fiocco, G., and Thompson, E., *Phys. Rev. Letters* **10**, 89 (1963).

485. Hughes, T. P., *Nature* **194**, 268 (1962).

486. Milburn, R. H., *Phys. Rev. Letters* **10**, 75 (1963).

487. Schwarz, S. E., *Proc. IEEE (Corres.)* **51**, 1362 (1963).

488. Ashby, D. E. T. F., and Jepheott, D. F., *Appl. Phys. Letters* **3**, 13 (1963).

489. George, T. V., Slama, L., Yokoyama, M., and Goldstein, L., *Phys. Rev. Letters* **11**, 403 (1963).

490. Heller, Z. H., *J. Opt. Soc. Am.* **53**, 395 (1963).

491. Chiao, R. Y., Townes, C. H., and Stoicheff, B. P., *Phys. Rev. Letters* **12**, 592 (1964).

492. Ekstein, H., and Rostocker, N., *Phys. Rev.* **100**, 1023 (1955).

493. Weber, J., *Phys. Rev.* **108**, 537 (1957).

494. Heitler, W., "The Quantum Theory of Radiation." Oxford Univ. Press, London and New York, 1954.

495. Malekov, G., and Rigsin, O., *in* "Quantum Electronics: Proceedings of the Third International Congress, Paris, 1963" (P. Grivet and N. Bloembergen, eds.), Vol. II, p. 1121. Columbia Univ. Press, New York, 1964.

496. McMullin, P. G., *Appl. Opt.* **3**, 641 (1964).

497. Bennett, W. R., Jr., Pawlikowski, A. T., and Knutson, J. W., *Bull. Am. Phys. Soc.* **9**, 500 (1964).

498. Doyle, W. M., *J. Appl. Phys.* **35**, 1348 (1964).

499. Bockasten, K., *Appl. Phys. Letters* **4**, 118 (1964).

500. Bridges, W. B., *Appl. Phys. Letters* **4**, 128 (1964).

500a. Bennett, W. R., Jr., Knuston, J. W., Jr., Mercer, G. N., and Detch, J. L., *Appl. Phys. Letters* **4**, 180 (1964).

501. Gordon, E. I., Labuda, E. F., and Bridges, W. B., *Appl. Phys. Letters* **4**, 178 (1964).

502. McFarlane, R. A., Faust, W. L., Patel, C. K. N., and Garrett, C. G. B., *Proc. IEEE (Corres.)* **52**, 318 (1964).

503. Mathias, L. E. S., and Parker, J. T., *Phys. Letters* **7**, 194 (1963).

504. Patel, C. K. N., *Phys. Rev. Letters* **12**, 588 (1964).

Author Index

Numbers in parentheses are reference numbers and indicate that an author's work is referred to although his name is not cited in the text. Numbers in italic show the page on which the complete reference is listed.

Subject Index